VECTOR AND TENSOR ANALYSIS

VECTOR AND TENSOR ANALYSIS

by

G. E. HAY

Associate Professor of Mathematics
University of Michigan

DOVER PUBLICATIONS, INC.

NEW YORK

TABLE OF CONTENTS

CHAPTER III. APPLICATION OF VECTORS TO MECHANICS

Motion of a Particle

Motion of a System of Particles

CHAPTER IV. PARTIAL DIFFERENTIATION

Chapter V. Integration

Chapter VI. Tensor Analysis

VECTOR AND TENSOR ANALYSIS

CHAPTER I

ELEMENTARY OPERATIONS

1. *Definitions.* Quantities which have magnitude only are called *scalars*. The following are examples: mass, distance, area, volume. A scalar can be represented by a number with an associated sign, which indicates its magnitude to some convenient scale.

There are quantities which have not only magnitude but also direction. The following are examples: force, displacement of a point, velocity of a point, acceleration of a point. Such quantities are called *vectors* if they obey a certain law of addition set forth in § 2 below. A vector can be represented by an arrow. The direction of the arrow indicates the direction of the vector, and the length of the arrow indicates the magnitude of the vector to some convenient scale.

Let us consider a vector represented by an arrow running from a point P to a point Q, as shown in Figure 1. The straight line through P and Q is called the *line of action* of the vector, the point P is called the *origin* of the vector, and the point Q is called the *terminus* of the vector.

To denote a vector we write the letter indicating its origin followed by the letter indicating its terminus, and place a bar over the two letters. The vector represented in Figure 1 is then represented by the symbols $\overline{PQ}$. In this book the superimposed bar will not be used in any capacity other than the above, and hence its presence can always

Figure 1

be interpreted as denoting vector character. This notation for vectors is somewhat cumbersome. Hence when convenient we shall use a simpler notation which consists in denoting a vector by a single symbol in bold-faced type. Thus, the vector in Figure 1 might be denoted by the symbol **a**. In this book no mathematical symbols will be printed in bold-faced type except those denoting vectors.*

The magnitude of a vector is a scalar which is never negative. The magnitude of a vector $\overline{PQ}$ will be denoted by either PQ or $|\overline{PQ}|$. Similarly, the magnitude of a vector **a** will be denoted by either a or $|\mathbf{a}|$.

Two vectors are said to be equal if they have the same magnitudes and the same directions. To denote the equality of two vectors the usual sign is employed. Hence, if **a** and **b** are equal vectors, we write

$$\mathbf{a} = \mathbf{b}.$$

A vector **a** is said to be equal to zero if its magnitude a is equal to zero. Thus $\mathbf{a} = 0$ if $a = 0$. Such a vector is called a zero vector.

2. *Addition of vectors.*   In § 1 it was stated that vectors are quantities with magnitude and direction, and which obey a certain law of addition. This law, which is called the *law of vector addition*, is as follows.

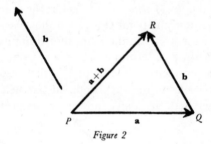

Figure 2

Let **a** and **b** be two vectors, as shown in Figure 2. The origin and terminus of **a** are P and Q. A vector equal to **b** is constructed with

---

* It is difficult to write bold-faced symbols on the blackboard or in the exercise book. When it is desired to write a single symbol denoting a vector, the reader will find it convenient to write the symbol in the ordinary manner, and to place a bar over it to indicate vector character.

its origin at Q. Its terminus falls at a point R. The sum $\mathbf{a}+\mathbf{b}$ is the vector $\overline{PR}$, and we write

$$\mathbf{a}+\mathbf{b} = \overline{PR}.$$

Theorem 1. Vectors satisfy the commutative law of addition; that is,

$$\mathbf{a}+\mathbf{b} = \mathbf{b}+\mathbf{a}.$$

Proof. Let $\mathbf{a}$ and $\mathbf{b}$ be the two vectors shown in Figure 2. Then

(2.1) $$\mathbf{a}+\mathbf{b} = \overline{PR}.$$

We now construct a vector equal to $\mathbf{b}$, with its origin at P. Its terminus falls at a point S. A vector equal to $\mathbf{a}$ is then constructed with its origin at S. The terminus of this vector will fall at R, and Figure 3 results. Hence.

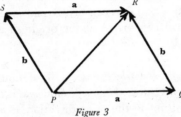

Figure 3

(2.2) $$\mathbf{b}+\mathbf{a} = \overline{PR}.$$

From (2.1) and (2.2) it follows that $\mathbf{a}+\mathbf{b} = \mathbf{b}+\mathbf{a}$.

Theorem 2. Vectors satisfy the associative law of addition; that is,

$$(\mathbf{a}+\mathbf{b})+\mathbf{c} = \mathbf{a}+(\mathbf{b}+\mathbf{c}).$$

Proof. Let us construct the polygon in Figure 4 having the vectors $\mathbf{a}$, $\mathbf{b}$, $\mathbf{c}$ as consecutive sides. The corners of this polygon are labelled P, Q, R and S. It then appears that

$$(\mathbf{a}+\mathbf{b})+\mathbf{c} = \overline{PR}+\mathbf{c}$$
$$= \overline{PS},$$
$$\mathbf{a}+(\mathbf{b}+\mathbf{c}) = \mathbf{a}+\overline{QS}$$
$$= \overline{PS}.$$

Hence the theorem is true.

According to Theorem 2 the sum of three vectors $\mathbf{a}$, $\mathbf{b}$, and $\mathbf{c}$ is

3

independent of the order in which they are added. Hence we can write $\mathbf{a}+\mathbf{b}+\mathbf{c}$ without ambiguity.

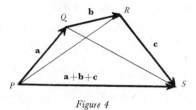

Figure 4

Figure 4 shows the construction of the vector $\mathbf{a}+\mathbf{b}+\mathbf{c}$. The sum of a larger number of vectors can be constructed similarly. Thus, to find the vector $\mathbf{a}+\mathbf{b}+\mathbf{c}+\mathbf{d}$ it is only necessary to construct the polygon having $\mathbf{a}$, $\mathbf{b}$, $\mathbf{c}$ and $\mathbf{d}$ as consecutive sides. The required vector is then the vector with its origin at the origin of $\mathbf{a}$, and its terminus at the terminus of $\mathbf{d}$.

3. *Multiplication of a vector by a scalar.* By definition, if m is a positive scalar and $\mathbf{a}$ is a vector, the expression $m\mathbf{a}$ is a vector with magnitude ma and pointing in the same direction as $\mathbf{a}$; and if m is negative, $m\mathbf{a}$ is a vector with magnitude $|m|\,a$, and pointing in the direction opposite to $\mathbf{a}$.

We note in particular that $-\mathbf{a}$ is a vector with the same magnitude as $\mathbf{a}$ but pointing in the direction opposite to $\mathbf{a}$. Figure 5 shows this vector, and as further examples of the multiplication of a vector by a scalar, the vectors $2\mathbf{a}$ and $-2\mathbf{a}$.

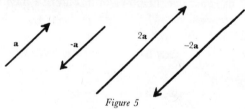

Figure 5

Theorem. The multiplication of a vector by a scalar satisfies the distributive laws; that is,

4

(3.1) $$(m+n)\mathbf{a} = m\mathbf{a}+n\mathbf{a},$$

(3.2) $$m(\mathbf{a}+\mathbf{b}) = m\mathbf{a}+m\mathbf{b}.$$

Proof of (3.1). If $m+n$ is positive, both sides of (3.1) represent a vector with magnitude $(m+n)a$ and pointing in the same direction as $\mathbf{a}$. If $m+n$ is negative, both sides of (3.1) represent a vector with magnitude $|m+n|a$ and pointing in the direction opposite to $\mathbf{a}$.

Proof of (3.2). Let m be positive, and let $\mathbf{a}$, $\mathbf{b}$, $m\mathbf{a}$ and $m\mathbf{b}$ be as shown in Figures 6 and 7. Then

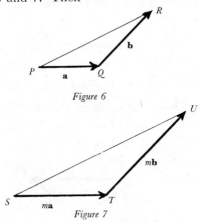

Figure 6

Figure 7

(3.3) $$m(\mathbf{a}+\mathbf{b}) = m\overline{PR}, \quad m\mathbf{a}+m\mathbf{b} = \overline{SU}.$$

The two triangles PQR and STU are similar. Corresponding sides are then proportional, the constant of proportionality being m. Thus

(3.4) $$mPR=SU.$$

Since $\overline{PR}$ and $\overline{SU}$ have the same directions, and since m is positive, then $m\overline{PR} = \overline{SU}$. Substitution in both sides of this equation from (3.3) yields (3.2).

Now, let m be negative. Then Figure 7 is replaced by Figure 8. Equations (3.3) apply in this case also. The triangles PQR and STU are again similar, but the constant of proportionality is $|m|$, so $|m|PR = SU$. Since $\overline{PR}$ and $\overline{SU}$ have opposite directions and m is negative,

5

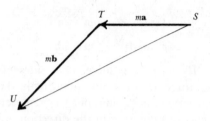

Figure 8

then $m\overline{PR} = \overline{SU}$. Substitution in both sides of this equation from (3.3) again yields (3.2).

4. *Subtraction of vectors.* If **a** and **b** are two vectors, their difference **a** − **b** is defined by the relation

$$\mathbf{a} - \mathbf{b} = \mathbf{a} + (-\mathbf{b}),$$

where the vector −**b** is as defined in the previous section. Figure 9 shows two vectors **a** and **b**, and also their difference **a** − **b**.

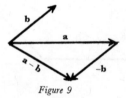

Figure 9

5. *Linear functions.* If **a** and **b** are any two vectors, and m and n are any two scalars, the expression $m\mathbf{a} + n\mathbf{b}$ is called a linear function of **a** and **b**. Similarly, $m\mathbf{a} + n\mathbf{b} + p\mathbf{c}$ is a linear function of **a**, **b**, and **c**. The extension of this to the cases involving more than three vectors follows the obvious lines.

Theorem 1. If **a** and **b** are any two nonparallel vectors in a plane, and if **c** is any third vector in the plane of **a** and **b**, then **c** can be expressed as a linear function of **a** and **b**.

Proof. Since **a** and **b** are not parallel, there exists a parallelogram with **c** as its diagonal and with edges parallel to **a** and **b**. Figure 10 shows this parallelogram. We note from this figure that

6

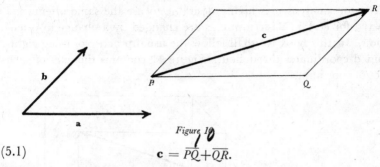

Figure 10

$$(5.1) \qquad\qquad \mathbf{c} = \overline{PQ} + \overline{QR}.$$

But $\overline{PQ}$ is parallel to $\mathbf{a}$, and $\overline{QR}$ is parallel to $\mathbf{b}$. Thus there exist scalars m and n such that

$$\overline{PQ} = m\mathbf{a}, \qquad \overline{QR} = n\mathbf{b}.$$

Substitution from these relations in (5.1) yields

$$\mathbf{c} = m\mathbf{a} + n\mathbf{b}.$$

Theorem 2.   If $\mathbf{a}$, $\mathbf{b}$ and $\mathbf{c}$ are any three vectors not all parallel to a single plane, and if $\mathbf{d}$ is any other vector, then $\mathbf{d}$ can be expressed as a linear function of $\mathbf{a}$, $\mathbf{b}$ and $\mathbf{c}$.

Proof.   This theorem is the extension of Theorem 1 to space. Since $\mathbf{a}$, $\mathbf{b}$ and $\mathbf{c}$ are not parallel to a single plane, there exists a parallelepiped with $\mathbf{d}$ as its diagonal and with edges parallel to $\mathbf{a}$, $\mathbf{b}$ and $\mathbf{c}$. Hence there exist scalars m, n and p such that

$$\mathbf{d} = m\mathbf{a} + n\mathbf{b} + p\mathbf{c}.$$

6. *Rectangular cartesian coordinates.*   In much of the theory and application of vectors it is convenient to introduce a set of rectangular cartesian coordinates. We shall *not* denote these by the usual symbols x, y and z, however, but shall use instead the symbols x_1, x_2 and x_3. These coordinates are said to have "right-handed orientation" or to be "right-handed" if when the thumb of the right hand is made to point in the direction of the positive x_3 axis, the fingers point in the direction of the 90° rotation which carries the positive x_1 axis into coincidence

7

with the positive x_2 axis. Otherwise the coordinates are "left-handed". In Vector Analysis it is highly desirable to use the same orientation always, for certain basic formulas are changed by a change in orientation. In this book we shall follow the usual practise of using right-handed coordinates throughout. Figure 11 contains the axes of such a set of coordinates.

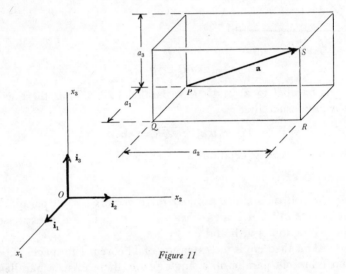

Figure 11

It is also convenient to introduce three vectors of unit magnitude, one pointing in the direction of each of the three positive coordinate axes. These vectors are denoted by $\mathbf{i}_1$, $\mathbf{i}_2$ and $\mathbf{i}_3$, and are shown in Figure 11.

Let us consider a vector $\mathbf{a}$. It has orthogonal projections in the directions of the positive coordinate axes. These are denoted by a_1, a_2 and a_3, as shown in Figure 11. They are called the components of $\mathbf{a}$. It should be noted that they can be positive or negative. Thus, for example, a_1 is positive when the angle between $\mathbf{a}$ and the direction of the positive x_1 axis (the angle QPS in the figure) is acute, and is negative when this angle is obtuse.

From Figure 11 it also appears that $\mathbf{a}$ is the diagonal of a rectangular

8

parallelepiped whose edges have lengths $|a_1|$, $|a_2|$ and $|a_3|$. Hence the magnitude a of the vector $\mathbf{a}$ is given by the relation

$$(6.1) \qquad a = \sqrt{a_1{}^2 + a_2{}^2 + a_3{}^2}.$$

From the figure it also appears that

$$(6.2) \qquad \mathbf{a} = \overline{PQ} + \overline{QR} + \overline{RS}.$$

Now the vector $\overline{PQ}$ is parallel to $\mathbf{i}_1$. Because of the definitions of a_1 and of the product of a scalar by a vector, we then have the relation $\overline{PQ} = a_1\mathbf{i}_1$. Similarly $\overline{QR} = a_2\mathbf{i}_2$ and $\overline{RS} = a_3\mathbf{i}_3$. Substitution in (6.2) from these relations yields

$$(6.3) \qquad \mathbf{a} = a_1\mathbf{i}_1 + a_2\mathbf{i}_2 + a_3\mathbf{i}_3.$$

This relation expresses the vector $\mathbf{a}$ as a linear function of the unit vectors $\mathbf{i}_1$, $\mathbf{i}_2$ and $\mathbf{i}_3$. We note that the coefficients are the components of $\mathbf{a}$.

Theorem. The components of the sum of a number of vectors are equal to the sums of the components of the vectors.

Proof. We consider two vectors $\mathbf{a}$ and $\mathbf{b}$ with components a_1, a_2, a_3, b_1, b_2 and b_3. Then

$$\mathbf{a} = a_1\mathbf{i}_1 + a_2\mathbf{i}_2 + a_3\mathbf{i}_3,$$
$$\mathbf{b} = b_1\mathbf{i}_1 + b_2\mathbf{i}_2 + b_3\mathbf{i}_3.$$

Addition of both sides of these equations leads to the relation

$$\mathbf{a} + \mathbf{b} = a_1\mathbf{i}_1 + a_2\mathbf{i}_2 + a_3\mathbf{i}_3 + b_1\mathbf{i}_1 + b_2\mathbf{i}_2 + b_3\mathbf{i}_3.$$

Now the sum of a number of vectors is independent of the order in which the vectors are added, by Theorem 1 of § 2. Hence we may write the above equation in the form

$$\mathbf{a} + \mathbf{b} = a_1\mathbf{i}_1 + b_1\mathbf{i}_1 + a_2\mathbf{i}_2 + b_2\mathbf{i}_2 + a_3\mathbf{i}_3 + b_3\mathbf{i}_3.$$

By the theorem in § 3 we may then write this in the form

$$\mathbf{a} + \mathbf{b} = (a_1 + b_1)\mathbf{i}_1 + (a_2 + b_2)\mathbf{i}_2 + (a_3 + b_3)\mathbf{i}_3.$$

Hence the components of $\mathbf{a} + \mathbf{b}$ are $a_1 + b_1$, $a_2 + b_2$ and $a_3 + b_3$. This proves the theorem when two vectors are added. The proof is similar when more than two vectors are added.

9

7. *The scalar product.* Let us consider two vectors **a** and **b** with magnitudes a and b, respectively. Let α be the smallest nonnegative angle between **a** and **b**, as shown in Figure 12. Then $0° \leqslant \alpha \leqslant 180°$.

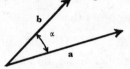

Figure 12

The scalar $ab \cos \alpha$ arises quite frequently, and hence it is convenient to give it a name. It is called the scalar product of **a** and **b**. It is also denoted by the symbols **a** · **b**, and hence we have

(7.1) $$\mathbf{a} \cdot \mathbf{b} = ab \cos \alpha.$$

The scalar product is sometimes referred to as the dot product.

If the components of **a** and **b** are denoted by a_1, a_2, a_3, b_1, b_2 and b_3 in the usual manner, the direction cosines of the directions of **a** and **b** are respectively

$$\frac{a_1}{a}, \frac{a_2}{a}, \frac{a_3}{a}; \quad \frac{b_1}{b}, \frac{b_2}{b}, \frac{b_3}{b}.$$

By a formula of analytic geometry, we then have

$$\cos \alpha = \frac{a_1}{a}\frac{b_1}{b} + \frac{a_2}{a}\frac{b_2}{b} + \frac{a_3}{a}\frac{b_3}{b}.$$

Substitution in (7.1) of this expression for $\cos \alpha$ yields

(7.2) $$\mathbf{a} \cdot \mathbf{b} = a_1 b_1 + a_2 b_2 + a_3 b_3.$$

This relation expresses the scalar product of two vectors in terms of the components of the vectors.

Theorem 1. The scalar product is commutative; that is,

$$\mathbf{a} \cdot \mathbf{b} = \mathbf{b} \cdot \mathbf{a}.$$

Proof. Because of (7.2), we have

$$\mathbf{a} \cdot \mathbf{b} = a_1 b_1 + a_2 b_2 + a_3 b_3,$$
$$\mathbf{b} \cdot \mathbf{a} = b_1 a_1 + b_2 a_2 + b_3 a_3.$$

10

Since $a_1b_1 = b_1a_1$, etc., the truth of the theorem follows immediately.

Theorem 2. The scalar product is distributive; that is,

$$\mathbf{a}\cdot(\mathbf{b}+\mathbf{c}) = \mathbf{a}\cdot\mathbf{b}+\mathbf{a}\cdot\mathbf{c}.$$

Proof. According to the theorem in § 6, the components of $\mathbf{b}+\mathbf{c}$ are b_1+c_1, b_2+c_2 and b_3+c_3. Hence, by (7.2) we have

$$\begin{aligned}
\mathbf{a}\cdot(\mathbf{b}+\mathbf{c}) &= a_1(b_1+c_1)+a_2(b_2+c_2)+a_3(b_3+c_3)\\
&= a_1b_1+a_2b_2+a_3b_3+a_1c_1+a_2c_2+a_3c_3\\
&= \mathbf{a}\cdot\mathbf{b}+\mathbf{a}\cdot\mathbf{c}.
\end{aligned}$$

This completes the proof.

If $\mathbf{a}$ and $\mathbf{b}$ are perpendicular, then

$$\mathbf{a}\cdot\mathbf{b} = 0.$$

However, if it is given that $\mathbf{a}\cdot\mathbf{b} = 0$, it does not necessarily follow that $\mathbf{a}$ is perpendicular to $\mathbf{b}$. It can be said only that at least one of the following must be true: $a = 0$; $b = 0$; $\mathbf{a}$ is perpendicular to $\mathbf{b}$. Similarly, if it is given that

$$\mathbf{a}\cdot\mathbf{b} = \mathbf{a}\cdot\mathbf{c},$$

it does not necessarily follow that $\mathbf{b} = \mathbf{c}$. For this relation can be written in the form $\mathbf{a}\cdot(\mathbf{b}-\mathbf{c}) = 0$, and hence it can be said only that at least one of the following is true: $a = 0$; $\mathbf{b} = \mathbf{c}$; $\mathbf{a}$ is perpendicular to the vector $\mathbf{b}-\mathbf{c}$.

We note the following expressions, in which $\mathbf{a}$ is any vector and $\mathbf{i}_1$, $\mathbf{i}_2$ and $\mathbf{i}_3$ are the unit vectors introduced in § 6:

$$\mathbf{a}\cdot\mathbf{a} = a^2,$$

(7.3)
$$\begin{array}{lll}
\mathbf{i}_1\cdot\mathbf{i}_1 = 1, & \mathbf{i}_1\cdot\mathbf{i}_2 = 0, & \mathbf{i}_1\cdot\mathbf{i}_3 = 0,\\
\mathbf{i}_2\cdot\mathbf{i}_1 = 0, & \mathbf{i}_2\cdot\mathbf{i}_2 = 1, & \mathbf{i}_2\cdot\mathbf{i}_3 = 0,\\
\mathbf{i}_3\cdot\mathbf{i}_1 = 0, & \mathbf{i}_3\cdot\mathbf{i}_2 = 0, & \mathbf{i}_3\cdot\mathbf{i}_3 = 1.
\end{array}$$

8. *The vector product.* Let us again consider two vectors $\mathbf{a}$ and $\mathbf{b}$, the smallest nonnegative angle between then being denoted by α, as shown in Figure 12. Then $0° \leqslant \alpha \leqslant 180°$. The vector product of $\mathbf{a}$ and $\mathbf{b}$ is a third vector $\mathbf{c}$ defined in terms of $\mathbf{a}$ and $\mathbf{b}$ by the following three conditions:

11

(i)   **c** is perpendicular to both **a** and **b**;

(ii)   the direction of **c** is that indicated by the thumb of the right hand when the fingers point in the sense of the rotation α from the direction of **a** to the direction of **b**;

(iii) $c = ab \sin \alpha$.

These conditions define **c** uniquely. Figure 13 shows **c**. The vector

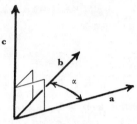

Figure 13

product of **a** and **b** is also denoted by **a** × **b**. Hence

(8.1) $$\mathbf{c} = \mathbf{a} \times \mathbf{b}.$$

The vector product is also called the cross product.

Theorem 1.   The area A of the parallelogram with the vectors **a** and **b** forming adjacent edges is given by the relation

(8.2) $$A = |\mathbf{a} \times \mathbf{b}|.$$

Proof.   Figure 14 shows the parallelogram. If p is the perpendicular distance from the terminus of **b** to the line of action of **a**, then $A = ap$. But $p = b \sin \alpha$. Hence

$$A = ab \sin \alpha$$
$$= |\mathbf{a} \times \mathbf{b}|.$$

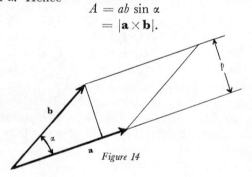

Figure 14

12

We shall now determine the components of the vector product $\mathbf{c}$ in (8.1) in terms of the components of $\mathbf{a}$ and $\mathbf{b}$. Because of condition (i) above, we have $\mathbf{a} \cdot \mathbf{c} = 0$, $\mathbf{b} \cdot \mathbf{c} = 0$. Because of (7.2), these equations can take the form

$$a_1c_1 + a_2c_2 + a_3c_3 = 0,$$
$$b_1c_1 + b_2c_2 + b_3c_3 = 0.$$

If these equations are solved for c_1 and c_2 in terms of c_3, it is found that

$$\frac{c_1}{a_2b_3 - a_3b_2} = \frac{c_2}{a_3b_1 - a_1b_3} = \frac{c_3}{a_1b_2 - a_2b_1}.$$

In order to preserve symmetry, we denote the common value o these three fractions by K, whence we have

(8.3)
$$\begin{aligned}
c_1 &= K(a_2b_3 - a_3b_2), \\
c_2 &= K(a_3b_1 - a_1b_3), \\
c_3 &= K(a_1b_2 - a_2b_1).
\end{aligned}$$

Now $c^2 = c_1{}^2 + c_2{}^2 + c_3{}^2$. Hence

$$\begin{aligned}
c^2 &= K^2[(a_2b_3 - a_3b_2)^2 + (a_3b_1 - a_1b_3)^2 + (a_1b_2 - a_2b_1)^2] \\
&= K^2[a_1{}^2(b_2{}^2 + b_3{}^2) + a_2{}^2(b_3{}^2 + b_1{}^2) + a_3{}^2(b_1{}^2 + b_2{}^2) \\
&\quad -2(a_2b_2a_3b_3 + a_3b_3a_1b_1 + a_1b_1a_2b_2)].
\end{aligned}$$

The first term inside the square brackets can be written in the form $a_1{}^2(b^2 - b_1{}^2)$. If the second and third terms are treated similarly it is found that

$$\begin{aligned}
c^2 &= K^2[(a_1{}^2 + a_2{}^2 + a_3{}^2) \; b^2 - (a_1b_1 + a_2b_2 + a_3b_3)^2] \\
&= K^2[a^2b^2 - (ab \cos \alpha)^2] \\
&= K^2a^2b^2(1 - \cos^2 \alpha) \\
&= K^2a^2b^2 \sin^2 \alpha.
\end{aligned}$$

But by condition (iii), above, $c^2 = a^2b^2 \sin^2 \alpha$. Thus $K = \pm 1$. If these two values of K are inserted in (8.3) two vectors $\mathbf{c}$ result with the same magnitude but pointing in opposite directions. Only one of these vectors satisfies condition (ii) above. Now both values of K are numerical, and are hence independent of $\mathbf{a}$ and $\mathbf{b}$. Thus the same value of K will satisfy condition (ii) for all vectors $\mathbf{a}$ and $\mathbf{b}$. Hence it is only necessary to find K for any one special case in which $\mathbf{c}$ can be found directly and with ease from conditions (i) – (iii) above. If we take $\mathbf{a} = \mathbf{i}_1$ and $\mathbf{b} = \mathbf{i}_2$, it is found from these conditions that $\mathbf{c} = \mathbf{i}_3$. Thus $a_1 = b_2 = c_3 = 1, a_2 = a_3 = b_1 = b_3 = c_1 = c_2 = 0$, and substitution in (8.3) yields $K = 1$. From (8.3) we then have in general,

$$(8.4) \qquad c_1 = a_2b_3 - a_3b_2, \;\; c_2 = a_3b_1 - a_1b_3, \;\; c_3 = a_1b_2 - a_2b_1.$$

Thus *the components of the vector product* $\mathbf{a} \times \mathbf{b}$ *are* $a_2b_3 - a_3b_2, \; a_3b_1 - a_1b_3, \; a_1b_2 - a_2b_1$. *Hence*

$$(8.5) \qquad \mathbf{a} \times \mathbf{b} = (a_2b_3 - a_3b_2)\mathbf{i}_1 + (a_3b_1 - a_1b_3)\mathbf{i}_2 + (a_1b_2 - a_2b_1)\mathbf{i}_3,$$

or, in determinant form

$$(8.6) \qquad \mathbf{a} \times \mathbf{b} = \begin{vmatrix} \mathbf{i}_1 & \mathbf{i}_2 & \mathbf{i}_3 \\ a_1 & a_2 & a_3 \\ b_1 & b_2 & b_3 \end{vmatrix}.$$

Theorem 2. The vector product is *not* commutative, because

$$(8.7) \qquad \mathbf{a} \times \mathbf{b} = -\mathbf{b} \times \mathbf{a}.$$

Proof. By (8.6) it follows that

$$\mathbf{b} \times \mathbf{a} = \begin{vmatrix} \mathbf{i}_1 & \mathbf{i}_2 & \mathbf{i}_3 \\ b_1 & b_2 & b_3 \\ a_1 & a_2 & a_3 \end{vmatrix}.$$

Since this determinant differs from the determinant in (8.6) only in that two rows are interchanged, the two determinants differ only in sign. Hence (8.7) is true. The truth of this theorem can also be seen easily by examining the three conditions which define the vector product. According to these conditions the effect of interchanging the order of $\mathbf{a}$ and $\mathbf{b}$ is only to reverse the direction of the vector product.

Theorem 3. The vector product is distributive; that is,

$$(8.8) \qquad \mathbf{a} \times (\mathbf{b} + \mathbf{c}) = \mathbf{a} \times \mathbf{b} + \mathbf{a} \times \mathbf{c}.$$

Proof. Let us write

$$\mathbf{d} = \mathbf{a} \times (\mathbf{b} + \mathbf{c}), \;\; \mathbf{e} = \mathbf{a} \times \mathbf{b}, \;\; \mathbf{f} = \mathbf{a} \times \mathbf{c}.$$

14

Then
$$d_1 = a_2(b_3+c_3) - a_3(b_2+c_2)$$
$$= (a_2b_3-a_3b_2) + (a_2c_3-a_3c_2)$$
$$= e_1+f_1.$$

Similarly $d_2 = e_2+f_2$ and $d_3 = e_3+f_3$. Hence $\mathbf{d} = \mathbf{e}+\mathbf{f}$, and so (8.8) is true.

We note the following expressions, in which $\mathbf{a}$ is any vector and $\mathbf{i}_1$, $\mathbf{i}_2$ and $\mathbf{i}_3$ are the unit vectors introduced in § 6:

$$\mathbf{a}\times\mathbf{a} = 0,$$

(8.9)
$$\mathbf{i}_1\times\mathbf{i}_1 = 0, \qquad \mathbf{i}_1\times\mathbf{i}_2 = \mathbf{i}_3, \qquad \mathbf{i}_1\times\mathbf{i}_3 = -\mathbf{i}_2,$$
$$\mathbf{i}_2\times\mathbf{i}_1 = -\mathbf{i}_3, \qquad \mathbf{i}_2\times\mathbf{i}_2 = 0, \qquad \mathbf{i}_2\times\mathbf{i}_3 = \mathbf{i}_1,$$
$$\mathbf{i}_3\times\mathbf{i}_1 = \mathbf{i}_2, \qquad \mathbf{i}_3\times\mathbf{i}_2 = -\mathbf{i}_1, \qquad \mathbf{i}_3\times\mathbf{i}_3 = 0.$$

If $\mathbf{a}$ and $\mathbf{b}$ are parallel, then

$$\mathbf{a}\times\mathbf{b} = 0.$$

Also, if it is given that $\mathbf{a}\times\mathbf{b} = 0$, then at least one of the following must be true: $a = 0$; $b = 0$; $\mathbf{a}$ is parallel to $\mathbf{b}$. Similarly, if

$$\mathbf{a}\times\mathbf{b} = \mathbf{a}\times\mathbf{c},$$

then $\mathbf{a}\times(\mathbf{b}-\mathbf{c}) = 0$ and at least one of the following must be true:

$$a = 0; \quad \mathbf{b} = \mathbf{c}; \quad \mathbf{a} \text{ is parallel to } \mathbf{b}-\mathbf{c}.$$

9. *Multiple products of vectors.* Let $\mathbf{a}$, $\mathbf{b}$ and $\mathbf{c}$ be any three vectors. The expression

$$\mathbf{a}\cdot(\mathbf{b}\times\mathbf{c})$$

is a scalar, and is called a *scalar triple product* of $\mathbf{a}$, $\mathbf{b}$ and $\mathbf{c}$.

If the components of $\mathbf{a}$, $\mathbf{b}$ and $\mathbf{c}$ are denoted in the usual way, then the components of $\mathbf{b}\times\mathbf{c}$ are $b_2c_3-b_3c_2$, $b_3c_1-b_1c_3$, $b_1c_2-b_2c_1$, and we have by (7.2)

$$\mathbf{a}\cdot(\mathbf{b}\times\mathbf{c}) = a_1(b_2c_3-b_3c_2) + a_2(b_3c_1-b_1c_3) + a_3(b_1c_2-b_2c_1),$$

or

(9.1)
$$\mathbf{a}\cdot(\mathbf{b}\times\mathbf{c}) = \begin{vmatrix} a_1 & a_2 & a_3 \\ b_1 & b_2 & b_3 \\ c_1 & c_2 & c_3 \end{vmatrix}.$$

15

Theorem 1. The permutation theorem for scalar triple products. If the vectors in a scalar triple product are subjected to an odd number of permutations, the value of this product is changed only in sign; and if the number of permutations is even the value of the product is not changed.

Proof. A permutation of the vectors in a scalar triple product is defined as the interchange of any two vectors which appear in the product. From (9.1) it appears that a single permutation produces an interchange of two rows in the determinant. Since such an interchange of rows results in a change of sign only, the truth of the theorem is established.

Because of this theorem we have

$$\mathbf{a}\cdot(\mathbf{b}\times\mathbf{c}) = \mathbf{b}\cdot(\mathbf{c}\times\mathbf{a}) = \mathbf{c}\cdot(\mathbf{a}\times\mathbf{b})$$
$$= -\mathbf{c}\cdot(\mathbf{b}\times\mathbf{a}) = -\mathbf{a}\cdot(\mathbf{c}\times\mathbf{b}) = -\mathbf{b}\cdot(\mathbf{a}\times\mathbf{c}).$$

Theorem 2. The volume V of the parallelepiped with the vectors **a**, **b** and **c** forming adjacent edges is given by the relation

$$(9.2) \qquad\qquad V = |\mathbf{a}\cdot(\mathbf{b}\times\mathbf{c})|,$$

where the vertical lines here denote the absolute value.

Proof. Figure 15 shows the parallelepiped. Let $\mathbf{d} = \mathbf{b}\times\mathbf{c}$. Then

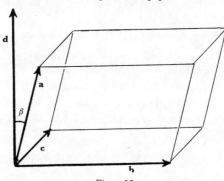

Figure 15

$d = |\mathbf{b}\times\mathbf{c}|$, and by Theorem 1 of § 8 the area of the parallelogram forming the base of the parallelepiped is then d. Hence $V = hd$,

16

where h is the altitude of the parallelepiped. But $\mathbf{d}$ is perpendicular to the base, and if β is the angle between $\mathbf{a}$ and $\mathbf{d}$, then $h = a \mid \cos \beta \mid$. (The absolute value signs are necessary here, since β lies in the range $0° \leqslant \beta \leqslant 180°$ and hence $\cos \beta$ may be negative.) Thus

$$\begin{aligned} V &= \mid ad \cos \beta \mid \\ &= \mid \mathbf{a} \cdot \mathbf{d} \mid \\ &= \mid \mathbf{a} \cdot (\mathbf{b} \times \mathbf{c}) \mid. \end{aligned}$$

The expression

$$\mathbf{a} \times (\mathbf{b} \times \mathbf{c})$$

is a vector, and is called a *vector triple product* of $\mathbf{a}$, $\mathbf{b}$ and $\mathbf{c}$. Let us write

$$\mathbf{d} = \mathbf{b} \times \mathbf{c}, \quad \mathbf{e} = \mathbf{a} \times \mathbf{d}.$$

Then $\mathbf{e}$ is equal to the vector triple product $\mathbf{a} \times (\mathbf{b} \times \mathbf{c})$. By (8.5) we have

$$\begin{aligned} e_1 &= a_2 d_3 - a_3 d_2 \\ &= a_2(b_1 c_2 - b_2 c_1) - a_3(b_3 c_1 - b_1 c_3) \\ &= b_1(a_2 c_2 + a_3 c_3) - c_1(a_2 b_2 + a_3 b_3). \end{aligned}$$

Because of (7.2), this can be written in the form

$$\begin{aligned} e_1 &= b_1(\mathbf{a} \cdot \mathbf{c} - a_1 c_1) - c_1(\mathbf{a} \cdot \mathbf{b} - a_1 b_1) \\ &= b_1(\mathbf{a} \cdot \mathbf{c}) - c_1(\mathbf{a} \cdot \mathbf{b}). \end{aligned}$$

Similarly

$$\begin{aligned} e_2 &= b_2(\mathbf{a} \cdot \mathbf{c}) - c_2(\mathbf{a} \cdot \mathbf{b}), \\ e_3 &= b_3(\mathbf{a} \cdot \mathbf{c}) - c_3(\mathbf{a} \cdot \mathbf{b}). \end{aligned}$$

Hence $\mathbf{e} = \mathbf{b}(\mathbf{a} \cdot \mathbf{c}) - \mathbf{c}(\mathbf{a} \cdot \mathbf{b})$, and since $\mathbf{e} = \mathbf{a} \times (\mathbf{b} \times \mathbf{c})$, we have

(9.3) $$\mathbf{a} \times (\mathbf{b} \times \mathbf{c}) = \mathbf{b}(\mathbf{a} \cdot \mathbf{c}) - \mathbf{c}(\mathbf{a} \cdot \mathbf{b}).$$

This is a rather important identity. It will be used frequently.

We note that the right side of (9.3) is a vector in the plane of $\mathbf{b}$ and $\mathbf{c}$. This is to be expected, since the vector $\mathbf{a} \times (\mathbf{b} \times \mathbf{c})$ is perpendicular to the vector $\mathbf{b} \times \mathbf{c}$ which is itself perpendicular to the plane of $\mathbf{b}$ and $\mathbf{c}$.

Let us now consider the expression

$$(\mathbf{a} \times \mathbf{b}) \times (\mathbf{c} \times \mathbf{d}).$$

17

It is a vector. If we regard it as a vector triple product of $\mathbf{a} \times \mathbf{b}$, $\mathbf{c}$ and $\mathbf{d}$, then by (9.3),

(9.4) $$(\mathbf{a} \times \mathbf{b}) \times (\mathbf{c} \times \mathbf{d}) = \mathbf{c}\,[(\mathbf{a} \times \mathbf{b}) \cdot \mathbf{d}] - \mathbf{d}\,[(\mathbf{a} \times \mathbf{b}) \cdot \mathbf{c}].$$

Since an interchange of the order of the vectors in a vector product only changes the sign,

$$(\mathbf{a} \times \mathbf{b}) \times (\mathbf{c} \times \mathbf{d}) = -(\mathbf{c} \times \mathbf{d}) \times (\mathbf{a} \times \mathbf{b}).$$

If we regard the right side of this equation as the vector triple product of $\mathbf{c} \times \mathbf{d}$, $\mathbf{a}$ and $\mathbf{b}$, then by (9.3),

(9.5) $$(\mathbf{a} \times \mathbf{b}) \times (\mathbf{c} \times \mathbf{d}) = -\mathbf{a}\,[(\mathbf{c} \times \mathbf{d}) \cdot \mathbf{b}] + \mathbf{b}\,[(\mathbf{c} \times \mathbf{d}) \cdot \mathbf{a}].$$

We next consider the expression

$$(\mathbf{a} \times \mathbf{b}) \cdot (\mathbf{c} \times \mathbf{d}).$$

It is a scalar. If we consider it as the scalar triple product of $\mathbf{a} \times \mathbf{b}$, $\mathbf{c}$ and $\mathbf{d}$, and subject these three vectors to two permutations, then according to Theorem 1 of § 9, we have

$$(\mathbf{a} \times \mathbf{b}) \cdot (\mathbf{c} \times \mathbf{d}) = \mathbf{c} \cdot [\mathbf{d} \times (\mathbf{a} \times \mathbf{b})].$$

If the vector triple product on the right-hand side of this equation is expanded by the identity in (9.3), we obtain

$$(\mathbf{a} \times \mathbf{b}) \cdot (\mathbf{c} \times \mathbf{d}) = (\mathbf{c} \cdot \mathbf{a})(\mathbf{d} \cdot \mathbf{b}) - (\mathbf{c} \cdot \mathbf{b})(\mathbf{d} \cdot \mathbf{a}),$$

or in a form more easily recalled,

(9.6) $$(\mathbf{a} \times \mathbf{b}) \cdot (\mathbf{c} \times \mathbf{d}) = (\mathbf{a} \cdot \mathbf{c})(\mathbf{b} \cdot \mathbf{d}) - (\mathbf{b} \cdot \mathbf{c})(\mathbf{a} \cdot \mathbf{d}).$$

There are many other multiple products of vectors. In general these can be simplified by means of the theorems and formulas above. In dealing with multiple products of vectors care must be exercised to avoid writing down expressions which are ambiguous or have not been defined. Thus, for example, the expression $\mathbf{a} \times \mathbf{b} \times \mathbf{c}$ is ambiguous since $\mathbf{a} \times (\mathbf{b} \times \mathbf{c}) \neq (\mathbf{a} \times \mathbf{b}) \times \mathbf{c}$, and the following expressions have not been defined:

$$\mathbf{ab}, \quad \mathbf{a} \cdot (\mathbf{b} \cdot \mathbf{c}), \quad \mathbf{a} \times (\mathbf{b} \cdot \mathbf{c}).$$

10.   *Moment of a vector about a point.*   Let $\mathbf{a}$ be a vector with origin at

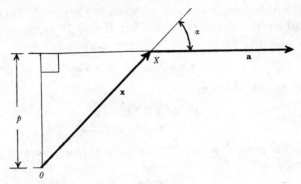

Figure 16

a point X, and let $\mathbf{x}$ be a vector with origin at a point 0 and terminus at X, as shown in Figure 16. The moment of $\mathbf{a}$ about the point 0 is by definition the vector $\mathbf{P}$ given by the relation

$$\mathbf{P} = \mathbf{x} \times \mathbf{a}.$$

Theorem 1. If $\mathbf{P}$ is the moment of $\mathbf{a}$ about a point 0, then

$$P = pa,$$

where p is the perpendicular distance from 0 to the line of action of $\mathbf{a}$.

Proof. Now $P = xa \sin \alpha$, where α is the angle between $\mathbf{x}$ and $\mathbf{a}$. But $p = x \sin \alpha$. Hence $P = pa$.

Theorem 2. The moments about a point of any two equal vectors with the same line of action are equal.

Proof. Let $\mathbf{a}$ and $\mathbf{a}$ be two equal vectors with the same line of ac-

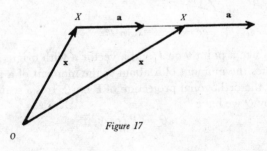

Figure 17

tion, and with origins X and X', as shown in Figure 17. Let 0 be any point, and let $\overline{OX} = \mathbf{x}$, $\overline{OX'} = \mathbf{x}'$. Let $\mathbf{P}$ and $\mathbf{P}'$ be the moments of $\mathbf{a}$ and $\mathbf{a}'$ about 0. Then

$$\mathbf{P} = \mathbf{x} \times \mathbf{a}, \quad \mathbf{P}' = \mathbf{x}' \times \mathbf{a}'.$$

But $\mathbf{x}' = \mathbf{x} + \overline{XX'}$. Hence

$$\begin{aligned}\mathbf{P}' &= (\mathbf{x} + \overline{XX'}) \times \mathbf{a}' \\ &= \mathbf{x} \times \mathbf{a}' + \overline{XX'} \times \mathbf{a}'.\end{aligned}$$

Since $\overline{XX'}$ is parallel to $\mathbf{a}'$, $\overline{XX'} \times \mathbf{a}' = 0$. Hence, since $\mathbf{a}' = \mathbf{a}$ we have finally

$$\mathbf{P}' = \mathbf{x} \times \mathbf{a} = \mathbf{P}.$$

11. *Moment of a vector about a directed line.* Each line defines two directions which are opposite. A line is said to be directed when one of these directions is labelled the positive direction and the other the negative direction.

Let us consider a directed line L, and let $\mathbf{b}$ denote a unit vector pointing in the positive direction of the line, as shown in Figure 18. We

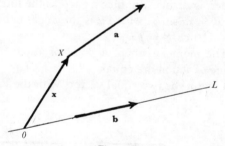

Figure 18

also introduce a point 0 on L and a vector $\mathbf{a}$ with origin at a point X. If $\mathbf{P}$ denotes the moment of $\mathbf{a}$ about 0, the moment of $\mathbf{a}$ about L is by definition the orthogonal projection of $\mathbf{P}$ on L. It is a scalar, and if it is denoted by Q we have

$$Q = P \cos \Phi,$$

20

where Φ is the angle between $\mathbf{P}$ and the unit vector $\mathbf{b}$. Hence $Q = \mathbf{b} \cdot \mathbf{P}$. But $\mathbf{P} = \mathbf{x} \times \mathbf{a}$, where $\mathbf{x} = \overline{OR}$. Thus

(11.1) $$Q = \mathbf{b} \cdot (\mathbf{x} \times \mathbf{a}).$$

Theorem 1.   The above definition of the moment of a vector about a directed line L is independent of the position of the point 0 on L.

Proof.   Let $0'$ be a second point on L, as shown in Figure 19. Also,

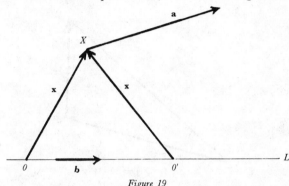

Figure 19

let $\mathbf{P}'$ be the moment of $\mathbf{a}$ about $0'$, and let Q' be the corresponding moment of $\mathbf{a}$ about L. Then

$$Q = \mathbf{b} \cdot (\mathbf{x} \times \mathbf{a}) , \quad Q' = \mathbf{b} \cdot (\mathbf{x}' \times \mathbf{a}) ,$$

where $\mathbf{x}'$ is as shown. But $\mathbf{x}' = \overline{O''O} + \mathbf{x}$. Thus

$$Q' = \mathbf{b} \cdot [(\overline{O''O} + \mathbf{x}) \times \mathbf{a}]$$
$$= \mathbf{b} \cdot (\overline{O''O} \times \mathbf{a}) + Q.$$

Since $\mathbf{b}$ and $\overline{O''O}$ have the same line of action L, then $\mathbf{b} \cdot (\overline{O''O} \times \mathbf{x}) = 0$ by Theorem 2 of §9. Thus $Q' = Q$, which proves the theorem.

Theorem 2.   If $\mathbf{P}$ denotes the moment of a vector $\mathbf{a}$ about the origin of the coordinates, then the three components of $\mathbf{P}$ are equal respectively to the moments of $\mathbf{a}$ about the three coordinate axes.

Proof.   The truth of this theorem follows immediately from the above definitions of the moments of a vector about a point and about a line.

21

12. *Differentiation with respect to a scalar variable.* Let u be a scalar variable. If there is a value of a vector **a** corresponding to each value of the scalar u, **a** is said to be a function of u. When it is desired to indicate such a correspondence, we write $\mathbf{a}(u)$.

Let us consider a general value of the scalar u and the corresponding vector $\mathbf{a}(u)$. Let the vector $\overline{OP}$ in Figure 20 denote this vector. We

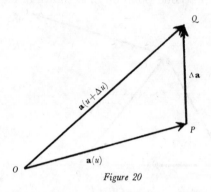

Figure 20

now increase the scalar u by an amount Δu. The vector corresponding to the scalar $u+\Delta u$ is $\mathbf{a}(u+\Delta u)$. Let the vector $\overline{OQ}$ in Figure 20 denote this vector. The change in $\mathbf{a}(u)$ corresponding to the change Δu in u is then $\mathbf{a}(u+\Delta u) - \mathbf{a}(u)$. In the usual notation of calculus we denote it by $\Delta\mathbf{a}$, so that

$$\Delta\mathbf{a} = \mathbf{a}(u+\Delta u) - \mathbf{a}(u).$$

From the figure it is seen that $\Delta\mathbf{a} = \overline{PQ}$. Since Δu is a scalar, the vector $\dfrac{\Delta\mathbf{a}}{\Delta u}$ has the same direction as $\overline{PQ}$. The vector

$$\underset{\Delta u \to 0}{\text{limit}} \frac{\Delta\mathbf{a}}{\Delta u}$$

is the rate of change of **a** with respect to u. It is also called the derivative of **a** with respect to u, and is denoted by the symbol $\dfrac{d\mathbf{a}}{du}$, so that

$$\frac{d\mathbf{a}}{du} = \underset{\Delta u \to 0}{\text{limit}} \frac{\Delta\mathbf{a}}{\Delta u}.$$

22

In precisely the same way, we define the derivative with respect to u of the vector $\frac{d\mathbf{a}}{du}$. This vector is denoted by

$$\frac{d}{du}\left(\frac{d\mathbf{a}}{du}\right) \text{ or } \frac{d^2\mathbf{a}}{du^2}.$$

Higher derivatives of $\mathbf{a}$ with respect to u are defined similarly.

Let $\mathbf{a}(u)$ and $\mathbf{b}(u)$ be any two vectors which are functions of a scalar u, and let m be a scalar function of u. We shall now derive the following formulas:

$$(12.1) \qquad \frac{d}{du}(\mathbf{a}+\mathbf{b}) = \frac{d\mathbf{a}}{du} + \frac{d\mathbf{b}}{du},$$

$$(12.2) \qquad \frac{d}{du}(m\mathbf{a}) = m\frac{d\mathbf{a}}{du} + \frac{dm}{du}\mathbf{a},$$

$$(12.3) \qquad \frac{d}{du}(\mathbf{a}\cdot\mathbf{b}) = \mathbf{a}\cdot\frac{d\mathbf{b}}{du} + \frac{d\mathbf{a}}{du}\cdot\mathbf{b},$$

$$(12.4) \qquad \frac{d}{du}(\mathbf{a}\times\mathbf{b}) = \mathbf{a}\times\frac{d\mathbf{b}}{du} + \frac{d\mathbf{a}}{du}\times\mathbf{b}.$$

Proof of (12.1). When u increases by an amount Δu, the change in the sum $\mathbf{a}+\mathbf{b}$ is

$$(12.5) \qquad \Delta(\mathbf{a}+\mathbf{b}) = (\mathbf{a}+\Delta\mathbf{a}+\mathbf{b}+\Delta\mathbf{b}) - (\mathbf{a}+\mathbf{b}).$$

According to Theorem 2 of § 2 the sum of a number of vectors is independent of the order of summation. Thus the right side of (12.5) can be written in the form $\mathbf{a}-\mathbf{a}+\mathbf{b}-\mathbf{b}+\Delta\mathbf{a}+\Delta\mathbf{b}$, which reduces to $\Delta\mathbf{a}+\Delta\mathbf{b}$. Thus

$$\Delta(\mathbf{a}+\mathbf{b}) = \Delta\mathbf{a}+\Delta\mathbf{b}.$$

If both sides of this equation are divided by Δu, and if Δu is then made to approach zero, (12.1) is obtained.

Proof of (12.2). When u increases by an amount Δu, the change in $m\mathbf{a}$ is

$$(12.6) \qquad \Delta(m\mathbf{a}) = (m+\Delta m)(\mathbf{a}+\Delta\mathbf{a}) - m\mathbf{a}.$$

According to the theorem in § 3 the multiplication of a vector by a scalar satisfies the distributive laws, as exemplified by Equations (3.1) and (3.2). Because of the law exemplified by (3.1) we can then write (12.6) in the form

(12.7) $$\Delta(m\mathbf{a}) = m(\mathbf{a}+\Delta\mathbf{a})+\Delta m(\mathbf{a}+\Delta\mathbf{a}) - m\mathbf{a},$$

and because of the law exemplified by (3.2), we can then write (12.7) in the form

$$\Delta(m\mathbf{a}) = m\mathbf{a}+m\Delta\mathbf{a}+\Delta m\ \mathbf{a}+\Delta m\ \Delta\mathbf{a} - m\mathbf{a}$$
$$= m\ \Delta\mathbf{a}+\Delta m\ \mathbf{a}+\Delta m\ \Delta\mathbf{a}.$$

If both sides of this equation are divided by Δu, and if Δu is then made to approach zero, (12.2) results.

Proof of (12.3). When u increases by an amount Δu, the change in $\mathbf{a}\cdot\mathbf{b}$ is

$$\Delta(\mathbf{a}\cdot\mathbf{b}) = (\mathbf{a}+\Delta\mathbf{a})\cdot(\mathbf{b}+\Delta\mathbf{b}) - \mathbf{a}\cdot\mathbf{b}.$$

Since the scalar product is distributive, this equation may be written in the form

$$\Delta(\mathbf{a}\cdot\mathbf{b}) = \mathbf{a}\cdot\mathbf{b}+\mathbf{a}\cdot\Delta\mathbf{b}+\Delta\mathbf{a}\cdot\mathbf{b}+\Delta\mathbf{a}\cdot\Delta\mathbf{b} - \mathbf{a}\cdot\mathbf{b}$$
$$= \mathbf{a}\cdot\Delta\mathbf{b}+\Delta\mathbf{a}\cdot\mathbf{b}+\Delta\mathbf{a}\cdot\Delta\mathbf{b}.$$

If both sides of this equation are divided by the scalar Δu, we have

$$\frac{\Delta(\mathbf{a}\cdot\mathbf{b})}{\Delta u} = \mathbf{a}\cdot\frac{\Delta\mathbf{b}}{\Delta u}+\frac{\Delta\mathbf{a}}{\Delta u}\cdot\mathbf{b}+\frac{\Delta\mathbf{a}}{\Delta u}\cdot\Delta\mathbf{b}.$$

If we now let Δu approach zero, (12.3) results.

Proof of (12.4). This proof follows exactly the same pattern as the proof of (12.3), and hence will not be given here.

It is important to note that in (12.4) the order in which the vectors $\mathbf{a}$ and $\mathbf{b}$ appear must be the same in all terms, since $\mathbf{a}\times\mathbf{b}$ is not equal to $\mathbf{b}\times\mathbf{a}$.

If $\mathbf{a}(u)$ is a vector with components a_1, a_2 and a_3, then

$$\mathbf{a} = a_1\mathbf{i}_1+a_2\mathbf{i}_2+a_3\mathbf{i}_3.$$

By (12.1) and (12.2) we then have

$$\frac{d\mathbf{a}}{du} = \frac{d}{du}\ (a_1\mathbf{i}_1)+\frac{d}{du}\ (a_2\mathbf{i}_2)+\frac{d}{du}\ (a_3\mathbf{i}_3)$$

$$= a_1\frac{d\mathbf{i}_1}{du}+a_2\frac{d\mathbf{i}_2}{du}+a_3\frac{d\mathbf{i}_3}{du}+\frac{da_1}{du}\ \mathbf{i}_1+\frac{da_2}{du}\ \mathbf{i}_2+\frac{da_3}{du}\ \mathbf{i}_3\ .$$

Now a_1, a_2 and a_3 are scalar functions of u. Also $\mathbf{i}_1$, $\mathbf{i}_2$ and $\mathbf{i}_3$ are unit vectors pointing in the directions of the positive coordinate axis. If they are the same for all values of u, then

$$\frac{d\mathbf{i}_1}{du} = \frac{d\mathbf{i}_2}{du} = \frac{d\mathbf{i}_3}{du} = 0,$$

and so

$$\frac{d\mathbf{a}}{du} = \frac{da_1}{du}\,\mathbf{i}_1 + \frac{da_2}{du}\,\mathbf{i}_2 + \frac{da_3}{du}\,\mathbf{i}_3.$$

From this equation we see that the components of the derivative of a vector are equal to the derivatives of the components, provided the directions of the coordinate axes are independent of the variable of differentiation.

13. *Integration with respect to a scalar variable.* Let $\mathbf{a}$ be a given function of a scalar u. We introduce orthogonal unit vectors $\mathbf{i}_1$, $\mathbf{i}_2$ and $\mathbf{i}_3$ with directions independent of u. Then

$$\mathbf{a}(u) = a_1\mathbf{i}_1 + a_2\mathbf{i}_2 + a_3\mathbf{i}_3.$$

We make the definition

$$(13.1) \qquad \int \mathbf{a}(u)\,du = \mathbf{i}_1\int a_1(u)\,du + \mathbf{i}_2\int a_2(u)\,du + \mathbf{i}_3\int a_3(u)\,du.$$

From this definition it follows that

$$\frac{d}{du}\int \mathbf{a}(u)\,du = \mathbf{i}_1\,a_1(u) + \mathbf{i}_2\,a_2(u) + \mathbf{i}_3\,a_3(u) = \mathbf{a},$$

as expected, since integration is the inverse of differentiation. It is to be noted that each integral on the right side of (13.1) gives rise to a constant of integration.

Theorem. If $\mathbf{a}(u)$ is a linear function of constant vectors, with coefficients which are functions of u, then $\int \mathbf{a}(u)\,du$ can be obtained by formal integration in which constant vectors are treated as are constants in ordinary integration, and arbitrary constant vectors are inserted where arbitrary constants would appear in ordinary integration.

Proof. We have
$$\mathbf{a}(u) = \mathbf{p}\,f(u) + \mathbf{q}\,g(u) + \cdots,$$
where $\mathbf{p}$, $\mathbf{q}$, $\cdots$ are constant vectors and $f(u)$, $g(u)$, $\cdots$ are given functions of u. By (13.1) it then follows that

$$\int \mathbf{a}(u)\,du = \mathbf{i}_1\,[\,p_1 \!\int\! f(u)\,du + q_1 \!\int\! g(u)\,du + \cdots]$$
$$+ \mathbf{i}_2[\,p_2\!\int\! f(u)\,du + \cdots] + \mathbf{i}_3[\,p_3\!\int\! f(u)\,du + \cdots]$$
$$= \mathbf{p}\!\int\! f(u)\,du + \mathbf{q}\!\int\! g(u)\,du + \cdots.$$

If k, l, $\cdots$ denote the integration constants of the integrals in the last line, then the total contribution of these constants to $\int \mathbf{a}(u)\,du$ is the single arbitrary constant vector $\mathbf{c}$ such that

$$\mathbf{c} = \mathbf{p}k + \mathbf{q}l + \cdots.$$

The following examples illustrate the above theorem:

$$\int (\mathbf{p}u + \mathbf{q})\,du = \tfrac{1}{2}\mathbf{p}u^2 + \mathbf{q}u + \mathbf{c},$$
$$\int \mathbf{p}\,\cos u\,du = \mathbf{p}\,\sin u + \mathbf{c}.$$

14. *Linear vector differential equations.* The equation

$$(14.1) \qquad (p_0\,\frac{d^n}{du^n} + p_1\,\frac{d^{n-1}}{du^{n-1}} + \cdots + p_{n-1}\,\frac{d}{du} + p_n)\,\mathbf{x} = \mathbf{a},$$

in which $\mathbf{a}$ and $p_0, p_1, \cdots, p_n$ are given functions of the scalar u and $\mathbf{x}$ is an unknown vector, is a linear vector differential equation of order n. Let F denote the differential operator in (14.1). Then (14.1) can be expressed in the form

$$(14.2) \qquad\qquad F[\mathbf{x}] = \mathbf{a}.$$

Theorem. The general solution of the linear vector differential equation $F[\mathbf{x}] = \mathbf{a}$ is $\mathbf{x} = \mathbf{Y} + \mathbf{A}$, where $\mathbf{A}$ is a particular solution of this differential equation, and

$$\mathbf{Y} = \mathbf{c}_1 y_1 + \mathbf{c}_2 y_2 + \mathbf{c}_3 y_3 + \cdots + \mathbf{c}_n y_n,$$

$\mathbf{c}_1$, $\mathbf{c}_2$, $\mathbf{c}_3$, $\cdots$, $\mathbf{c}_n$ *being arbitrary constant vectors and* $y_1, y_2, y_3, \cdots, y_n$ *being* n *linearly independent solutions* of the homogeneous scalar differential equation $F[y] = 0$.

Proof. Let us introduce the unit vectors $\mathbf{i}_1$, $\mathbf{i}_2$ and $\mathbf{i}_3$ with directions independent of u. Then

$$\mathbf{a} = a_1\mathbf{i}_1 + a_2\mathbf{i}_2 + a_3\mathbf{i}_3,$$
$$\mathbf{x} = x_1\mathbf{i}_1 + x_2\mathbf{i}_2 + x_3\mathbf{i}_3,$$
$$F[\mathbf{x}] = F[x_1]\mathbf{i}_1 + F[x_2]\mathbf{i}_2 + F[x_3]\mathbf{i}_3.$$

Hence, from (14.2) we have

(14.3) $\qquad F[x_1] = a_1, \quad F[x_2] = a_2, \quad F[x_3] = a_3.$

Let A_1, A_2 and A_3 denote particular solutions of these three scalar differential equations, and let $y_1, y_2, \cdots, y_n$ denote u linearly independent particular solutions of the scalar differential equation $F[y] = 0$. Then the general solutions of Equations (14.3) are

$$x_1 = c_{11}y_1 + c_{12}y_2 + c_{13}y_3 + \cdots + c_{1n}y_n + A_1,$$
$$x_2 = c_{21}y_1 + c_{22}y_2 + c_{23}y_3 + \cdots + c_{2n}y_n + A_2,$$
$$x_3 = c_{31}y_1 + c_{32}y_2 + c_{33}y_3 + \cdots + c_{3n}y_n + A_3,$$

where the c's are arbitrary constants. Let us multiply these three equations by $\mathbf{i}_1$, $\mathbf{i}_2$ and $\mathbf{i}_3$, respectively, and then add. The result can be written in the form

(14.4) $\qquad\qquad \mathbf{x} = \mathbf{Y} + \mathbf{A},$

where

$$\mathbf{Y} = \mathbf{c}_1 y_1 + \mathbf{c}_2 y_2 + \mathbf{c}_3 y_3 + \cdots + \mathbf{c}_n y_n,$$
$$\mathbf{A} = A_1\mathbf{i}_1 + A_2\mathbf{i}_2 + A_3\mathbf{i}_3,$$

the vectors $\mathbf{c}_1$, $\mathbf{c}_2$, $\mathbf{c}_3$, $\cdots$, $\mathbf{c}_n$ being arbitrary constant vectors. Equation (14.4) gives the general solution of Equation (14.1). We note that $\mathbf{Y}$ is the general solution of the homogeneous equation $F[\mathbf{x}] = 0$, and that $\mathbf{A}$ is a particular solution of Equation (14.1). The particular solution $\mathbf{A}$ can be found by procedures very similar to those used to find particular solutions of linear scalar differential equations. This is demonstrated below.

As an example, let us find the general solution of the differential equation

$$(14.5) \qquad \frac{d^2\mathbf{x}}{du^2} - \frac{d\mathbf{x}}{du} - 2\mathbf{x} = 10\mathbf{p}\sin u + \mathbf{q}(2u+1),$$

where $\mathbf{p}$ and $\mathbf{q}$ are constant vectors. We must first find two linearly independent solutions of the equation

$$(14.6) \qquad \frac{d^2 y}{du^2} - \frac{dy}{du} - 2y = 0.$$

The auxiliary equation of this differential equation is

$$m^2 - m - 2 = 0.$$

It has roots -1, 2, whence the required solutions of (14.6) are e^{-u} and e^{2u}. Thus

$$\mathbf{Y} = \mathbf{c}_1 e^{-u} + \mathbf{c}_2 e^{2u}.$$

We now use the method of undetermined coefficients to find a particular solution $\mathbf{A}$ of Equation (14.5). The function on the right side of (14.5), and the derivatives of this function, are linear functions of $\sin u$, $\cos u$, u, 1, none of which are particular solutions of (14.6). Hence, we look for a particular solution $\mathbf{A}$ in the form

$$\mathbf{A} = \mathbf{b}\sin u + \mathbf{c}\cos u + \mathbf{d}u + \mathbf{e},$$

where $\mathbf{b}$, $\mathbf{c}$, $\mathbf{d}$ and $\mathbf{e}$ are constant vectors. By substitution in (14.5) we readily find by equating coefficients that

$$3\mathbf{b} - \mathbf{c} = -10\mathbf{p}, \qquad \mathbf{b} + 3\mathbf{c} = 0,$$
$$\mathbf{d} = -\mathbf{q}, \qquad \mathbf{d} + 2\mathbf{e} = -\mathbf{q}.$$

Solving these four equations for $\mathbf{b}$, $\mathbf{c}$, $\mathbf{d}$, $\mathbf{e}$, we find that

$$\mathbf{b} = -3\mathbf{p}, \qquad \mathbf{c} = \mathbf{p}, \qquad \mathbf{d} = -\mathbf{q}, \qquad \mathbf{e} = 0.$$

The general solution of Equation (14.5) is then

$$\mathbf{x} = \mathbf{c}_1 e^{-u} + \mathbf{c}_2 e^{2u} + \mathbf{p}(-3\sin u + \cos u) - \mathbf{q}u.$$

Problems

1. The vectors $\mathbf{a}$, $\mathbf{b}$, $\mathbf{c}$ and $\mathbf{d}$ all lie in a horizontal plane. Their

magnitudes are 1, 2, 3 and 2, and their directions are east, northeast, north and northwest, respectively. Construct these vectors.

2. If $\mathbf{a}$, $\mathbf{b}$ and $\mathbf{c}$ are defined as in Problem 1, construct the vectors $(\mathbf{a}+\mathbf{b})+\mathbf{c}$, $(\mathbf{b}+\mathbf{a})+\mathbf{c}$, $\mathbf{c}+(\mathbf{a}+\mathbf{b})$, and by measuring their magnitudes and directions verify that they are equal.

3. If $\mathbf{a}$ and $\mathbf{b}$ are defined as in Problem 1, contruct the vectors $\mathbf{a}+2\mathbf{b}$, $2\mathbf{a}+\mathbf{b}$, $3\mathbf{a}-\mathbf{b}$, $-2\mathbf{a}-2\mathbf{b}$.

4. If $\mathbf{a}$, $\mathbf{b}$ and $\mathbf{c}$ are defined as in Problem 1, express each of these vectors as a linear function of the other two, determining the coefficients graphically to two decimal places in each case.

5. Given that

$$\mathbf{a}+2\mathbf{b} = \mathbf{m}, \qquad 2\mathbf{a}-\mathbf{b} = \mathbf{n},$$

where $\mathbf{m}$ and $\mathbf{n}$ are known vectors, solve for $\mathbf{a}$ and $\mathbf{b}$.

6. If $\mathbf{a}$ and $\mathbf{b}$ are vectors with a common origin 0 and terminuses A and B, in terms of $\mathbf{a}$ and $\mathbf{b}$ find the vector $\overline{OC}$, where C is the middle point of AB.

7. The vectors $\mathbf{a}$ and $\mathbf{b}$ form consecutive sides of a regular hexagon, the terminus of $\mathbf{a}$ coinciding with the origin of $\mathbf{b}$. In terms of $\mathbf{a}$ and $\mathbf{b}$ find the vectors forming the other four sides.

8. If $\mathbf{a}$, $\mathbf{b}$, $\mathbf{c}$ and $\mathbf{d}$ have a common origin and terminuses A, B, C and D, and if $\mathbf{b}-\mathbf{a} = \mathbf{c}-\mathbf{d}$, show that $ABCD$ is a parallelogram.

9. The vectors $\mathbf{a}$, $\mathbf{b}$ and $\mathbf{c}$ have a common origin and form adjacent edges of a parallelepiped. Show that $\mathbf{a}+\mathbf{b}+\mathbf{c}$ forms a diagonal.

10. Vectors are drawn from the center of a regular pentagon to its vertices. Show that their sum is zero.

11. Consider the vectors $\mathbf{a}$, $\mathbf{b}$, $\mathbf{c}$ and $\mathbf{d}$ defined in Problem 1. Introduce rectangular cartesian coordinate axes such that the four vectors lie in the $x_1 x_2$ plane with the x_1 axis pointing east and the x_2 axis pointing north. Find the components of the vectors $\mathbf{a}$, $\mathbf{b}$, $\mathbf{c}$, $\mathbf{d}$, $\mathbf{a}+2\mathbf{b}$, and $3\mathbf{a}-2\mathbf{b}$; also, express these vectors in terms of their components and the unit vectors $\mathbf{i}_1$, $\mathbf{i}_2$ and $\mathbf{i}_3$.

12. Do Problem 4, making an exact determination of the coefficients analytically by the use of components.

13. Given that

$$a = i_1 + 2i_2 + i_3,$$
$$b = 2i_1 + i_2,$$
$$c = 3i_1 - 4i_2 - 5i_3,$$

verify that $a \cdot (b+c) = a \cdot b + a \cdot c$, $a \times (b+c) = a \times b + a \times c$. Also, find $|a \times b|$, $|a \times b + a \times c|$.

14. Show that $(a+b) \cdot (a-b) = a^2 - b^2$.

15. Show that $(a-b) \times (a+b) = 2a \times b$.

16. The two vectors $a = i_1 + 3i_2 - 2i_3$, $b = 3i_1 + 2i_2 - 2i_3$ have a common origin. Show that the line joining their terminuses is parallel to the $x_1 x_2$ plane, and find its length.

17. Show that the vectors $a = i_1 + 4i_2 + 3i_3$, $b = 4i_1 + 2i_2 - 4i_3$ are perpendicular.

18. If a, b and c are as defined in Problem 13, find $a \cdot (b \times c)$, $(b \times a) \cdot c$, $a \times (b \times c)$, $(a \times b) \cdot (a \times c)$, $(a \times b) \times (a \times c)$.

19. If the vectors drawn from the origin to three points A, B and C are respectively equal to the three vectors a, b and c defined in Problem 13, find a unit vector n perpendicular to the plane ABC. Hence find the distance from the origin to this plane.

20. Show that

$$a \times (b \times c) + b \times (c \times a) + c \times (a \times b) = 0.$$

21. Show that

$$a \times [b \times (c \times d)] = [a \cdot (c \times d)]b - (a \cdot b)(c \times d)$$
$$= (b \cdot d)(a \times c) - (b \cdot c)(a \times d).$$

22. Show that

$$[a \times b] \cdot [(b \times c) \times (c \times a)] = [a \cdot (b \times c)]^2.$$

23. Show that

$$a[b \cdot (c \times d)] - b[c \cdot (d \times a)] + c[d \cdot (a \times b)] - d[a \cdot (b \times c)] = 0.$$

24. Show that

$$[a \cdot (b \times c)](f \times g) = \begin{vmatrix} a & b & c \\ f \cdot a & f \cdot b & f \cdot c \\ g \cdot a & g \cdot b & g \cdot c \end{vmatrix}.$$

30

25. Show that

$$\mathbf{n} = \frac{\mathbf{n}\cdot(\mathbf{b}\times\mathbf{c})}{\mathbf{a}\cdot(\mathbf{b}\times\mathbf{c})}\,\mathbf{a} + \frac{\mathbf{n}\cdot(\mathbf{c}\times\mathbf{a})}{\mathbf{b}\cdot(\mathbf{c}\times\mathbf{a})}\,\mathbf{b} + \frac{\mathbf{n}\cdot(\mathbf{a}\times\mathbf{b})}{\mathbf{c}\cdot(\mathbf{a}\times\mathbf{b})}\,\mathbf{c}\,.$$

This formula can be used to express any vector $\mathbf{n}$ as a linear function of any three vectors $\mathbf{a}$, $\mathbf{b}$ and $\mathbf{c}$ not lying in the same plane.

26. Express the vector $\mathbf{n} = \mathbf{i}_1 + 2\mathbf{i}_2 + 3\mathbf{i}_3$ as a linear function of the vectors $\mathbf{a}$, $\mathbf{b}$ and $\mathbf{c}$ defined in Problem 13. (See Problem 25.)

27. Express the vector $\mathbf{n} = 2\mathbf{i}_1 - 2\mathbf{i}_2 - 3\mathbf{i}_3$ as a linear function of the vectors $\mathbf{a}$, $\mathbf{b}$ and $\mathbf{c}$ defined in Problem 13. (See Problem 25.)

28. Show that

$$\mathbf{a}\times[(\mathbf{f}\times\mathbf{b})\times(\mathbf{g}\times\mathbf{c})] + \mathbf{b}\times[(\mathbf{f}\times\mathbf{c})\times(\mathbf{g}\times\mathbf{a})]$$
$$+\mathbf{c}\times[(\mathbf{f}\times\mathbf{a})\times(\mathbf{g}\times\mathbf{b})] = 0.$$

29. If 0 is the origin of the coordinates and A, B and C are three points such that

$$\overline{OA} = 2\mathbf{i}_1 + 2\mathbf{i}_2 - \mathbf{i}_3,$$
$$\overline{AB} = \mathbf{i}_1 - \mathbf{i}_2 + 2\mathbf{i}_3,$$
$$\overline{BC} = -2\mathbf{i}_1 + 2\mathbf{i}_2 - 3\mathbf{i}_3,$$

find (i) the moment of $\overline{BC}$ about A, (ii) the moment of $\overline{CB}$ about O, (iii) the moment of $\overline{BC}$ about the directed line OA, (iv) the moments of $\overline{BC}$ about the coordinate axes.

30. If $\mathbf{a}$ and $\mathbf{b}$ are two vectors, prove that a times the moment of $\mathbf{b}$ about the line of action of $\mathbf{a}$ is equal to b times the moment of $\mathbf{a}$ about the line of action of $\mathbf{b}$.

31. If $\mathbf{a}(u)$ has a constant magnitude, show that

$$\mathbf{a}\cdot\frac{d\mathbf{a}}{du} = 0\,.$$

32. If $\mathbf{a} = \mathbf{p}\cos u + \mathbf{q}\sin u$, where $\mathbf{p}$ and $\mathbf{q}$ are constant vectors and u is a variable, show that

$$\mathbf{a}\cdot\left[\frac{d\mathbf{a}}{du}\times\frac{d^2\mathbf{a}}{du^2}\right] = 0\,.$$

33. If $\mathbf{a}$ is a function of a variable u, show that

$$\frac{d}{du}\left[\mathbf{a}\cdot\left(\frac{d\mathbf{a}}{du}\times\frac{d^2\mathbf{a}}{du^2}\right)\right] = \left(\mathbf{a}\times\frac{d\mathbf{a}}{du}\right)\cdot\frac{d^3\mathbf{a}}{du^3}\,.$$

34. Given that the unit vectors $\mathbf{i}_1$, $\mathbf{i}_2$ and $\mathbf{i}_3$ are independent of a variable u, evaluate $\int \mathbf{a}\, du$ when

(i) $\qquad\qquad\qquad \mathbf{a} = \mathbf{i}_1 + 2u\mathbf{i}_2 + 8u^3\mathbf{i}_3$,

(ii) $\qquad\qquad\qquad \mathbf{a} = \mathbf{i}_1 \cos u + \mathbf{i}_2 \sin u - \mathbf{i}_3\, e^u$,

(iii) $\qquad\qquad\qquad \mathbf{a} = \dfrac{2\mathbf{i}_1}{4-u^2} + \dfrac{2\mathbf{i}_2}{4+u^2}$.

35. Evaluate the following integrals, in which $\mathbf{p}$ and $\mathbf{q}$ are constant vectors:

(i) $\qquad\qquad\qquad \int (\mathbf{p} + \mathbf{q}u^2)\, du$,

(ii) $\qquad\qquad\qquad \int (\mathbf{p} \cos u + \mathbf{q} \sec^2 u)\, du$,

(iii) $\qquad\qquad\qquad \int \dfrac{\mathbf{p} + \mathbf{q}u}{4-u^2}\, du$.

36. Find the vector $\mathbf{x}(u)$ in each of the following cases, given that $\mathbf{p}$, $\mathbf{q}$ and $\mathbf{r}$ are constant vectors:

(i) $\qquad\qquad\qquad \dfrac{d\mathbf{x}}{du} = \mathbf{p}\, u^2 + \mathbf{q}\, e^{2u}$,

(ii) $\qquad\qquad\qquad \dfrac{d^2\mathbf{x}}{du^2} = \mathbf{p} \cos u + \mathbf{q} \sin u$,

(iii) $\qquad\qquad\qquad \dfrac{d^2\mathbf{x}}{du^2} = (\mathbf{p} \sin u - \mathbf{q} \cos u) \times \mathbf{r}$.

37. Find the general solutions of the differential equations

(i) $\qquad\qquad\qquad \dfrac{d^2\mathbf{x}}{du^2} - \dfrac{d\mathbf{x}}{du} - 6\mathbf{x} = 0$,

(ii) $\qquad\qquad\qquad \dfrac{d^2\mathbf{x}}{du^2} + 4\dfrac{d\mathbf{x}}{du} + 4\mathbf{x} = 0$,

(iii) $\qquad\qquad\qquad \dfrac{d^2\mathbf{x}}{du^2} - 2\dfrac{d\mathbf{x}}{du} + 5\mathbf{x} = 0$,

(iv) $\qquad\qquad\qquad \dfrac{d^4\mathbf{x}}{du^4} - 6\dfrac{d^3\mathbf{x}}{du^3} + 11\dfrac{d^2\mathbf{x}}{du^2} - 6\dfrac{d\mathbf{x}}{du} = 0$.

38. Find the general solutions of the following differential equations, given that $\mathbf{p}$ and $\mathbf{q}$ are constant vectors:

(i) $$\frac{d\mathbf{x}}{du} - 3\mathbf{x} = \mathbf{p}(3u^2+1),$$

(ii) $$\frac{d^2\mathbf{x}}{du^2} - 4\mathbf{x} = 16\mathbf{p}\cos 2u,$$

(iii) $$\frac{d^2\mathbf{x}}{du^2} + 2\frac{d\mathbf{x}}{du} = -6\mathbf{p}e^u + 5\mathbf{q}\sin u.$$

39. Find the general solutions of the following differential equations, given that $\mathbf{p}$ and $\mathbf{q}$ are constant vectors:

(i) $$\frac{d^2\mathbf{x}}{du^2} - 2\frac{d\mathbf{x}}{du} + \mathbf{x} = 2\mathbf{p}e^u,$$

(ii) $$\frac{d^2\mathbf{x}}{du^2} - 3\frac{d\mathbf{x}}{du} = 2\mathbf{p}e^u + 18\mathbf{q}u^2,$$

(iii) $$u^2\frac{d^2\mathbf{x}}{du^2} - u\frac{d\mathbf{x}}{du} - 3\mathbf{x} = 6\mathbf{p}.$$

CHAPTER II

APPLICATIONS TO GEOMETRY

15. *Introduction.* This chapter contains a treatment by vector methods of various elementary topics in geometry. This treatment is included in the present volume for two reasons. First, it indicates the ease and power which vector methods lend to studies in geometry. Secondly, it affords the student an opportunity to gain additional skill in the use of the vector operations introduced in the previous chapter.

Proofs of some well-known theorems of plane geometry will first be given. Then a fairly broad treatment of solid analytic geometry will be presented, in which some of the more familiar formulas will be deduced in vector form and by vector methods. Finally, the differential geometry of curves in space will be considered briefly. For more complete treatments of analytic geometry and differential geometry by vector methods, the reader is referred to the excellent books by F. D. Murnaghan,[1] W. C. Graustein[2] and C. E. Weatherburn.[3]

16. *Some theorems of plane geometry.* In this section we shall consider proofs by vector methods of two well-known theorems of plane geometry.

Theorem 1. The diagonals of a parallelogram bisect each other.

Proof. Let us consider the parallelogram *OABC* in Figure 21. The diagonals cut each other at the point *D*. We must prove that *D* bisects both of the line segments *OB* and *AC*.

For convenience we denote the vectors drawn from *O* to the points

---

[1] F. D. Murnaghan, Analytic geometry, Prentice-Hall, New York, 1946.

[2] W. C. Graustein, Differential geometry, The Macmillan Company, New York, 1935.

[3] C. E. Weatherburn, Differential geometry of three dimensions, Cambridge University Press, Cambridge, England. Vol. 1, 1927. Vol. 2, 1930.

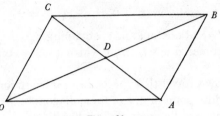

Figure 21

A, B, C and D by $\mathbf{a}$, $\mathbf{b}$, $\mathbf{c}$ and $\mathbf{d}$, respectively. Since D lies on the line OB, there exists a scalar u such that

(16.1) $$\mathbf{d} = u\mathbf{b}.$$

Also, from the figure we see that

(16.2) $$\mathbf{d} = \overline{OA} + \overline{AD}.$$

Since D lies on the line AC there exists a scalar v such that

$$\overline{AD} = v\overline{AC}.$$

Hence we can write (16.2) in the form

(16.3) $$\mathbf{d} = \mathbf{a} + v\overline{AC}.$$

We now equate the above two expressions given for $\mathbf{d}$ in (16.1) and (16.3), obtaining

(16.4) $$\mathbf{a} + v\overline{AC} = u\,\mathbf{b}.$$

The next step is to express all vectors in this equation as linear functions of any two vectors in the plane, say $\mathbf{a}$ and $\mathbf{c}$. From the figure we see that

$$\overline{AC} = -\mathbf{a} + \mathbf{c}, \qquad \mathbf{b} = \mathbf{a} + \mathbf{c},$$

whence (16.4) becomes

$$\mathbf{a} + v\,(-\mathbf{a} + \mathbf{c}) = u\,(\mathbf{a} + \mathbf{c}),$$

or

$$(1 - u - v)\,\mathbf{a} = (u - v)\,\mathbf{c}.$$

35

Since **a** and **c** do not have the same line of action it then follows that

$$1 - u - v = 0, \qquad u - v = 0.$$

We solve these equations for u and v, obtaining $u = v = \frac{1}{2}$. Thus Equation (16.1) becomes $\mathbf{d} = \frac{1}{2} \mathbf{b}$, from which it follows that D is the middle point of OB.

We have now proved that the point of intersection D of the diagonals is the middle point of one of these diagonals. From symmetry, D must also be the middle point of the other diagonal.

Theorem 2. The medians of a triangle meet in a single point which trisects each of them.

Proof. Let us consider the triangle OAB in Figure 22. The points

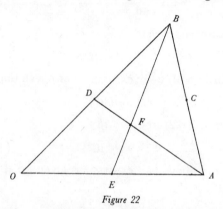

Figure 22

C, D and E are the middle points of the sides, and F is the point of intersection of the medians AD and BE. We must prove that F is a point of trisection of each of the three medians AD, BE and OC.

For convenience we denote the vectors drawn from O to the points A, B, C, D, E and F by **a**, **b**, **c**, **d**, **e** and **f**, respectively. Now F lies on the median AD. Thus there exists a scalar u such that

(16.5) $$\overline{DF} = u\overline{DA}$$

and we then have

$$\mathbf{f} = \overline{OD} + u\overline{DA}.$$

36

Similarly, since F lies on the median BE, we have

$$\mathbf{f} = \overline{OE} + v\overline{EB},$$

where v is some scalar. We now equate these two expressions for $\mathbf{f}$, obtaining

(16.6) $$\overline{OD} + u\overline{DA} = \overline{OE} + v\overline{EB}.$$

The next step is to express all vectors in this equation as linear functions of any two vectors in the plane, say $\mathbf{a}$ and $\mathbf{b}$. From Figure 22 we see that

(16.7) $$\overline{OD} = \tfrac{1}{2}\mathbf{b}, \qquad \overline{OE} = \tfrac{1}{2}\mathbf{a},$$
$$\overline{DA} = -\tfrac{1}{2}\mathbf{b} + \mathbf{a}, \qquad \overline{EB} = -\tfrac{1}{2}\mathbf{a} + \mathbf{b}.$$

Thus (16.6) becomes, after substitution from (16.7) and collection of like terms,

$$(\tfrac{1}{2} - u - \tfrac{1}{2}v)\mathbf{a} = (\tfrac{1}{2} - \tfrac{1}{2}u - v)\mathbf{b}.$$

Since $\mathbf{a}$ and $\mathbf{b}$ do not have the same line of action, it follows that

$$\tfrac{1}{2} - u - \tfrac{1}{2}v = 0, \qquad \tfrac{1}{2} - \tfrac{1}{2}u - v = 0.$$

We solve these equations for u and v, obtaining $u = v = \tfrac{1}{3}$. Thus Equation (16.5) becomes $\overline{DF} = \tfrac{1}{3}\overline{DA}$, from which it follows that F is a point of trisection of the median DA.

We have now proved that the point of intersection F of two medians is a point of trisection of one of these medians. From symmetry, F must also be a point of trisection of the other of these medians. From symmetry F must also be a point of trisection of the third median.

Solid Analytic Geometry

17. *Notation.* We shall now consider the analytic geometry of points in space. A right-handed set of rectangular cartesian coordinates is introduced, with origin at a point 0. Just as in Chapter I, we denote these coordinates by the symbols x_1, x_2 and x_3, as shown in Figure 23. Unit vectors $\mathbf{i}_1$, $\mathbf{i}_2$ and $\mathbf{i}_3$ pointing in the directions of the positive coordinate axes are also introduced, as shown.

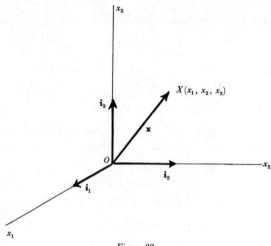

Figure 23

To denote a general point in space we shall use the letter X, and we shall call the vector $\overline{OX}$ the *position-vector* of X. For convenience we shall denote this vector also by the symbol $\mathbf{x}$, and its components by the symbols (x_1, x_2, x_3). We then have

$$\mathbf{x} = x_1\mathbf{i}_1 + x_2\mathbf{i}_2 + x_3\mathbf{i}_3.$$

The quantities x_1, x_2 and x_3 are also the coordinates of the point X.

We shall use the letters $A, B, C, \cdots$ to denote specific points in space, and shall denote the position-vectors of these points by $\mathbf{a}, \mathbf{b}, \mathbf{c}, \cdots$. The component of these vectors will be denoted in the usual way by the symbols (a_1, a_2, a_3), (b_1, b_2, b_3), (c_1, c_2, c_3), $\cdots$. We note that these quantities are also the coordinates of the points $A, B, C, \cdots$.

18. *Division of a line segment in a given ratio.* Let us suppose that we are given two points A and B, and that it is desired to find a third point C which divides the line segment AB in the given ratio m to n. Figure 24 illustrates the problem. If C lies between A and B, then $0 < m/n < +\infty$; if C lies beyond B then $-\infty < m/n < -1$; if C lies beyond A, then $-1 < m/n < 0$. In any event we have

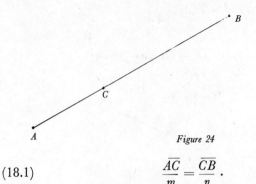

Figure 24

(18.1)
$$\frac{\overline{AC}}{m} = \frac{\overline{CB}}{n}.$$

If we now denote the position-vectors of A, B and C by $\mathbf{a}$, $\mathbf{b}$ and $\mathbf{c}$, respectively, then

$$\overline{AC} = \mathbf{c} - \mathbf{a}, \qquad \overline{CB} = \mathbf{b} - \mathbf{c},$$

and (18.1) can then be written in the form

$$n(\mathbf{c} - \mathbf{a}) = m(\mathbf{b} - \mathbf{c}).$$

Solving this equation for $\mathbf{c}$, we obtain

(18.2)
$$\mathbf{c} = \frac{m\mathbf{b} + n\mathbf{a}}{m + n}.$$

This formula expresses the position-vector $\mathbf{c}$ of the desired point C in terms of the known quantities $\mathbf{a}$, $\mathbf{b}$, m and n.

In books on Analytic Geometry, formulas are usually given which express the coordinates of C in terms of m, n and the coordinates of A and B. It should be noted that (18.2) is entirely equivalent to these formulas, for these formulas can be deduced from (18.2) simply by equating the components of the left side of (18.2) to the components of the right side of (18.2).

19. *The distance between two points.* Let us suppose that A and B are two given points, and that it is desired to find the distance d between A and B in terms of the position-vectors $\mathbf{a}$ and $\mathbf{b}$ of A and B. Figure 25 illustrates the problem. Now

39

$$d = |\overline{AB}|\,.$$

But $\overline{AB} = \mathbf{b} - \mathbf{a}$. Thus

$$d^2 = |\overline{AB}|^2 = \overline{AB}\cdot\overline{AB} = (\mathbf{b} - \mathbf{a})\cdot(\mathbf{b} - \mathbf{a})$$

whence

$$d = \sqrt{(\mathbf{b} - \mathbf{a})\cdot(\mathbf{b} - \mathbf{a})}.$$

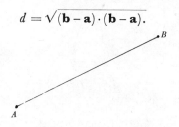

Figure 25

20. *The area of a triangle.* Let us suppose that A, B and C are three given points, and that it is desired to find the area Δ_{abc} of the triangle ABC in terms of the position-vectors $\mathbf{a}$, $\mathbf{b}$ and $\mathbf{c}$ of A, B and C. Figure 26 illustraties the problem.

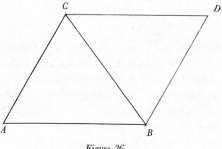

Figure 26

We first construct the parallelogram of which AB and AC form two adjacent edges, as shown. Then Δ_{abc} is equal to one half the area of this parallelogram. But, by Theorem 1 of § 8, the area of this parallelogram is $|\overline{AB}\times\overline{AC}|$. Hence we can write

(20.1) $$\Delta_{abc} = \tfrac{1}{2}\varphi,$$

where

(20.2) $$\boldsymbol{\varphi} = \overline{AB} \times \overline{AC}.$$

Now $\overline{AB} = \mathbf{b} - \mathbf{a}$, $\overline{AC} = \mathbf{c} - \mathbf{a}$. Thus

$$\boldsymbol{\varphi} = (\mathbf{b} - \mathbf{a}) \times (\mathbf{c} - \mathbf{a}).$$

This simplifies to

(20.3) $$\boldsymbol{\varphi} = \mathbf{b} \times \mathbf{c} + \mathbf{c} \times \mathbf{a} + \mathbf{a} \times \mathbf{b}.$$

The required area of the triangle is thus given by (20.1), φ being the magnitude of the vector given by (20.3).

A property of the vector $\boldsymbol{\varphi}$ will now be recorded, for future use. Since this vector is equal to $\overline{AB} \times \overline{AC}$ we conclude that *the vector $\boldsymbol{\varphi}$ is perpendicular to the plane of the triangle ABC, and its direction is that indicated by the thumb of the right hand when the fingers are placed to indicate the direction of the passage around the triangle from A to B to C.*

21. *The equation of a plane.* There are several ways in which a plane can be specified. For example, three points which are on the plane and do not lie on a single straight line can be given, or a line in the plane and a point on the plane but not on the line can be given. In each of several such cases we shall now deduce the equation which must be satisfied by the position-vector $\mathbf{x}$ of every point X on the plane. This equation will be referred to simply as the *equation of the plane*. In books on analytic geometry the equation of a plane usually appears as an equation which involves scalars only, and is satisfied only by the co-ordinates of points on the plane. We shall refer to this latter equation as the *cartesian form of the equation of the plane*.

(i) *To find the equation of the plane through a given point and perpendicular to a given vector.* Let A be the given point and $\mathbf{b}$ be the given vector. Figure 27 illustrates the problem, the plane P being the plane in question.

Let X be a general point on P, and let $\mathbf{a}$ and $\mathbf{x}$ denote the position-vectors of A and X, respectively. Now $\overline{AX}$ is perpendicular to $\mathbf{b}$. Thus

$$\overline{AX} \cdot \mathbf{b} = 0.$$

41

But $\overline{AX} = \mathbf{x} - \mathbf{a}$, whence it follows that

(21.1)
$$(\mathbf{x} - \mathbf{a}) \cdot \mathbf{b} = 0 .$$

This is the desired equation of the plane P.

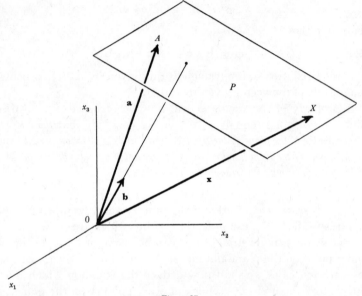

Figure 27

The cartesian form of the equation of the plane P can be obtained readily from (21.1). It is only necessary to express (21.1) in terms of the components of the vectors involved. In this way we obtain the equation

$$(x_1 - a_1) b_1 + (x_2 - a_2) b_2 + (x_3 - a_3) b_3 = 0 .$$

(ii) *To find the equation of the plane through three given points.* Let A, B and C be three given points. It is desired to find the equation of the plane P containing these three points. Figure 28 illustrates the problem.

Let X be a general point on the plane P, and let $\mathbf{a}$, $\mathbf{b}$, $\mathbf{c}$ and $\mathbf{x}$ denote the position-vectors of the points A, B, C and X, respectively. In § 20 we saw that the vector $\boldsymbol{\varphi}$ given by the relation

42

$$\boldsymbol{\varphi} = \mathbf{b}\times\mathbf{c}+\mathbf{c}\times\mathbf{a}+\mathbf{a}\times\mathbf{b}$$

is perpendicular to the plane P. Hence, by Problem (i) above the equation of P is

(21.2) $$(\mathbf{x}-\mathbf{a})\cdot\boldsymbol{\varphi} = 0.$$

Since $\mathbf{a}\cdot\boldsymbol{\varphi} = \mathbf{a}\cdot(\mathbf{b}\times\mathbf{c}+\mathbf{c}\times\mathbf{a}+\mathbf{a}\times\mathbf{b}) = \mathbf{a}\cdot(\mathbf{b}\times\mathbf{c})$,

Equation (21.2) can be written in the equivalent form

(21.3) $$\mathbf{x}\cdot\boldsymbol{\varphi} = \mathbf{a}\cdot(\mathbf{b}\times\mathbf{c}).$$

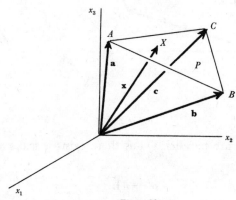

Figure 28

22. *The vector-perpendicular from a point to a plane.* The vector-perpendicular from a point D to a plane P is the vector with origin at D and terminus at the point on P nearest D.

(i) *To find the vector-perpendicular from a point D to a plane P through a given point and perpendicular to a given vector.* Let A be the given point and let $\mathbf{b}$ be the given vector. Figure 29 illustrates the problem. We denote the position-vectors of the points A and D by $\mathbf{a}$ and $\mathbf{d}$, respectively. If the point E is the foot of the perpendicular from the point D to the plane P, then $\overline{DE}$ is the vector-perpendicular from the point D to the plane P. We shall denote it by the symbol $\mathbf{p}$. It is required to find $\mathbf{p}$ in terms of $\mathbf{a}$ and $\mathbf{b}$.

43

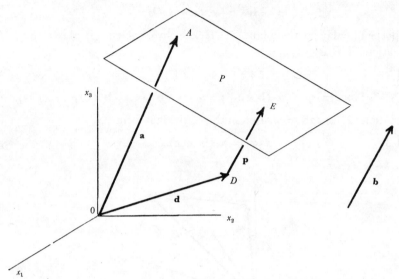

Figure 29

Now **p** and **b** are parallel. Thus there exists a scalar constant K such that

(22.1) $$\mathbf{p} = K\mathbf{b}.$$

From the figure we see that

$$\overline{OD} + \overline{DE} + \overline{EA} + \overline{AO} = 0,$$

or

(22.2) $$\mathbf{d} + K\mathbf{b} + \overline{EA} - \mathbf{a} = 0.$$

Now **b** is perpendicular to $\overline{EA}$. Hence $\mathbf{b} \cdot \overline{EA} = 0$, and so scalar multiplication of (22.2) by **b** yields

(22.3) $$(\mathbf{d} - \mathbf{a}) \cdot \mathbf{b} + Kb^2 = 0.$$

Thus

$$K = \frac{(\mathbf{a} - \mathbf{d}) \cdot \mathbf{b}}{b^2},$$

and substitution for K in Equation (22.1) then yields

(22.4)
$$\mathbf{p} = \frac{(\mathbf{a} - \mathbf{d}) \cdot \mathbf{b}}{b^2} \, \mathbf{b} \, .$$

In particular, if the point D is at the origin, then $\mathbf{d} = 0$ and

(22.5)
$$\mathbf{p} = \frac{\mathbf{a} \cdot \mathbf{b}}{b^2} \, \mathbf{b} \, .$$

(ii) *To find the vector-perpendicular from a point D to a plane P through three given points.* Let A, B and C be the three given points, with position-vectors $\mathbf{a}$, $\mathbf{b}$ and $\mathbf{c}$, respectively. Figure 30 illustrates the problem. It is desired to find the vector-perpendicular $\mathbf{p}$ in terms of $\mathbf{a}$, $\mathbf{b}$, $\mathbf{c}$ and $\mathbf{d}$.

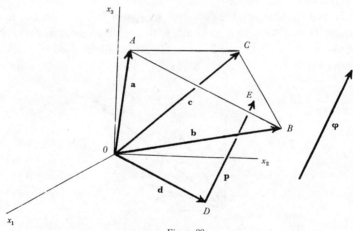

Figure 30

In § 20 we saw that the vector $\boldsymbol{\varphi}$ given by the relation

$$\boldsymbol{\varphi} = \mathbf{b} \times \mathbf{c} + \mathbf{c} \times \mathbf{a} + \mathbf{a} \times \mathbf{b}$$

is perpendicular to the plane P. Hence we may regard P as the plane through the given point A and perpendicular to the given vector $\boldsymbol{\varphi}$. Thus, from Equation (22.4) it follows that the required vector-perpendicular is given by the relation

45

$$\mathbf{p} = \frac{(\mathbf{a} - \mathbf{d}) \cdot \boldsymbol{\varphi}}{\varphi^2} \, \boldsymbol{\varphi}.$$

Since $\mathbf{a} \cdot \boldsymbol{\varphi} = \mathbf{a} \cdot (\mathbf{b} \times \mathbf{c})$ it follows that

(22.6)
$$\mathbf{p} = \frac{\mathbf{a} \cdot (\mathbf{b} \times \mathbf{c}) - \mathbf{d} \cdot \boldsymbol{\varphi}}{\varphi^2} \, \boldsymbol{\varphi}.$$

23. *The equation of a line.* There are several ways in which a line in space can be specified. For example, two points on the line can be given, or two planes through the line can be given. In each of several such cases we shall now deduce the equation which must be satisfied by the position-vector $\mathbf{x}$ of every point X on the line. This equation will be referred to simply as the *equation of the line*.

(i) *To find the equation of the line through a given point and parallel to a given vector.* Let A be the given point, with position-vector $\mathbf{a}$, and let $\mathbf{b}$ be the given vector. Figure 31 illustrates the problem, L being the line in question.

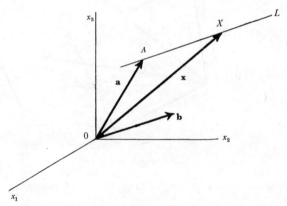

Figure 31

Let X be a general point on L, and let $\mathbf{x}$ denote the position-vector of X. Now $\overline{AX}$ is parallel to $\mathbf{b}$. Thus

$$\overline{AX} \times \mathbf{b} = 0.$$

46

But $\overline{AX} = \mathbf{x} - \mathbf{a}$, whence it follows that

(23.1) $$(\mathbf{x} - \mathbf{a}) \times \mathbf{b} = 0.$$

This is the desired equation of the line L.

(ii) *To find the equation of the line through two given points.* Let A and B be the given points, with position-vectors $\mathbf{a}$ and $\mathbf{b}$, respectively. Figure 32

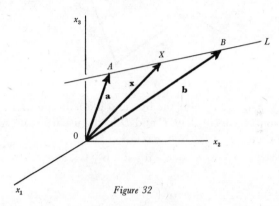

Figure 32

illustrates the problem, L being the line in question. Now L is parallel to the vector $\overline{AB}$, and $\overline{AB} = \mathbf{b} - \mathbf{a}$. Thus, by Problem (i) above, the desired equation of L is

(23.2) $$(\mathbf{x} - \mathbf{a}) \times (\mathbf{b} - \mathbf{a}) = 0.$$

(iii) *To find the equation of the line through a given point and perpendicular to two given vectors.* Let A be the given point with position-vector $\mathbf{a}$, and let $\mathbf{b}$ and $\mathbf{c}$ be the given vectors. Figure 33 illustrates the problem, L being the line in question. Now L is parallel to the vector $\mathbf{b} \times \mathbf{c}$. Hence, by Problem (i) above, the desired equation of L is

(23.3) $$(\mathbf{x} - \mathbf{a}) \times (\mathbf{b} \times \mathbf{c}) = 0.$$

(iv) *To find the equation of the line through a given point and perpendicular to the plane through three given points.* Let A be the given point on the line, and let B, C and D be the given points on the plane. Figure 34 illustrates

47

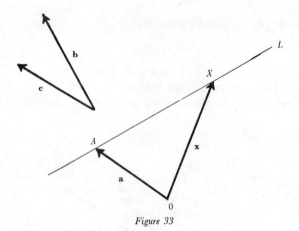

Figure 33

the problem, L and P being the line and plane in question. We denote the position-vectors of A, B, C and D in the usual manner. Let us consider the vector $\boldsymbol{\varphi}$ given by the relation

$$\boldsymbol{\varphi} = \mathbf{c}\times\mathbf{d}+\mathbf{d}\times\mathbf{b}+\mathbf{b}\times\mathbf{c}.$$

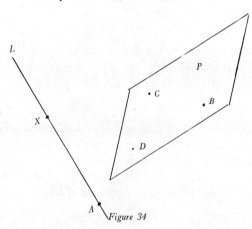

Figure 34

According to § 20, this vector is perpendicular to the plane P. Thus L is the line through A and parallel to $\boldsymbol{\varphi}$, and hence by Problem (i) above the desired equation of L is

48

$$(23.4) \qquad (\mathbf{x} - \mathbf{a}) \times \boldsymbol{\varphi} = 0.$$

24. *The equation of a sphere.* Let S be a sphere of radius a with center at a point C, as shown in Figure 35. If X is general point on the sphere S, then

$$\overline{CX} \cdot \overline{CX} = |\overline{CX}|^2 = a^2.$$

But $\overline{CX} = \mathbf{x} - \mathbf{c}.$ Thus

$$(24.1) \qquad (\mathbf{x} - \mathbf{c}) \cdot (\mathbf{x} - \mathbf{c}) = a^2.$$

This is an equation satisfied by the position-vector of a general point X on the sphere. It is thus the equation of the sphere.

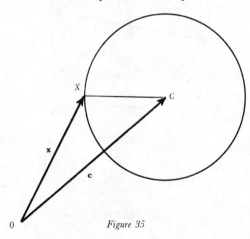

Figure 35

We shall now prove the following well-known property of a sphere: the angle at the surface of a sphere subtended by a diameter of the sphere is a right angle. For convenience, the origin of the coordinate system is chosen at the center of the sphere, as shown in Figure 36. Let D and E be points at the ends of a diameter, and let X be a general point on the sphere. We denote the position-vectors of these points in the usual manner. From the figure

$$\overline{DX} = \mathbf{x} - \mathbf{d}, \qquad \overline{EX} = \mathbf{x} - \mathbf{e}.$$

49

Thus
$$\overline{DX} \cdot \overline{EX} = (\mathbf{x} - \mathbf{d}) \cdot (\mathbf{x} - \mathbf{e}) = \mathbf{x} \cdot \mathbf{x} - \mathbf{x} \cdot (\mathbf{d} + \mathbf{e}) + \mathbf{d} \cdot \mathbf{e}.$$
But $\mathbf{d} + \mathbf{e} = 0$, and if a denotes the radius of the sphere then $\mathbf{x} \cdot \mathbf{x} = a^2$, $\mathbf{d} \cdot \mathbf{e} = -a^2$. Hence it follows that
$$\overline{DX} \cdot \overline{EX} = 0,$$
and so $\overline{DX}$ is perpendicular to $\overline{EX}$.

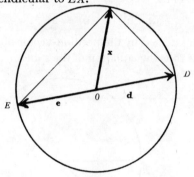

Figure 36

25. *The tangent plane to a sphere.* Let S be a sphere of radius a with center at a point C, as shown in Figure 37. We shall now find

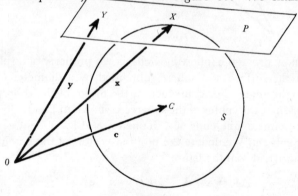

Figure 37

50

the equation of the plane P which touches S at a given point X.

Let Y be a general point on P. We denote the position-vectors of the various points in the usual manner. From the figure it follows that

$$\overline{CY} = \overline{CX} + \overline{XY},$$

or

$$\mathbf{y} - \mathbf{c} = \overline{CX} + \overline{XY}.$$

We now multiply this equation scalarly by $\overline{CX}$. Now $\overline{CX} \cdot \overline{CX} = a^2$, and $\overline{CX} \cdot \overline{XY} = 0$ because $\overline{CX}$ is perpendicular to $\overline{XY}$. Thus we have

(25.1) $$\overline{CX} \cdot (\mathbf{y} - \mathbf{c}) = a^2.$$

But $\overline{CX} = \mathbf{x} - \mathbf{c}$. Thus Equation (25.1) becomes

$$(\mathbf{x} - \mathbf{c}) \cdot (\mathbf{y} - \mathbf{c}) = a^2.$$

This is the desired equation of the plane P.

Differential Geometry

26. *Introduction.* We shall consider here only a small portion of the differential geometry of curves in space. Rectangular cartesian co-ordinates x_1, x_2 and x_3 are introduced, with origin at a point O. The quantities x_1, x_2 and x_3 denote the coordinates of a general point X with position-vector $\mathbf{x}$. If $\mathbf{i}_1$, $\mathbf{i}_2$ and $\mathbf{i}_3$ are unit vectors in the directions of the positive coordinate axes, then as before,

(26.1) $$\mathbf{x} = x_1\mathbf{i}_1 + x_2\mathbf{i}_2 + x_3\mathbf{i}_3.$$

A curve consists of the set of points the position-vectors of which satisfy the relation

$$\mathbf{x} = \mathbf{x}(u),$$

where $\mathbf{x}(u)$ is a function of a scalar parameter u. We shall consider only those parts of the curve which are free of singularities of all kinds.

If the set of points comprising a curve all lie in a single plane, the curve is said to be a *plane curve*. If this set of points does not lie in a single plane, the curve is said to be a *skew curve*.

It is convenient to choose as the scalar parameter the length s of the arc of the curve measured from some fixed point A. The quantity s is

51

positive for points on one side of A, and negative for points on the other side of A. The equation of the curve may then take the form

$$\mathbf{x} = \mathbf{x}(s).$$

The derivatives with respect to s of the function $\mathbf{x}(s)$ will be denoted by $\mathbf{x}'$, $\mathbf{x}''$, $\mathbf{x}'''$, etc.

27. *The principal triad.* Let us consider a general point X on a curve C. The position-vector of X is $\mathbf{x}$. We shall now define a set of three orthogonal unit vectors $\mathbf{j}_1$, $\mathbf{j}_2$ and $\mathbf{j}_3$ at X. They are functions of the parameter s, and their derivatives respect to s will be denoted in the usual

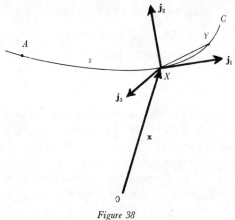

Figure 38

way by the symbols $\mathbf{j}_1'$, $\mathbf{j}_2'$ and $\mathbf{j}_3'$. They are shown in Figure 38, and are defined by the conditions:

(i) $\mathbf{j}_1$ is tangent to the curve C, and points in the direction of s increasing;

(ii) $\mathbf{j}_2$ lies in the plane of the vectors $\mathbf{j}_1$ and $\mathbf{j}_1'$, and makes an acute angle with $\mathbf{j}_1'$;

(iii) $\mathbf{j}_3$ is such that the vectors $\mathbf{j}_1$, $\mathbf{j}_2$ and $\mathbf{j}_3$ form a right-handed triad[1].

---

[1] At points on the curve where $\mathbf{j}_1'$ is equal to zero, these conditions are not sufficient for a unique determination of $\mathbf{j}_2$ and $\mathbf{j}_3$. We exclude such points from consideration here.

The straight line through the point X and parallel to $\mathbf{j}_2$ is called the *principal normal* to the curve. The straight line through X and parallel to $\mathbf{j}_3$ is called the *binormal* to the curve. The vectors $\mathbf{j}_1$, $\mathbf{j}_2$ and $\mathbf{j}_3$ are called the *unit tangent vector*, *unit normal vector*, and *unit binormal vector*, respectively. The triad formed by these vectors is called the *principal triad*. The plane through X and perpendicular to $\mathbf{j}_1$ is called the *normal plane*. The plane through X and perpendicular to $\mathbf{j}_3$ is called the *osculating plane*.

28. *The Serret-Frenet formulas.* Let Y be a point on the curve C and near the point X, as shown in Figure 38. We denote the length of the arc XY by the symbol Δs, and the vector $\overline{XY}$ by the symbol $\Delta\mathbf{x}$. Let us now consider the vector

$$\mathbf{x}' = \underset{\Delta s \to 0}{\text{limit}} \ \frac{\Delta\mathbf{x}}{\Delta s}.$$

Now

$$\underset{\Delta s \to 0}{\text{limit}} \ \frac{|\Delta\mathbf{x}|}{\Delta s} = 1.$$

Thus $\mathbf{x}'$ is a unit vector. Further, the vector $\Delta\mathbf{x}/\Delta s$ lies along $\overline{XY}$, and its direction then tends to that of $\mathbf{j}_1$ as Δs tends to zero. Since $\mathbf{j}_1$ is a unit vector, we can then write

(28.1) $$\mathbf{j}_1 = \mathbf{x}'.$$

The vectors $\mathbf{j}_1'$, $\mathbf{j}_2'$ and $\mathbf{j}_3'$ can each be expressed as a linear function of any three non-coplaner vectors. In particular, they can be expressed as linear functions of the vectors $\mathbf{j}_1$, $\mathbf{j}_2$ and $\mathbf{j}_3$, and we then have relations of the form

(28.2) $$\begin{aligned}
\mathbf{j}_1' &= a_{11}\mathbf{j}_1 + a_{12}\mathbf{j}_2 + a_{13}\mathbf{j}_3\,, \\
\mathbf{j}_2' &= a_{21}\mathbf{j}_1 + a_{22}\mathbf{j}_2 + a_{23}\mathbf{j}_3\,, \\
\mathbf{j}_3' &= a_{31}\mathbf{j}_1 + a_{32}\mathbf{j}_2 + a_{33}\mathbf{j}_3\,,
\end{aligned}$$

where the scalar coefficients are functions of the parameter s. Since the vectors $\mathbf{j}_1$, $\mathbf{j}_2$ and $\mathbf{j}_3$ are orthogonal unit vectors, they satisfy the relations

53

$$(28.3) \quad \begin{array}{lll} \mathbf{j}_1 \cdot \mathbf{j}_1 = 1, & \mathbf{j}_1 \cdot \mathbf{j}_2 = 0, & \mathbf{j}_1 \cdot \mathbf{j}_3 = 0, \\ \mathbf{j}_2 \cdot \mathbf{j}_1 = 0, & \mathbf{j}_2 \cdot \mathbf{j}_2 = 1, & \mathbf{j}_2 \cdot \mathbf{j}_3 = 0, \\ \mathbf{j}_3 \cdot \mathbf{j}_1 = 0, & \mathbf{j}_3 \cdot \mathbf{j}_2 = 0, & \mathbf{j}_3 \cdot \mathbf{j}_3 = 1. \end{array}$$

We differentiate with respect to s the first equation in the first line of (28.3). This yields the relation

$$\mathbf{j}_1 \cdot \mathbf{j}_1' + \mathbf{j}_1' \cdot \mathbf{j}_1 = 0.$$

Since in a scalar product the order in which the vectors appear is immaterial, we can interchange the vectors in the second scalar product. It then follows that

$$\mathbf{j}_1 \cdot \mathbf{j}_1' = 0.$$

If we substitute here for $\mathbf{j}_1'$ from the first equation in (28.2), and then make use of Equations (28.3), we find that $a_{11} = 0$. Similarly $a_{22} = a_{33} = 0$, and we may write

$$(28.4) \qquad a_{11} = a_{22} = a_{33} = 0.$$

We now differentiate with respect to s the second relation in the first line of (28.3). This yields

$$\mathbf{j}_1 \cdot \mathbf{j}_2' + \mathbf{j}_1' \cdot \mathbf{j}_2 = 0.$$

If we substitute here for $\mathbf{j}_1'$ and $\mathbf{j}_2'$ from the first two equations in (28.2), and then make use of Equations (28.3), we find that $a_{12} + a_{21} = 0$. Similarly we can find two similar relations, and we have altogether

$$(28.5) \qquad a_{12} + a_{21} = 0, \qquad a_{23} + a_{32} = 0, \qquad a_{31} + a_{13} = 0.$$

So far, only conditions (i) and (iii) above have been used. By condition (ii) the vector $\mathbf{j}_1'$ is to be in the plane of $\mathbf{j}_1$ and $\mathbf{j}_2$. This can be true only if

$$(28.6) \qquad a_{13} = 0.$$

By condition (ii), the vector $\mathbf{j}_1'$ is to make an acute angle with $\mathbf{j}_2$. If this angle is denoted by α, then $\cos \alpha$ must be positive. But

$$|\mathbf{j}_1'| \cos \alpha = \mathbf{j}_2 \cdot \mathbf{j}_1'.$$

If we substitute here for $\mathbf{j}_1'$ from Equations (28.2) and then use Equations (28.3) we find that

$$|\mathbf{j}_1'| \cos \alpha = a_{12}.$$

Thus

(28.7)
$$a_{12} > 0.$$

We now define two quantities $\varkappa$ and τ by the relations

(28.8)
$$\varkappa = a_{12}, \qquad \tau = a_{23}.$$

Then, by (28.7) it follows that

(28.9)
$$\varkappa > 0,$$

and because of Equations (28.4), (28.5), (28.6) and (28.8), we can now express Equations (28.2) in the form

(28.10)
$$\begin{aligned}
\mathbf{j}_1' &= \varkappa \mathbf{j}_2, \\
\mathbf{j}_2' &= \tau \mathbf{j}_3 - \varkappa \mathbf{j}_1, \\
\mathbf{j}_3' &= - \tau \mathbf{j}_2.
\end{aligned}$$

These are the Serret-Frenet formulas. They were given originally by Serret (1851) and Frenet (1852) in an equivalent form which did not involve vectors. The quantities $\varkappa$ and τ, which are functions of the arc length s of the curve C, will be considered in some detail in the next section.

29. *Curvature and torsion.* The quantity $\varkappa$ appearing in Equations (28.10) is called the *curvature* of the curve. It can be shown that

$$\varkappa = \lim_{\Delta s \to 0} \frac{\Delta \theta}{\Delta s},$$

where $\Delta \theta$ is the angle between the tangents to the curve C at the points X and Y in Figure 38. Thus $\varkappa$ is the rate at which the tangent at the point X rotates as X moves along the curve. The reciprocal of $\varkappa$ is called the *radius of curvature*, and will be denoted by the symbol ρ.

The quantity τ appearing in Equations (28.10) is called the *torsion* of the curve. It can be shown that

$$\tau = \lim_{\Delta s \to 0} \frac{\Delta \Phi}{\Delta s},$$

where $\Delta \Phi$ is the angle between the binormals to the curve C at the points X and Y in Figure 38. Thus τ is the rate at which the unit binormal at the point X rotates as X moves along the curve. The reciprocal of τ is called the *radius of torsion*, and will be denoted by σ.

To find $\varkappa$, we note from Equation (28.1) that

$$(29.1) \qquad \mathbf{j}_1 = \mathbf{x}', \qquad \mathbf{j}_1' = \mathbf{x}''.$$

Substitution from the second of these relations for $\mathbf{j}_1'$ in the first of the Serret-Frenet formulas then yields the equation

$$(29.2) \qquad \mathbf{x}'' = \varkappa\mathbf{j}_2.$$

We now multiply each side of this equation scalarly by itself, obtaining

$$\varkappa^2 = \mathbf{x}'' \cdot \mathbf{x}''.$$

Because of (28.9), $\varkappa$ is positive, and so

$$(29.3) \qquad \varkappa = \sqrt{\mathbf{x}'' \cdot \mathbf{x}''}.$$

To find the torsion τ we differentiate Equation (29.2) with respect to s. This yields

$$\mathbf{x}''' = \varkappa\mathbf{j}_2' + \varkappa'\mathbf{j}_2.$$

We now substitute for $\mathbf{j}_2'$ from the second Serret-Frenet formula, obtaining

$$(29.4) \qquad \mathbf{x}''' = \varkappa\,(\tau\,\mathbf{j}_3 - \varkappa\,\mathbf{j}_1) + \varkappa'\mathbf{j}_2.$$

From Equations (29.1), (29.2) and (29.4) it now follows that

$$\begin{aligned}
\mathbf{x}' \cdot (\mathbf{x}'' \times \mathbf{x}''') &= \mathbf{j}_1 \cdot [\varkappa\,\mathbf{j}_2 \times (\varkappa\tau\mathbf{j}_3 - \varkappa^2\mathbf{j}_1 + \varkappa'\mathbf{j}_2)] \\
&= \mathbf{j}_1 \cdot [\varkappa^2\tau\,\mathbf{j}_1 + \varkappa^3\mathbf{j}_3] \\
&= \varkappa^2\tau.
\end{aligned}$$

Thus

$$(29.5) \qquad \tau = \frac{1}{\varkappa^2}\,\mathbf{x}' \cdot (\mathbf{x}'' \times \mathbf{x}''').$$

The curvature and torsion can be computed from Equations (29.3) and (29.5). We can express these equations in different forms. Now

$$\begin{aligned}
\mathbf{x} &= x_1\mathbf{i}_1 + x_2\mathbf{i}_2 + x_3\mathbf{i}_3, \\
\mathbf{x}' &= x_1'\mathbf{i}_1 + x_2'\mathbf{i}_2 + x_3'\mathbf{i}_3, \\
\mathbf{x}'' &= x_1''\mathbf{i}_1 + x_2''\mathbf{i}_2 + x_3''\mathbf{i}_3, \\
\mathbf{x}''' &= x_1'''\mathbf{i}_1 + x_2'''\mathbf{i}_2 + x_3'''\mathbf{i}_3.
\end{aligned}$$

Substitution from these relations in Equations (29.3) and (29.4) then yields

$$(29.6) \qquad \varkappa = \sqrt{{x_1''}^2 + {x_2''}^2 + {x_3''}^2},$$

$$(29.7) \qquad \tau = \frac{1}{\varkappa^2} \begin{vmatrix} x_1' & x_2' & x_3' \\ x_1'' & x_2'' & x_3'' \\ x_1''' & x_2''' & x_3''' \end{vmatrix}.$$

Since $\varkappa$ can now be found, we can obtain the unit tangent vector $\mathbf{j}_1$ and the unit normal vector $\mathbf{j}_2$ by use of Equations (29.1) and (29.2). The unit binormal vector $\mathbf{j}_3$ can then be found easily, since it is equal to $\mathbf{j}_1 \times \mathbf{j}_2$. We have the collected results

$$(29.8) \qquad \mathbf{j}_1 = \mathbf{x}' , \quad \mathbf{j}_2 = \frac{1}{\varkappa} \mathbf{x}'' , \quad \mathbf{j}_3 = \frac{1}{\varkappa} \mathbf{x}' \times \mathbf{x}'' .$$

Let us now find the equation of the tangent to the curve at the point X. If Y is a general point on this tangent, the desired equation is easily seen to be

$$(\mathbf{y} - \mathbf{x}) \times \mathbf{j}_1 = 0 .$$

Because of Equation (29.8), this can be written in the form

$$(29.9) \qquad (\mathbf{y} - \mathbf{x}) \times \mathbf{x}' = 0 .$$

In the same way, the equations of the principal normal and binormal can be found in the forms

$$(29.10) \qquad (\mathbf{y} - \mathbf{x}) \times \mathbf{x}'' = 0 ,$$

$$(29.11) \qquad (\mathbf{y} - \mathbf{x}) \times (\mathbf{x}' \times \mathbf{x}'') = 0 .$$

The equation of the normal plane at the point X is easily seen to be

$$(\mathbf{y} - \mathbf{x}) \cdot \mathbf{j}_1 = 0 .$$

Because of Equation (29.8), this can be written in the form

$$(29.12) \qquad (\mathbf{y} - \mathbf{x}) \cdot \mathbf{x}' = 0 .$$

In the same way we can find the equation of the osculating plane in the form

$$(29.13) \qquad (\mathbf{y} - \mathbf{x}) \cdot (\mathbf{x}' \times \mathbf{x}'') = 0 .$$

1. Prove that the line joining the middle points of any two sides of a triangle is parallel to the third side, and is equal in length to one half the length of the third side.

2. Prove that the lines joining the middle points of the sides of a quadrilateral form a parallelogram.

3. If O is a point in space, ABC is a triangle, and D, E and F are the middle points of the sides, prove that

$$\overline{OA}+\overline{OB}+\overline{OC} = \overline{OD}+\overline{OE}+\overline{OF}.$$

4. If O is a point in space, $ABCD$ is a parallelogram, and E is the point of intersection of the diagonals, prove that

$$\overline{OA}+\overline{OB}+\overline{OC}+\overline{OD} = 4\overline{OE}.$$

5. Prove that the line joining one vertex of a parallelogram to the middle point of an opposite side trisects a diagonal of the parallelogram.

6. Prove that it is possible to construct a triangle with sides equal and parallel to the medians of a given triangle.

7. Prove that the lines joining the middle points of opposite sides of a skew quadrilateral bisect each other. Prove also that the point where these lines cross is the middle point of the line joining the middle points of the diagonals of the quadrilateral.

8. Prove that the three perpendiculars from the vertices of a triangle to the opposite sides meet in a point.

9. Prove that the bisectors of the angles of a triangle meet in a point. Hint: the sum of unit vectors along two sides lies along the bisector of the contained angle.

10. Prove that the perpendicular bisectors of the sides of a triangle meet in a point.

11. If O is a point in space and ABC is a triangle with sides of lengths l, m and n, then

$$l\,\overline{OA}+m\,\overline{OB}+n\,\overline{OC} = (l+m+n)\,\overline{OD},$$

where D is the center of the inscribed circle.

12. If ABC is a given triangle, the middle points of the sides BC, CA

58

and AB are denoted by D, E and F respectively, G is the point of intersection of the perpendiculars from the vertices to the opposite sides, and H is the center of the circumscribed circle, prove that

$$\overline{AG} = 2\,\overline{HD}, \quad \overline{BG} = 2\,\overline{HE}, \quad \overline{CG} = 2\,\overline{HF}.$$

Hence prove that

$$\overline{GA} + \overline{GB} + \overline{GC} = 2\,\overline{GH}.$$

In problems 13–22 the points A, B, C and D have the following coordinates: $A(-1, 2, 3)$, $B(2, 5, -3)$, $C(4, 1, -1)$, $D(1, 3, -3)$.

13. Find the position-vectors of the points of trisection of the line segment AB.

14. Find the distance between the points A and B.

15. Find the area of the triangle ABC.

16. Find the cartesian form of the equation of the plane through A and perpendicular to $\overline{OB}$.

17. Find the cartesian form of the equation of the plane through (i) the origin and the points A and B, (ii) the points A, B and C.

18. Find the distance from the point D to the plane through A and perpendicular to $\overline{OB}$.

19. Find the distance from D to the plane ABC.

20. Find the cartesian form of the equation of the line through A and parallel to $\overline{BC}$.

21. Find the cartesian form of the equation of the line through A and B.

22. Find the cartesian form of the equation of the line through D and (i) perpendicular to the plane through A, B and C, (ii) perpendicular to $\overline{BC}$ and $\overline{OC}$.

23. A plane passes through a given point A with position-vector $\mathbf{a}$, and is parallel to each of two given vectors $\mathbf{b}$ and $\mathbf{c}$. Derive the equation of this plane in the form

$$(\mathbf{x} - \mathbf{a}) \cdot (\mathbf{b} \times \mathbf{c}) = 0.$$

24. A straight line L passes through a point A with position-vector $\mathbf{a}$, and is parallel to a vector $\mathbf{b}$. A vector $\mathbf{p}$ has its origin at a point C

with position-vector $\mathbf{c}$, its line of action along the perpendicular from C to L, and its terminus on L. Show that

$$\mathbf{p} = \mathbf{a} - \mathbf{c} - \frac{(\mathbf{a} - \mathbf{c}) \cdot \mathbf{b}}{b^2} \, \mathbf{b} \, .$$

25. A straight line L passes through a point A with position-vector $\mathbf{a}$, and is parallel to a vector $\mathbf{b}$. A second straight line L' passes through a point A' with position-vector $\mathbf{a}'$, and is parallel to a vector $\mathbf{b}'$. The vector $\mathbf{p}$ runs from L to L' along the common perpendicular. Show that

$$\mathbf{p} = \frac{(\mathbf{a}' - \mathbf{a}) \cdot \mathbf{c}}{c^2} \, \mathbf{c} \, ,$$

where $\mathbf{c} = \mathbf{b} \times \mathbf{b}'$.

26. Prove that if the torsion of a curve is equal to zero, the curve is a plane curve.

27. Prove that

$$\mathbf{x}'''' = -3\varkappa \varkappa' \mathbf{j}_1 + (\varkappa'' - \varkappa^3 - \varkappa\tau^2)\mathbf{j}_2 + (2\,\varkappa'\tau + \varkappa\tau')\mathbf{j}_3 \, .$$

28. If the position-vector $\mathbf{x}$ of a general point on a curve is given as a function of a parameter t, and if primes denote differentiations with respect to t prove that

$$\varkappa = \frac{1}{s'^2} \sqrt{\mathbf{x}'' \cdot \mathbf{x}'' - s''^2} \, , \qquad \tau = \frac{1}{\varkappa^2 s'^6} \, \mathbf{x}' \cdot (\mathbf{x}'' \times \mathbf{x}''') \, ,$$

$$\mathbf{j}_1 = \frac{\mathbf{x}'}{s'} \, , \quad \mathbf{j}_2 = \frac{1}{\varkappa s'^2} \left(\mathbf{x}'' - \frac{s''}{s'} \, \mathbf{x}' \right) , \quad \mathbf{j}_3 = \frac{\mathbf{x}' \times \mathbf{x}''}{\varkappa s'^3} \, .$$

Also, derive the equations of the tangent, principal normal, binormal, normal plane and osculating plane in the following forms:

tangent,	$(\mathbf{y} - \mathbf{x}) \times \mathbf{x}' = 0;$
principal normal,	$(\mathbf{y} - \mathbf{x}) \times \left(\mathbf{x}'' - \dfrac{s''}{s'} \, \mathbf{x}' \right) = 0;$
binormal,	$(\mathbf{y} - \mathbf{x}) \times (\mathbf{x}' \times \mathbf{x}'') = 0;$
normal plane,	$(\mathbf{y} - \mathbf{x}) \cdot \mathbf{x}' = 0;$
osculating plane,	$(\mathbf{y} - \mathbf{x}) \cdot (\mathbf{x}' \times \mathbf{x}'') = 0.$

29. The position-vector $\mathbf{x}$ of a general point on a circular helix is given by the relation

$$\mathbf{x} = a \cos t\, \mathbf{i}_1 + a \sin t\, \mathbf{i}_2 + at \cot \alpha\, \mathbf{i}_3,$$

where a and α are constants, and t is a parameter. Find ρ, σ and the principal triad. Answer: $\rho = a \operatorname{cosec}^2 \alpha$, $\sigma = 2a \operatorname{cosec} 2\alpha$, $\mathbf{j}_1 = \sin \alpha$ $(-\mathbf{i}_1 \sin t + \mathbf{i}_2 \cos t + \mathbf{i}_3 \cot \alpha)$, $\mathbf{j}_2 = -\mathbf{i}_1 \cos t - \mathbf{i}_2 \sin t$, $\mathbf{j}_3 = \cos \alpha\, (\mathbf{i}_1 \sin t - \mathbf{i}_2 \cos t + \mathbf{i}_3 \tan \alpha)$.

30. The position-vector $\mathbf{x}$ of a general point on a curve is given by the relation

$$\mathbf{x} = a(3t - t^3)\mathbf{i}_1 + 3at^2\mathbf{i}_2 + a(3t + t^3)\mathbf{i}_3,$$

where a is a constant and t is a parameter. Find ρ, σ and the principal triad. Answer: $\rho = \sigma = 3a\, \gamma^2$, $\sqrt{2}\, \mathbf{j}_1 = \gamma^{-1}(\alpha\, \mathbf{i}_1 + \beta \mathbf{i}_2 + \gamma \mathbf{i}_3)$, $\mathbf{j}_2 = \gamma^{-1}(-\beta \mathbf{i}_1 + \alpha\, \mathbf{i}_2)$, $\sqrt{2}\, \mathbf{j}_3 = \gamma^{-1}(-\alpha\, \mathbf{i}_1 - \beta\, \mathbf{i}_2 + \gamma\, \mathbf{i}_3)$, where $\alpha = 1 - t^2$, $\beta = 2t$, $\gamma = 1 + t^2$.

31. The position-vector $\mathbf{x}$ of a general point on a curve is given by the relation

$$\mathbf{x} = a[(t - \sin t)\mathbf{i}_1 + (1 - \cos t)\mathbf{i}_2 + t\, \mathbf{i}_3],$$

where a is a constant and t is a parameter. Find ρ and σ. Answer: $\rho = a\, \alpha^{3/2}, \beta^{-1/2}$, $\sigma = -a\, \beta$, where $\alpha = 3 - 2 \cos t$, $\beta = 2 - 2 \cos t + \cos^2 t$.

Chapter III

APPLICATION OF VECTORS TO MECHANICS

Motion of a particle

30. *Kinematics of a particle.* The phrase ,,kinematics of a particle''
refers to that portion of the study of the motion of a particle which is
not concerned with the forces producing the motion, but is concerned
rather with the mathematical concepts useful in describing the motion.

Let us consider a moving particle. It is necessary to introduce a
,,frame of reference'' relative to which the motion of the particle can
be measured. For a frame of reference we take a rigid body. Such a
body is one having the property that the distances between all pairs
of particles in it do not vary with the time. We then introduce a set of
rectangular cartesian coordinate axes fixed in the frame of reference.
Figure 39 shows these axes and the associated unit vectors $\mathbf{i}_1$, $\mathbf{i}_2$ and $\mathbf{i}_3$.

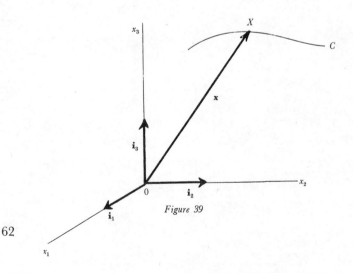

Figure 39

Let the curve C in this figure be the path of the particle, and let the point X denote the position of the particle at time t. The vector $\overline{OX}$ is the *position-vector* of the particle. We denote this vector also by $\mathbf{x}$. It is a function of the time t.

The velocity $\mathbf{v}$ of the particle relative to the frame of reference, and the acceleration $\mathbf{a}$ of the particle relative to the frame of reference, are defined by the relations

$$(30.1) \qquad \mathbf{v} = \frac{d\mathbf{x}}{dt}, \qquad \mathbf{a} = \frac{d\mathbf{v}}{dt} = \frac{d^2\mathbf{x}}{dt^2}.$$

The magnitude v of the velocity $\mathbf{v}$ is called the *speed* of the particle. Thus, velocity is a vector and speed is a scalar. We shall now compute various sets of components of the vectors $\mathbf{v}$ and $\mathbf{a}$.

(i) *The components of the velocity and acceleration in the directions of rectangular cartesian coordinate axes.* Let x_1, x_2, x_3 denote the rectangular cartesian coordinates of the point X in Figure 39. Then

$$\mathbf{x} = x_1\mathbf{i}_1 + x_2\mathbf{i}_2 + x_3\mathbf{i}_3.$$

If we now adopt the convention that a single superimposed dot denotes a first time derivative, and a pair of superimposed dots denotes a second time derivative, then

$$\mathbf{v} = \frac{d\mathbf{x}}{dt} = \dot{x}_1\mathbf{i}_1 + \dot{x}_2\mathbf{i}_2 + \dot{x}_3\mathbf{i}_3,$$

$$\mathbf{a} = \frac{d\mathbf{v}}{dt} = \ddot{x}_1\mathbf{i}_1 + \ddot{x}_2\mathbf{i}_2 + \ddot{x}_3\mathbf{i}_3.$$

Thus *the desired components of* $\mathbf{v}$ *and* $\mathbf{a}$ *are*

$$(30.2) \qquad \dot{x}_1, \dot{x}_2, \dot{x}_3; \qquad \ddot{x}_1, \ddot{x}_2, \ddot{x}_3.$$

(ii) *The components of the velocity and acceleration in the directions of the principal triad of the curve traced out by the particle.* The curve C in Figure 39 is the path of the particle. Let $\mathbf{j}_1$, $\mathbf{j}_2$ and $\mathbf{j}_3$ denote the principal triad at the general point X on C. The principal triad was discussed in § 27. If s denotes the arc length of C, then from Equations (28.1) and (28.10) we have

$$(30.3) \qquad \mathbf{j}_1 = \frac{d\mathbf{x}}{ds}, \qquad \frac{d\mathbf{j}_1}{ds} = \varkappa\mathbf{j}_2,$$

where $\varkappa$ is the curvature of C. Now

$$\mathbf{v} = \frac{d\mathbf{x}}{dt} = \frac{d\mathbf{x}}{ds}\,\dot{s},$$

and because of the first equation in (30.3) we then have

(30.4) $$\mathbf{v} = \dot{s}\,\mathbf{j}_1.$$

Thus *the velocity of the particle is directed along the tangent to its path, and the speed is $v = \dot{s}$.*

Because of (30.4) we have

$$\mathbf{a} = \frac{d\mathbf{v}}{dt} = \ddot{s}\,\mathbf{j}_1 + \dot{s}\,\frac{d\mathbf{j}_1}{dt}.$$

But because of the second equation in (30.3) we have

$$\frac{d\mathbf{j}_1}{dt} = \frac{d\mathbf{j}_1}{ds}\,\dot{s} = \varkappa\dot{s}\,\mathbf{j}_2,$$

and hence

(30.5) $$\mathbf{a} = \ddot{s}\,\mathbf{j}_1 + \varkappa\dot{s}^2\,\mathbf{j}_2.$$

Thus *the acceleration $\mathbf{a}$ lies in the osculating plane of C. Also, the components of $\mathbf{a}$ in the directions of the tangent, normal and binormal are*

(30.6) $$\ddot{s} = \dot{v} = v\,\frac{dv}{ds}, \qquad \varkappa\dot{s}^2 = \varkappa v^2 = \frac{v^2}{\rho}, \qquad 0,$$

where ρ is the radius of curvature of C.

(iii)   *The components of the velocity and acceleration in the directions of the parametric lines of cylindrical coordinates.*   Let r, θ, x_3 be cylindrical coordinates of a general point X on the path C of the particle. Figure 40 shows these coordinates. We introduce a triad of unit vectors $\mathbf{k}_1, \mathbf{k}_2, \mathbf{k}_3$ at O as shown; $\mathbf{k}_1$ points toward the point X' which is the projection of X on the $x_1 x_2$ plane, $\mathbf{k}_3$ is equal to $\mathbf{i}_3$, and $\mathbf{k}_2$ is such that the triad is right-handed. It will be noted that $\mathbf{k}_1, \mathbf{k}_2, \mathbf{k}_3$ point in the directions of the parametric lines[1] of the cylindrical coordinates r, θ, x_3 at X.

---

[1] It will be recalled that the directions of the parametric lines of a coordinate system at a point X are those directions in which one of the coordinates increases while the other coordinates do not vary.

64

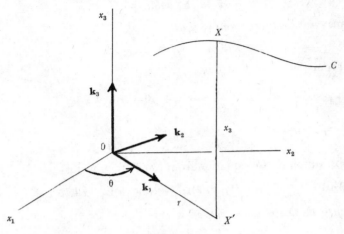

Figure 40

If $\mathbf{i}_1$, $\mathbf{i}_2$ and $\mathbf{i}_3$ are the usual unit vectors associated with the rectangular cartesian coordinate axes in Figure 40, then

$$\mathbf{k}_1 = \mathbf{i}_1 \cos \theta + \mathbf{i}_2 \sin \theta,$$
$$\mathbf{k}_2 = -\mathbf{i}_1 \sin \theta + \mathbf{i}_2 \cos \theta,$$
$$\mathbf{k}_3 = \mathbf{i}_3,$$

and so

$$\frac{d\mathbf{k}_1}{dt} = \frac{d\mathbf{k}_1}{d\theta} \dot{\theta} = (-\mathbf{i}_1 \sin \theta + \mathbf{i}_2 \cos \theta) \dot{\theta} = \mathbf{k}_2 \dot{\theta},$$

(30.7) $$\frac{d\mathbf{k}_2}{dt} = \frac{d\mathbf{k}_2}{d\theta} \dot{\theta} = (-\mathbf{i}_1 \cos \theta - \mathbf{i}_2 \sin \theta) \dot{\theta} = -\mathbf{k}_1 \dot{\theta},$$

$$\frac{d\mathbf{k}_3}{dt} = 0.$$

From Figure 40 it follows that the position-vector $\mathbf{x}$ of the particle is given by the relation $\mathbf{x} = r\mathbf{k}_1 + x_3\mathbf{k}_3$. Thus

$$\mathbf{v} = \frac{d\mathbf{x}}{dt} = \dot{r}\mathbf{k}_1 + \dot{x}_3\mathbf{k}_3 + r\frac{d\mathbf{k}_1}{dt} + x_3\frac{d\mathbf{k}_3}{dt}.$$

Because of (30.7) we then obtain

65

(30.8) $$\mathbf{v} = \dot{r}\mathbf{k}_1 + r\dot{\theta}\mathbf{k}_2 + \dot{x}_3\mathbf{k}_3 .$$

Thus *the desired components of* $\mathbf{v}$ *are*

(30.9) $$\dot{r}, \; r\dot{\theta}, \; \dot{x}_3 .$$

From (30.8) we find that

$$\mathbf{a} = \frac{d\mathbf{v}}{dt} = \ddot{r}\,\mathbf{k}_1 + (\dot{r}\dot{\theta} + r\ddot{\theta})\mathbf{k}_2 + \ddot{x}_3\mathbf{k}_3$$

$$+ \dot{r}\,\frac{d\mathbf{k}_1}{dt} + r\dot{\theta}\,\frac{d\mathbf{k}_2}{dt} + \dot{x}_3\,\frac{d\mathbf{k}_3}{dt} .$$

Substitution in this equation from (30.7) then yields

(30.10) $$\mathbf{a} = (\ddot{r} - r\dot{\theta}^2)\mathbf{k}_1 + (2\dot{r}\dot{\theta} + r\ddot{\theta})\mathbf{k}_2 + \ddot{x}_3\mathbf{k}_3 .$$

Hence *the desired components of* $\mathbf{a}$ *are*

(30.11) $$\ddot{r} - r\dot{\theta}^2, \quad 2\dot{r}\dot{\theta} + r\ddot{\theta} = \frac{1}{r}\frac{d}{dt}(r^2\dot{\theta}), \quad \ddot{x}_3 .$$

Of course, if the particle is confined to the x_1x_2 plane then $x_3 = 0$, $r = x$, and we find from (30.9) and (30.11) that the components of $\mathbf{v}$ and $\mathbf{a}$ in the directions of the parametric lines of the plane polar coordinates x, θ are

(30.12) $$x, \quad x\dot{\theta}; \quad \ddot{x} - x\dot{\theta}^2, \frac{1}{x}\frac{d}{dt}(x^2\dot{\theta}) .$$

31. *Newton's laws.* The concept of force is intuitive. We can define a unit force as that force which produces a standard deflection of a standard spring. Hence we can assign a numerical value to the magnitude of any force.

We know that forces have magnitude and direction. It has been verified experimentally to within the limits of experimental error that forces obey the law of vector addition. Hence we shall assume that *forces are vectors.* The sum of two or more forces is sometimes called the resultant of the forces.

The term "mass of a body" refers to the quantity of matter present in the body. We can define a unit mass as that mass which, when sus-

66

pended from a standard spring at a standard place in the earth's gravitational field, produces a standard deflection of the spring. Hence we can assign a numerical value to the mass of any body.

We now introduce the laws governing the motion of a particle. These laws, which were first stated by Isaac Newton and are called Newton's laws, are as follows:

(i) Every particle continues in a state of rest or uniform motion in a straight line unless compelled by some external force to change that state.

(ii) The product of the mass and acceleration of a particle is proportional to the force applied to the particle, and the acceleration is in the same direction as the force.

(iii) When two particles exert forces on each other, the forces have the same magnitudes and act in opposite directions along the line joining the two particles.

In the second law, the acceleration of the particle enters. This acceleration depends on the frame of reference employed. It thus appears that Newton's second law cannot apply in all frames of reference. Those frames of reference in which this law does apply are called *Newtonian frames of reference*. A frame of reference fixed with respect to the stars is Newtonian, and in making an accurate study of any motion such a frame of reference should be used. However, for many problems we may consider the earth as a Newtonian frame of reference, when effects due to the motion of the earth are negligible.

Let us now consider a particle of mass m acted upon by a force $\mathbf{F}$. Let $\mathbf{a}$ denote the acceleration of the particle relative to a Newtonian frame of reference. Then according to Newton's second law

$$\mathbf{F} = k\,m\,\mathbf{a},$$

where k is a constant of proportionality. It is customary to choose units of length, mass, time and force so that k is equal to unity. We then have

(31.1) $$\mathbf{F} = m\,\mathbf{a}.$$

There are three such systems of units in general use. These are indicated in Table 1, together with abbreviations commonly used for these units. Thus, for example, when a force of one pdl. acts on a particle with a mass of one lb., the acceleration of the particle is one ft./sec.². The systems of units in the second and third columns of Table 1 are called foot-pound-second sytems, or simply f.p.s. systems. The system of units in the fourth column is called the centimeter–gram–second system, or simply the c.g.s. system.

	f.p.s.		c.g.s.
Unit of length	foot (ft.)	foot (ft.)	centimeter (cm.)
Unit of mass	pound (lb.)	slug	gram (gm.)
Unit of time	second (sec.)	second (sec.)	second (sec.)
Unit of force	poundal (pdl.)	pound-weight (lb.wt.)	dyne

TABLE 1. Systems of units used in mechanics.

The lb. wt. is the force exerted on a mass of one lb. by the earth's gravitational field. If G denotes the acceleration due to gravity, expressed in ft./sec.², then

$$1 \text{ lb. wt.} = G \text{ pdl.},$$

$$1 \text{ slug} = G \text{ lb.}$$

At points near the surface of the earth, G is approximately equal to 32.

Equation (31.1), which governs the motion of a particle, may also be written in the equivalent forms

$$(31.2) \qquad \mathbf{F} = m \frac{d\mathbf{v}}{dt}, \qquad \mathbf{F} = m \frac{d^2\mathbf{x}}{dt^2}.$$

32. *Motion of a particle acted upon by a force which is a given function of the time.* When the force $\mathbf{F}$ acting on a particle is a given function of the time, Equations (31.2) can be solved by integration for the velocity $\mathbf{v}$ and position-vector $\mathbf{x}$ of the particle.

As an example, let us suppose that

$$\mathbf{F} = 12 \, \mathbf{p} + \mathbf{q} \cos t,$$

where $\mathbf{p}$ and $\mathbf{q}$ are given constant vectors. Because of the first equation in (31.2) we then have

$$m \frac{d\mathbf{v}}{dt} = 12\mathbf{p} + \mathbf{q} \cos t,$$

whence

$$m\mathbf{v} = \int (12\mathbf{p} + \mathbf{q} \cos t) \, dt.$$

We now carry out this integration in the manner outlined in § 13, obtaining

(32.1) $$m\mathbf{v} = 12\mathbf{p}t + \mathbf{q} \sin t + \mathbf{r},$$

where $\mathbf{r}$ is an arbitrary constant vector.

Now $\mathbf{v} = d\mathbf{x}/dt$. Thus from (32.1) we have

(32.2) $$m\mathbf{x} = \int (12\mathbf{p}t + \mathbf{q} \sin t + \mathbf{r}) \, dt$$
$$= 6\mathbf{p}t^2 - \mathbf{q} \cos t + \mathbf{r}t + \mathbf{s},$$

where $\mathbf{s}$ is an arbitrary constant vector. The arbitrary constant vectors $\mathbf{r}$ and $\mathbf{s}$ can be found if the initial values of $\mathbf{x}$ and $\mathbf{v}$ are known. If these initial values are $\mathbf{x}_0$ and $\mathbf{v}_0$, it is readily found that

$$\mathbf{r} = m\mathbf{v}_0, \qquad \mathbf{s} = m\mathbf{x}_0 + \mathbf{q}.$$

33. *Simple harmonic motion.* Let O be a point fixed in a Newtonian frame of reference. Let us consider a particle moving under the action of a force directed toward O, the force having a magnitude proportional to the distance from the particle to O. If $\mathbf{x}$ denotes the position-vector of the particle relative to O, then the force $\mathbf{F}$ acting on the particle satisfies the relation

$$\mathbf{F} = -k\mathbf{x},$$

where k is a constant. From Equation (31.2) we then have

$$-k\mathbf{x} = m \frac{d^2\mathbf{x}}{dt^2},$$

or

$$\frac{d^2\mathbf{x}}{dt^2} + \frac{k}{m}\mathbf{x} = 0.$$

69

This is a differential equation of the type considered in § 14. According to the procedure demonstrated there, the general solution of this differential equation is

$$\mathbf{x} = \mathbf{c}_1 \cos \sqrt{\frac{k}{m}}\, t + \mathbf{c}_2 \sin \sqrt{\frac{k}{m}}\, t,$$

where $\mathbf{c}_1$ and $\mathbf{c}_2$ are arbitrary constant vectors. These arbitrary constant vectors can be found if the initial values of $\mathbf{x}$ and $\mathbf{v}$ are known. If these initial values are $\mathbf{x}_0$ and $\mathbf{v}_0$, it is readily found that

$$\mathbf{c}_1 = \mathbf{x}_0, \qquad \mathbf{c}_2 = \sqrt{\frac{m}{k}}\, \mathbf{v}_0,$$

whence we have

$$\mathbf{x} = \mathbf{x}_0 \cos \sqrt{\frac{k}{m}}\, t + \mathbf{v}_0 \sqrt{\frac{m}{k}} \sin \sqrt{\frac{k}{m}}\, t.$$

It will be noted that $\mathbf{x}$ is a linear function of $\mathbf{x}_0$ and $\mathbf{v}_0$; hence it follows that the motion of the particle is confined to the plane P containing the given vectors $\mathbf{x}_0$ and $\mathbf{v}_0$. This result could have been anticipated, for the force $\mathbf{F}$ acting on the particle has no component perpendicular to the plane P.

34. *Central orbits.* Let O be a point fixed in a Newtonian frame of reference. Let us consider a particle acted upon by a force $\mathbf{F}$ directed toward O, the magnitude of $\mathbf{F}$ being a function of the distance from O to the particle. The path of the particle is called a *central orbit*. It will be noted that the problem considered in § 33 dealt with a special type of central orbit.

Denoting the vector $\overline{OX}$ by $\mathbf{x}$, we then have

$$F = F(x).$$

The equation of motion is

$$\mathbf{F} = m\mathbf{a}.$$

Let $\mathbf{x}_0$ and $\mathbf{v}_0$ be the initial values of $\mathbf{x}$ and the velocity $\mathbf{v}$. The entire path of the particle will be in the plane P containing the vectors $\mathbf{x}_0$ and $\mathbf{v}_0$. Let x and θ be polar coordinates in this plane. The components of $\mathbf{F}$ in the directions of the parametric lines of these coordi-

70

nates are $-F$, 0. Also, the components of **a** in these directions are given in Equation (30.12). Hence we have

(34.1)
$$- F = m \, (\ddot{x} - x\dot{\theta}^2) ,$$

(34.2)
$$0 = \frac{m}{x} \frac{d}{dt} \, (x^2\dot{\theta}) \, .$$

These are two equations from which x and θ can be determined as functions of the time t. It is more convenient, however, to determine from (34.1) and (34.2) a single equation by elimination of the time variable. This single equation will now be deduced.

We first introduce a variable y defined by the relation

(34.3)
$$y = 1/x.$$

Then from (34.2) we have

$$\dot{\theta}y^{-2} = \text{const.} = h$$

whence

(34.4)
$$\dot{\theta} = h \, y^2 .$$

Then

$$\dot{x} = -y^{-2}\dot{y} = - \, y^{-2} \frac{dy}{d\theta} \, \dot{\theta} = - h \frac{dy}{d\theta} ,$$

(34.5)
$$\ddot{x} = - h \frac{d^2y}{d\theta^2} \, \dot{\theta} = - h^2y^2 \frac{d^2y}{d\theta^2} .$$

By substitution in (34.1) for x, $\dot{\theta}$ and $\ddot{x}$ from (34.3), (34.4) and (34.5), we finally obtain

(34.6)
$$\frac{d^2y}{d\theta^2} + y = \frac{F}{mh^2y^2} .$$

Now F is a function of y alone. Once the form of this function has been assigned, we can find the path of the particle by solving Equation (34.6).

Let us now consider the special case when F varies inversely as the square of x. Then we can write

$$F = \gamma my^2,$$

where γ is a constant, and Equation (34.6) becomes

$$\frac{d^2y}{d\theta^2} + y = \frac{\gamma}{h^2}.$$

The general solution of this equation, expressed in terms of x, is

(34.7) $$\frac{1}{x} = \frac{\gamma}{h^2} + c_1 \cos \theta + c_2 \sin \theta,$$

where c_1 and c_2 are arbitrary constants. These constants can be found if the initial values $\mathbf{x}_0$ and $\mathbf{v}_0$ are known. It can be shown that (34.7) represents either an ellipse, parabola or hyperbola, depending on the values of x_0 and v_0.

Motion of a system of particles

35. *The center of mass of a system of particles.* Let us consider a system of N particles. We denote their masses by the symbols m_1, m_2, m_3, $\cdots$, m_N. The total mass m of the system is then given by the relation

(35.1) $$m = \sum_{j=1}^{N} m_j.$$

We denote the coordinates of the particle of mass m_j by the symbols (x_{j1}, x_{j2}, x_{j3}). The position-vector $\mathbf{x}_j$ of this particle then satisfies the relation

$$\mathbf{x}_j = x_{j1}\mathbf{i}_1 + x_{j2}\mathbf{i}_2 + x_{j3}\mathbf{i}_3 \quad (j = 1, 2, \cdots, N).$$

We have then a set of $3N$ scalars x_{jk} ($j = 1, 1, 3, \cdots, N; k = 1, 2, 3$) which denotes the coordinates of the particles.

The center of mass of the system of particles is defined to be the point C with position-vector $\mathbf{x}_C$ determined by the equation

(35.2) $$m\,\mathbf{x}_C = \sum_{j=1}^{N} m_j\,\mathbf{x}_j.$$

The center of mass is sometimes called the mass center or centroid or center of gravity.

If the distances between the individual particles in a system remain unaltered, as mentioned previously the system is called a *rigid body*. A rigid body often consists of a continuous distribution of matter, and in this case the summations in Equations (35.1) and (35.2) above must

72

then be replaced by integrations. Thus, if ρ is the density of matter in the body, V is the region occupied by the body, dV is the volume of an element of the body and $\mathbf{x}$ is the position-vector of a point in dV, then

(35.3)
$$m = \int_V \rho \, dV,$$

(35.4)
$$m\mathbf{x}_C = \int_V \rho \, \mathbf{x} \, dV.$$

36. *The moments and products of inertia of a system of particles.* Let us first consider a single particle of mass m. Let l denote the length of the perpendicular from the particle to a line L, as shown in Figure 41.

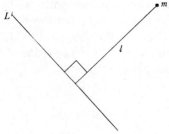

Figure 41

The moment of inertia of the particle about the line L is defined to be the scalar I given by the relation

$$I = m \, l^2.$$

Let p and q denote the lengths of the perpendiculars from the particle to two perpendicular planes P and Q, as shown in Figure 42. The product of inertia of the particle with respect to these two planes is defined to be the scalar K given by the relation

$$K = m \, p \, q.$$

The moment of inertia about a line of a system of particles is defined to be the sum of the moments of inertia about the line of the individual particles. Also, the product of inertia with respect to two planes of

73

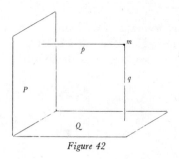

Figure 42

a system of particles is defined to be the sum of the products of inertia with respect to the two planes of the individual particles.

We now consider a set of N particles and introduce a set of rectangular cartesian coordinate axes with origin at a point 0. As in § 35 we denote the masses of these particles by m_j $(j = 1, 2, 3, \cdots, N)$ and their coordinates by the $3N$ symbols x_{jk} $(j = 1, 2, \cdots, N;$ $k = 1, 2, 3)$. The moments of inertia of this system of particles about the three coordinate axes are denoted by I_1, I_2, and I_3. It is easily seen that

$$I_1 = \sum_{j=1}^{N} m_j \, (x^2_{j2} + x^2_{j3}) ,$$

(36.1)
$$I_2 = \sum_{j=1}^{N} m_j \, (x^2_{j3} + x^2_{j1}) ,$$

$$I_3 = \sum_{j=1}^{N} m_j \, (x^2_{j1} + x^2_{j2}) .$$

The products of inertia of this system of particles with respect to the three coordinate planes, taken in pairs, are denoted by K_1, K_2 and K_3. It is easily seen that

$$K_1 = \sum_{j=1}^{N} m_j \, x_{j2} \, x_{j3} ,$$

(36.2)
$$K_2 = \sum_{j=1}^{N} m_j \, x_{j3} \, x_{j1} ,$$

$$K_3 = \sum_{j=1}^{N} m_j \, x_{j1} \, x_{j2} .$$

74

Of course, if the system of particles forms a rigid body, the summations in Equations (36.1) and (36.2) must be replaced by integrations.

If I_1, I_2, I_3, K_1, K_2 and K_3 are known, the moment of inertia I of the system about any line L through the origin can be found easily.

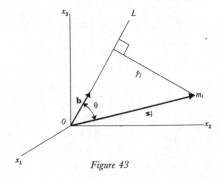

Figure 43

In order to prove this we let p_j denote the length of the perpendicular from the particle of mass m_j to the line L, as shown in Figure 43. Then

$$I = \sum_{j=1}^{N} m_j p_j{}^2.$$

But from the figure we see that

$$p_j = x_j \sin \theta = |\mathbf{b} \times \mathbf{x}_j|,$$

where $\mathbf{x}_j$ is the position-vector of the particle of mass m_j, x_j is the magnitude of $\mathbf{x}_j$, $\mathbf{b}$ is a unit vector on L, and θ is the angle between $\mathbf{x}_j$ and $\mathbf{b}$. The components of the vector $\mathbf{b} \times \mathbf{x}_j$ are

$$b_2\, x_{j3} - b_3\, x_{j2}, \quad b_3\, x_{j1} - b_1\, x_{j3}, \quad b_1\, x_{j2} - b_2\, x_{j1},$$

and hence $p_j{}^2$ is equal to the sum of the squares of these three components. Thus

$$I = \sum_{j=1}^{N} m_j \left[(b_2 x_{j3} - b_3\, x_{j2})^2 + (b_3\, x_{j1} - b_1\, x_{j3})^2 + (b_1\, x_{j2} - b_2\, x_{j1})^2 \right]$$

$$= b_1{}^2 \sum_{j=1}^{N} m_j\, (x_{j2}{}^2 + x_{j3}{}^2) + b_2{}^2 \sum_{j=1}^{N} m_j\, (x_{j3}{}^2 + x_{j1}{}^2) +$$

$$+ b_3^2 \sum_{j=1}^{N} m_j \, (x_{j1}^2 + x_{j2}^2) - 2 \, b_2 b_3 \sum_{j=1}^{N} m_j \, x_{j2} \, x_{j3}$$

$$- 2 \, b_3 \, b_1 \sum_{j=1}^{N} m_j \, x_{j3} \, x_{j1} - 2 \, b_1 \, b_2 \sum_{j=1}^{N} m_j \, x_{j1} \, x_{j2} \, .$$

Because of (36.1) and (36.2) we then have

$$(36.3) \qquad I = I_1 \, b_1^2 + I_2 \, b_2^2 + I_3 \, b_3^2 - 2 \, K_1 \, b_2 \, b_3 - 2 \, K_2 \, b_3 \, b_1 - 2 \, K_3 \, b_1 \, b_2 \, .$$

It will be noted that b_1, b_2 and b_3, which are the components of the unit vector **b** on the line L, are also the direction cosines of L. Equation (36.3) is the desired equation which permits a simple determination of the moment of inertia I of a system about any line L through the origin, once I_1, I_2, I_3, K_1, K_2 and K_3 have been found.

If it happens that $K_1 = K_2 = K_3 = O$, the coordinate axes are said to be *principal axes of inertia* at the point O. It can be proved that at every point there is at least one set of principal axes of inertia.[1] In many cases, principal axes of inertia can be deduced readily by considerations of symmetry of the system of particles. For example, at the center of a rectangular parallelepiped the principal axes of inertia are parallel to the edges of the body.

We shall now state without proof two theorems the proofs of which are very simple and may be found in almost any text book on calculus.

The theorem of perpendicular axes. If a system of particles lies entirely in a plane P, the moment of inertia of the system with respect to a line L perpendicular to the plane P is equal to the sum of the moments of inertia of the system with respect to any two perpendicular lines intersecting L and lying in P.

The theorem of parallel axes. The moment of inertia I of a system of particles about a line L satisfies the relation

$$I = I' + m \, l^2 \, ,$$

where I' is the moment of inertia of the system about a line L' parallel to L and through the center of mass of the system, m is the total mass

---

[1] See J. L. Synge and B. A. Griffith, *Principles of Mechanics*, McGraw–Hill Book Co., 1942, pp. 311–321.

of the system, and l is the perpendicular distance between L and L'.

In most books of mathematical tables there are listed the moments of inertia of many bodies with respect to certain axes associated with these bodies. By the use of such tables together with Equation (36.3) and the above two theorems, it is frequently possible to determine rapidly the moment of inertia of a body with respect to any given line.

37. *Kinematics of a rigid body.* Let us consider a rigid body which is rotating about a line L at the rate of ω radians per unit time. The body is said to have an angular velocity. We can represent this angular velocity completely by an arrow defined as follows: its length represents the scalar to some convenient scale; its origin is an arbitrary point on L; its line of action coincides with L; it points in the direction indicated by the thumb of the right hand when the fingers are placed to indicate the sense of the rotation about L. To prove that angular velocity is a vector, it is then only necessary to prove that it obeys the law of vector addition. This will be done presently. We shall anticipate this result, and denote angular velocities by symbols in bold-faced type.

We shall first determine the velocity $\mathbf{v}$ of a general point X in a body which has an angular velocity $\boldsymbol{\omega}$. Let 0 denote a point on the line of action of $\boldsymbol{\omega}$, and let $\mathbf{x}$ denote the vector $\overline{OX}$, as shown in Figure 44.

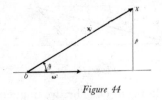

Figure 44

Let θ denote the angle between $\boldsymbol{\omega}$ and $\mathbf{x}$, and let p denote the length of the perpendicular from X to the line of action of $\boldsymbol{\omega}$. The displacement $d\mathbf{x}$ of the point X in time dt has the following properties:

(i)   its direction is perpendicular to both $\boldsymbol{\omega}$ and $\mathbf{x}$;

(ii)   its direction is that indicated by the thumb of the right hand when the fingers are placed to indicate the sense of the rotation θ from $\boldsymbol{\omega}$ to $\mathbf{x}$;

(iii) its magnitude is $p\omega dt$, which is equal to $x\omega dt \sin \theta$, x being the magnitude of the vector $\mathbf{x}$.

In view of the definition in § 8 of the vector product of two vectors, it then appears that $d\mathbf{x} = \boldsymbol{\omega} \times \mathbf{x}\, dt$. Thus

$$\frac{d\mathbf{x}}{dt} = \boldsymbol{\omega} \times \mathbf{x}.$$

If the point O is fixed in a frame of reference S, the velocity $\mathbf{v}$ of the point X relative to S is then

(37.1) $$\mathbf{v} = \boldsymbol{\omega} \times \mathbf{x}.$$

On the other hand, if the point O has a velocity $\mathbf{u}$ relative to a frame of reference S, the velocity of the point X relative to S is

(37.2) $$\mathbf{v} = \mathbf{u} + \boldsymbol{\omega} \times \mathbf{x}.$$

We shall now prove that angular velocity obeys the law of vector addition. Let us consider a body which is rotating simultaneously about two lines L and L' which intersect at a point O fixed in a frame of reference S. These angular velocities can be represented by the arrows $\boldsymbol{\omega}$ and $\boldsymbol{\omega}'$ in Figure 45. Let X be a general point in the body,

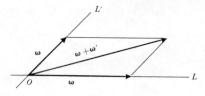

Figure 45

with position-vector $\mathbf{x}$ relative to O. The two angular velocities impart to X the two velocities $\boldsymbol{\omega} \times \mathbf{x}$ and $\boldsymbol{\omega}' \times \mathbf{x}$ which, being vectors, can be added to yield the resultant velocity

(37.3) $$\mathbf{v} = \boldsymbol{\omega} \times \mathbf{x} + \boldsymbol{\omega}' \times \mathbf{x}.$$

To complete the proof we must show that (37.3) can be written in the form $\mathbf{v} = \boldsymbol{\omega}'' \times \mathbf{x}$, where $\boldsymbol{\omega}''$ is an arrow obtained by the application

78

of the law of vector addition to the arrows $\boldsymbol{\omega}$ and $\boldsymbol{\omega}'$. Even though angular velocity has not been assumed to satisfy the law of vector addition, Equation (8.5) may be applied to the two products in (37.3) to yield

$$v_1 = \omega_2\, x_3 - \omega_3\, x_2 + \omega'_2\, x_3 - \omega'_3\, x_2$$
$$= (\omega_2 + \omega'_2)\, x_3 - (\omega_3 + \omega'_3)\, x_2,$$

and two similar expressions for v_2 and v_3. Hence we can write

$$\mathbf{v} = \boldsymbol{\omega}'' \times \mathbf{x},$$

where $\boldsymbol{\omega}''$ is an arrow having components $\omega_1 + \omega_1'$, $\omega_2 + \omega'_2$, $\omega_3 + \omega'_3$. But these are the components of the vector obtained by application of the law of vector addition to the arrows $\boldsymbol{\omega}$ and $\boldsymbol{\omega}'$. Hence $\boldsymbol{\omega}''$ is equal to the vector sum of $\boldsymbol{\omega}$ and $\boldsymbol{\omega}'$, and so angular velocity is a vector.

It will be noted that two angular velocities can be added only when their lines of action have a point of intersection, and that the line of action of the sum passes through this point of intersection.

38. *The time derivative of a vector.* Let us consider a set of rectangular cartesian coordinate axes with origin O fixed in a frame of reference S, and with axes rotating relative to S with angular velocity $\boldsymbol{\omega}$. Then the line of action of $\boldsymbol{\omega}$ passes though O.

If $\mathbf{i}_1$, $\mathbf{i}_2$ and $\mathbf{i}_3$ are the usual unit vectors associated with these coordinate axes, then the velocities relative to S of the terminuses of these vectors are

$$\frac{d\mathbf{i}_1}{dt}, \qquad \frac{d\mathbf{i}_2}{dt}, \qquad \frac{d\mathbf{i}_3}{dt}.$$

But by the previous section these velocities are

$$\boldsymbol{\omega} \times \mathbf{i}_1, \quad \boldsymbol{\omega} \times \mathbf{i}_2, \quad \boldsymbol{\omega} \times \mathbf{i}_3.$$

Hence

(38.1) $\qquad \dfrac{d\mathbf{i}_1}{dt} = \boldsymbol{\omega} \times \mathbf{i}_1, \quad \dfrac{d\mathbf{i}_2}{dt} = \boldsymbol{\omega} \times \mathbf{i}_2, \quad \dfrac{d\mathbf{i}_3}{dt} = \boldsymbol{\omega} \times \mathbf{i}_3.$

Let $\mathbf{a}$ be a vector with components a_1, a_2, a_3 relative to the rotating coordinate axes. Then

$$\mathbf{a} = a_1 \mathbf{i}_1 + a_2 \mathbf{i}_2 + a_3 \mathbf{i}_3 ,$$

and the time derivative of $\mathbf{a}$, relative to S, is then

$$\frac{d\mathbf{a}}{dt} = \frac{da_1}{dt}\mathbf{i}_1 + \frac{da_2}{dt}\mathbf{i}_2 + \frac{da_3}{dt}\mathbf{i}_3 + a_1\frac{d\mathbf{i}_1}{dt} + a_2\frac{d\mathbf{i}_2}{dt} + a_3\frac{d\mathbf{i}_3}{dt} .$$

Because of Equations (38.1) we can write the last three terms in the form

$$a_1\boldsymbol{\omega} \times \mathbf{i}_1 + a_2\boldsymbol{\omega} \times \mathbf{i}_2 + a_3\boldsymbol{\omega} \times \mathbf{i}_3 ,$$

which reduces to $\boldsymbol{\omega} \times \mathbf{a}$. Hence we can write

(38.2)
$$\frac{d\mathbf{a}}{dt} = \frac{\delta\mathbf{a}}{\delta t} + \boldsymbol{\omega} \times \mathbf{a} ,$$

where

(38.3)
$$\frac{\delta\mathbf{a}}{\delta t} = \frac{da_1}{dt}\mathbf{i}_1 + \frac{da_2}{dt}\mathbf{i}_2 + \frac{da_3}{dt}\mathbf{i}_3 .$$

Equation (38.2) expresses $d\mathbf{a}/dt$ as the sum of two parts. The part $\delta\mathbf{a}/\delta t$ is the time derivative of $\mathbf{a}$ relative to the moving coordinate system. The part $\boldsymbol{\omega} \times \mathbf{a}$ is the time derivative of $\mathbf{a}$ relative to S when $\mathbf{a}$ is fixed relative to the moving coordinate system.

When the origin of the coordinate system is not at rest relative to S but has a velocity $\mathbf{u}$, Equations (38.1) still hold, and hence also does Equation (38.2).

39. *Linear and angular momentum.* Let us consider a particle of mass m, with a position-vector $\mathbf{x}$ relative to a point O fixed in a frame of

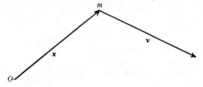

Figure 46

reference S. Let $\mathbf{v}$ denote the velocity of the particle, as shown in Figure 46. The linear momentum of the particle is a vector $\mathbf{M}$ defined by the relation

80

$$\mathbf{M} = m\,\mathbf{v}.$$

The angular momentum of the particle about the point O is by definition the moment of $\mathbf{M}$ about O. We shall denote it by the symbol $\mathbf{h}$. Hence, by § 10 where the moment of a vector about a point is considered, we have

$$\mathbf{h} = \mathbf{x} \times \mathbf{M} = \mathbf{x} \times m\mathbf{v} = m\mathbf{x} \times \mathbf{v}.$$

Let us now consider a system of N particles. As before, we denote the mass and position-vector of the j-th particle by m_j and $\mathbf{x}_j$, respectively. Also, we denote the velocity of this particle relative to S by $\mathbf{v}_j$. Then for this system the linear momentum $\mathbf{M}$ and the angular momentum $\mathbf{h}$ about O are defined by the relations

$$(39.1) \qquad \mathbf{M} = \sum_{j=1}^{N} m_j \mathbf{v}_j, \qquad \mathbf{h} = \sum_{j=1}^{N} m_j \mathbf{x}_j \times \mathbf{v}_j.$$

Theorem. The linear momentum of a system of particles is equal to the product of the total mass of the system and the velocity of the center of mass of the system.

Proof. The position-vector $\mathbf{x}_C$ of the center of mass of the system is given by Equation (35.2). We differentiate this equation with respect to the time t, obtaining

$$m\,\frac{d\mathbf{x}_C}{dt} = \sum_{j=1}^{N} m_j\,\frac{d\mathbf{x}_j}{dt}.$$

But

$$\frac{d\mathbf{x}_C}{dt} = \mathbf{v}_C, \qquad \frac{d\mathbf{x}_j}{dt} = \mathbf{v}_j,$$

where $\mathbf{v}_C$ is the velocity of the center of mass C relative to S. Hence

$$(39.2) \qquad m\mathbf{v}_C = \sum_{j=1}^{N} m_j \mathbf{v}_j = \mathbf{M}.$$

This completes the proof.

Let us now suppose that the system of particles constitutes a rigid body, and that the body is rotating about the point O which is fixed in the frame of reference S. The body then has an angular velocity $\boldsymbol{\omega}$

with a line of action which passes through O. The velocity relative to S of the *j-th* particle in the body is then

$$\mathbf{v}_j = \boldsymbol{\omega} \times \mathbf{x}_j,$$

and by Equation (39.1) the angular momentum of the system about O is then

(39.3)
$$\mathbf{h} = \sum_{j=1}^{N} m_j \, \mathbf{x}_j \times (\boldsymbol{\omega} \times \mathbf{x}_j).$$

Because of the identity (9.3), we can then write

$$\mathbf{h} = \sum_{j=1}^{N} m_j \left[\boldsymbol{\omega} \, x_j^2 - \mathbf{x}_j (\mathbf{x}_j \cdot \boldsymbol{\omega}) \right].$$

Now let us introduce coordinate axes with origin at the point O fixed in S. The directions of these coordinate axes need not be fixed in S. As before we denote the coordinates of the *j-th* particle by (x_{j1}, x_{j2}, x_{j3}). The component h_1 of $\mathbf{h}$ then has the value

$$\mathbf{h}_1 = \sum_{j=1}^{N} m_j \left[\omega_1 \left(x_{j1}^2 + x_{j2}^2 + x_{j3}^2 \right) - x_{j1} \left(x_{j1}\omega_1 + x_{j2}\omega_2 + x_{j3}\omega_3 \right) \right]$$

$$= \omega_1 \sum_{j=1}^{N} m_j \left(x_{j2}^2 + x_{j3}^2 \right) - \omega_2 \sum_{j=1}^{N} m_j \, x_{j1} \, x_{j2} - \omega_3 \sum_{j=1}^{N} m_j \, x_{j3} \, x_{j1}$$

$$= I_1\omega_1 - K_3\omega_2 - K_2\omega_3 \, ,$$

where I_1, K_2 and K_3 are moments and products of inertia defined in § 36. There are similar expressions for h_2 and h_3. We have finally

(39.4)
$$\begin{aligned}
h_1 &= I_1\omega_1 - K_3\omega_2 - K_2\omega_3 \, , \\
h_2 &= -K_3\omega_1 + I_2\omega_2 - K_1\omega_3 \, , \\
h_3 &= -K_2\omega_1 - K_1\omega_2 + I_3\omega_3 \, .
\end{aligned}$$

Let us now consider a rigid body which is moving in a general fashion relative to a frame of reference S. Let us introduce coordinate axes with origin at the center of mass C of the body. The directions of the coordinate axes need not be fixed in the body, however. We may consider the body as having a velocity of translation $\mathbf{v}_C$ plus an angular velocity about a line through C. Then, as seen in § 37, the velocity of the *j-th* particle can be expressed in the form

$$\mathbf{v}_j = \mathbf{v}_C + \boldsymbol{\omega} \times \mathbf{x}_j.$$

82

Hence the angular momentum **h** of the system about the center of mass C has the value

$$\mathbf{h} = \sum_{j=1}^{N} m_j\, \mathbf{x}_j \times (\mathbf{v}_C + \boldsymbol{\omega} \times \mathbf{x}_j)$$

$$= \left(\sum_{j=1}^{N} m_j\, \mathbf{x}_j \right) \times \mathbf{v}_C + \sum_{j=1}^{N} m_j\, \mathbf{x}_j \times (\boldsymbol{\omega} \times \mathbf{x}_j) \ .$$

By Equation (35.2) the first sum is equal to $m\mathbf{x}_C$. Since the origin of the coordinate system and the center of mass C of the body coincide, $\mathbf{x}_C = 0$. Thus

$$\mathbf{h} = \sum_{j=1}^{N} m_j\, \mathbf{x}_j \times (\boldsymbol{\omega} \times \mathbf{x}_j) \ .$$

The right side of this equation is the same as the right side of Equation (39.3). Hence in the present case the components of **h** are also given by Equations (39.4).

We have then the important result: *Equations (39.4) may be used for the determination of the components of the angular momentum* **h** *of a rigid body about either a fixed point O in the body or the center of mass C of the body. In the two cases the origin of the coordinates is at O and C, respectively, the directions of the coordinate axes being quite general.* Equations (39.4) cannot be used in the case of the angular momentum of a rigid body about a moving point which is not the center of mass of the body.

40. *The motion of a system of particles.* Let us consider a general system of N particles. Let m_j denote the mass of the j-th particle, and let $\mathbf{v}_j$ denote its velocity relative to a Newtonian system. The forces acting on the j-th particle can be divided into two groups called *internal forces* and *external forces*. Internal forces are those due to other particles in the system. External forces include all other forces. Let $\mathbf{F}_{jk}$ denote the internal force exerted on the j-th particle by the k-th particle, and let $\mathbf{F}_j$ denote the total external force exerted on the j-th particle.

Theorem 1. The rate of change of the linear momentum of the system is equal to the sum the *external* forces acting on the system.

Proof. Applying to the *j-th* particle Newton's Second Law as stated in § 31, we have

$$(40.1) \qquad m_j \frac{d\mathbf{v}_j}{dt} = \mathbf{F}_j + \sum_{k=1}^{N} \mathbf{F}_{jk} .$$

We now sum the N equations in (40.1), obtaining

$$(40.2) \qquad \sum_{j=1}^{N} m_j \frac{d\mathbf{v}_j}{dt} = \sum_{j=1}^{N} \mathbf{F}_j + \sum_{j=1}^{N} \sum_{k=1}^{N} \mathbf{F}_{jk} .$$

Because of Newton's Third Law, as stated in § 31, $\mathbf{F}_{jk} = -\mathbf{F}_{jk}$. Thus the double sum in Equation (40.2) vanishes, and we can then write (40.2) in the form

$$(40.3) \qquad \frac{d\mathbf{M}}{dt} = \mathbf{F} ,$$

where $\mathbf{M}$ is the linear momentum of the system and $\mathbf{F}$ is the sum of the external forces acting on the system.

Theorem 2. The center of mass of a system of particles moves like a particle with a mass equal to the total mass of the system acted upon by a force equal to the sum of the external forces acting on the system.

Proof. In § 39 we saw that $\mathbf{M} = m\mathbf{v}_C$, where m is the total mass of the system, and $\mathbf{v}_C$ is the velocity of the center of mass of the system. Thus Equation (40.3) can be written in the form

$$(40.4) \qquad m \frac{d\mathbf{v}_C}{dt} = \mathbf{F} .$$

This completes the proof.

41. *The motion of a rigid body with a fixed point.* Let us now consider a system of particles which constitutes a rigid body with a point O fixed relative to a Newtonian frame of reference.

Theorem 1. The rate of change of the angular momentum of the body about O is equal to the total moment about O of the external forces.

Proof. Let us introduce coordinates with origin at O. Then

$$(41.1) \qquad \mathbf{v}_j = \frac{d\mathbf{x}_j}{dt} ,$$

where $\mathbf{v}_j$, $\mathbf{x}_j$ and t have the usual meanings. By Equation (39.1), the angular momentum $\mathbf{h}$ of the body about the fixed point O is

$$\mathbf{h} = \sum_{j=1}^{N} m_j\, \mathbf{x}_j \times \mathbf{v}_j\,,$$

and so

(41.2) $$\frac{d\mathbf{h}}{dt} = \mathbf{A} + \mathbf{B}\,,$$

where

$$\mathbf{A} = \sum_{j=1}^{N} m_j \frac{d\mathbf{x}_j}{dt} \times \mathbf{v}_j\,, \quad \mathbf{B} = \sum_{j=1}^{N} m_j\, \mathbf{x}_j \times \frac{d\mathbf{v}_j}{dt}\,.$$

Because of Equation (41.1) we have

$$\mathbf{A} = \sum_{j=1}^{N} m_j\, \mathbf{v}_j \times \mathbf{v}_j = 0.$$

Equation (40.1) gives an expression for $m_j d\mathbf{v}_j/dt$. Because of this we have

$$\mathbf{B} = \sum_{j=1}^{N} \mathbf{x}_j \times \left(\mathbf{F}_j + \sum_{k=1}^{N} \mathbf{F}_{jk} \right) = \mathbf{G} + \mathbf{H},$$

where

(41.3) $$\mathbf{G} = \sum_{j=1}^{N} \mathbf{x}_j \times \mathbf{F}_j,$$

$$\mathbf{H} = \sum_{j=1}^{N} \sum_{k=1}^{N} \mathbf{x}_j \times \mathbf{F}_{jk}.$$

It will be recalled that $\mathbf{F}_j$ is the external force acting on the *j-th* particle and $\mathbf{F}_{jk}$ is the internal force exerted on the *j-th* particle by *k-th* particle. We note that $\mathbf{G}$ is the sum of the moments about O of the external forces. Now

$$\mathbf{H} = \sum_{j=1}^{N} \sum_{k=1}^{N} \mathbf{x}_j \times \mathbf{F}_{jk} = \sum_{k=1}^{N} \sum_{j=1}^{N} \mathbf{x}_k \times \mathbf{F}_{kj}.$$

Thus

(41.4) $$2\,\mathbf{H} = \sum_{j=1}^{N} \sum_{k=1}^{N} (\mathbf{x}_j \times \mathbf{F}_{jk} + \mathbf{x}_k \times \mathbf{F}_{kj})\,.$$

But $\mathbf{F}_{kj} = -\mathbf{F}_{jk}$. Thus (41.4) becomes

$$2\mathbf{H} = \sum_{j=1}^{N} \sum_{k=1}^{N} (\mathbf{x}_j - \mathbf{x}_k) \times \mathbf{F}_{jk}.$$

Since the lines of action of the vectors $\mathbf{x}_j - \mathbf{x}_k$ and $\mathbf{F}_{jk}$ coincide, their vector product vanishes. Hence $\mathbf{H} = 0$, and $\mathbf{B} = \mathbf{G}$, so Equation (41.2) reduces to the form

$$(41.5) \qquad \frac{d\mathbf{h}}{dt} = \mathbf{G},$$

where $\mathbf{h}$ is the angular momentum of the system about the fixed point O, and $\mathbf{G}$ is the total moment about O of the external forces. This completes the proof.

We have placed the origin of the coordinate system at the fixed point O. Let us now choose as coordinate axes a set of principal axes of inertia of the body at O. (Principal axes of inertia are defined in § 36.) Then the products of inertia K_1, K_2, K_3 all vanish, and from Equations (39.4) we obtain for the components of the angular momentum $\mathbf{h}$ of the body about 0 the expressions

$$(41.6) \qquad h_1 = I_1\omega_1, \quad h_2 = I_2\omega_2, \quad h_3 = I_3\omega_3,$$

where I_1, I_2, I_3 are the moments of inertia of the body about the coordinate axes, and ω_1, ω_2, ω_3 are the components of the angular velocity $\boldsymbol{\omega}$ of the body about O.

In most cases the coordinate axes will be fixed in the body and will hence have an angular velocity $\boldsymbol{\omega}$ about O. However, in a few special cases when the body has a certain symmetry it will be found possible and desirable to choose coordinate axes not fixed in the body. To include such special cases we denote the angular velocity of the axes about O by $\boldsymbol{\Omega}$, which may or may not differ from $\boldsymbol{\omega}$. According to Equation (38.3) we then have

$$\frac{d\mathbf{h}}{dt} = \frac{\delta\mathbf{h}}{\delta t} + \boldsymbol{\Omega} \times \mathbf{h}$$

or

$$(41.7) \qquad \frac{d\mathbf{h}}{dt} = \dot{h}_1\mathbf{i}_1 + \dot{h}_2\mathbf{i}_2 + \dot{h}_3\mathbf{i}_3 + (\Omega_2 h_3 - \Omega_3 h_2)\,\mathbf{i}_1$$
$$+ (\Omega_3 h_1 - \Omega_1 h_3)\,\mathbf{i}_2 + (\Omega_1 h_2 - \Omega_2 h_1)\,\mathbf{i}_3.$$

From this equation we can read off the components of the vector $d\mathbf{h}/dt$. According to Equation (41.5) these components are equal to the components of $\mathbf{G}$. Hence we have the equations

$$\dot{h}_1 + \Omega_2 h_3 - \Omega_3 h_2 = G_1,$$
$$\dot{h}_2 + \Omega_3 h_1 - \Omega_1 h_3 = G_2,$$
$$\dot{h}_3 + \Omega_1 h_2 - \Omega_2 h_1 = G_3,$$

where G_1, G_2, G_3 are the components of $\mathbf{G}$. Because of Equations (41.6) these relations can be written in the form

(41.8)
$$I_1\dot{\omega}_1 - I_2\omega_2\Omega_3 + I_3\omega_3\Omega_2 = G_1,$$
$$I_2\dot{\omega}_2 - I_3\omega_3\Omega_1 + I_1\omega_1\Omega_3 = G_2,$$
$$I_3\dot{\omega}_3 - I_1\omega_1\Omega_2 + I_2\omega_2\Omega_1 = G_3.$$

In the case when the coordinate axes are fixed in the rigid body, then $\boldsymbol{\Omega} = \boldsymbol{\omega}$ and so (12.8) reduce to the form

(41.9)
$$I_1\dot{\omega}_1 - (I_2 - I_3)\,\omega_2\omega_3 = G_1,$$
$$I_2\dot{\omega}_2 - (I_3 - I_1)\,\omega_3\omega_1 = G_2,$$
$$I_3\dot{\omega}_3 - (I_1 - I_2)\,\omega_1\omega_2 = G_3.$$

These equations are called Euler's equations of motion.

Theorem 3. The total moment about O of the gravity forces acting on a system of particles is equal to the moment about O of a single force equal to the resultant of the gravity forces and acting at the center of mass of the system.

Proof. Let us introduce a coordinate system with origin at the point O. Let $\mathbf{k}$ be a unit vector in the direction of the gravity forces. Then the gravity force acting on the j-*th* particle is $m_j g\mathbf{k}$, and the total moment about O of the gravity forces is

$$\mathbf{G}' = \sum_{j=1}^{N} \mathbf{x}_j \times m_j g\mathbf{k} = \left(\sum_{j=1}^{N} m_j\,\mathbf{x}_j\right) \times g\mathbf{k}.$$

But by Equation (35.2) we have

$$\sum_{j=1}^{N} m_j\,\mathbf{x}_j = m\,\mathbf{x}_C$$

87

where m is the total mass and $\mathbf{x}_C$ is the position-vector of the center of mass. Thus

$$\mathbf{G}' = m\mathbf{x}_C \times g\mathbf{k} = \mathbf{x}_C \times (mg\mathbf{k}).$$

But $\mathbf{x}_C \times (mg\mathbf{k})$ is the moment about O of a single force $mg\mathbf{k}$ equal to the resultant of the gravity forces and acting at the center of mass C of the system. This completes the proof.

Example 1. *A sphere of radius a is placed on a rough plane which makes an angle α with the horizontal, and is then released. Find the distance the sphere moves down the plane in time t.*

Figure 47 shows the configuration of the system at a general time t.

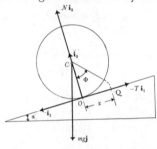

Figure 47

The center of mass of the sphere is at its geometrical center. The point Q is the initial point of contact of the sphere and plane, and in the time t the sphere has rolled through an angle Φ, as shown. The point on the sphere which is in contact with the plane is at rest. Hence the sphere has a fixed point, and we select this point as the origin O of the coordinate system. We must select the coordinate axes to coincide with principal directions of inertia of the sphere at O. This requirement is satisfied if the unit vectors $\mathbf{i}_1$ and $\mathbf{i}_3$ are chosen as shown in the figure. The unit vector $\mathbf{i}_2$ is then perpendicular to $\mathbf{i}_1$ and $\mathbf{i}_3$, and points up from the page. We note that the coordinate axes are not fixed in the body, and that consequently Equations (41.8) apply.

The external forces acting on the sphere consist of gravity and the reaction of the plane. Because of Theorem 3 above, the forces exerted by gravity on all the particles of the sphere may be replaced by a single force $mg\mathbf{j}$ acting at C, as shown, where $\mathbf{j}$ is a unit vector. The reaction of the plane is a force which may be resolved into a force $N\mathbf{i}_3$ normal to the plane and a force $-T\mathbf{i}_1$ along the plane, as shown. The moment $\mathbf{G}$ of the external forces about O is given by the relation

$$\mathbf{G} = \overline{OC} \times mg\mathbf{j},$$

since the moments of $\mathbf{N}$ and $\mathbf{T}$ about O are equal to zero. But

$$\overline{OC} = a\mathbf{i}_3, \quad \mathbf{j} = \mathbf{i}_1 \sin \alpha - \mathbf{i}_3 \cos \alpha.$$

Thus

$$\mathbf{G} = a\mathbf{i}_3 \times mg \,(\mathbf{i}_1 \sin \alpha - \mathbf{i}_3 \cos \alpha)$$
$$= mga\mathbf{i}_2 \sin \alpha,$$

so

(41.10) $\qquad G_1 = 0, \quad G_2 = mga \sin \alpha, \quad G_3 = 0.$

The coordinate axes have no angular velocity, so

(41.11) $\qquad \Omega_1 = \Omega_2 = \Omega_3 = 0.$

The angular velocity $\boldsymbol{\omega}$ of the sphere about 0 is

$$\boldsymbol{\omega} = \dot{\Phi}\,\mathbf{i}_2,$$

where the superimposed dot denotes differentiation with respect to t. Thus

(41.12) $\qquad \omega_1 = 0, \quad \omega_2 = \dot{\Phi}, \quad \omega_3 = 0.$

The moments of inertia of the sphere about the coordinate axes are

(41.13) $\qquad I_1 = I_2 = \tfrac{7}{5}ma^2, \quad I_3 = \tfrac{2}{5}ma^2.$

We now substitute in Euler's equations (41.8) from Equations (41.10), (41.11), (41.12) and (41.13) to obtain the relation

$$\tfrac{7}{5}ma^2\ddot{\Phi}\mathbf{i}_2 = mga\mathbf{i}_2 \sin \alpha.$$

Thus

$$\ddot{\Phi} = \frac{5g \sin \alpha}{7a},$$

and two integrations then yield

89

$$\Phi = \frac{5g \sin \alpha}{14a} t^2,$$

since $\Phi = \dot{\Phi} = 0$ when $t = 0$.

If z is the distance the sphere has rolled down the plane in time t, then $z = a\Phi$ and we have

(41.14) $z = \frac{5}{14} gt^2 \sin \alpha.$

Example 2.   Two shafts are attached to the corners A and C of a rectangular plate ABCD, in such a way that the axes of the shafts are continuations of the diagonal AC. The shafts turn in two bearings each at a distance c from the center of the plate. The system is made to rotate at a constant rate of ω radians per unit time. Find the forces exerted on the bearings.

The system is shown in Figure 48. We choose the center O of the

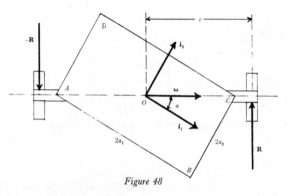

Figure 48

plate as the origin of the coordinate system. We also choose the unit vectors $\mathbf{i}_1$ and $\mathbf{i}_2$ parallel to edges of the plate, as shown. The unit vector $\mathbf{i}_3$ is then perpendicular to the plane of the plate. The directions of these three vectors are principal directions of inertia of the plate at O. The moments of inertia of the plate about the coordinate axes are

(41.15) $I_1 = \frac{1}{3}ma_2^2, \quad I_2 = \frac{1}{3}ma_1^2, \quad I_3 = \frac{1}{3}m(a_1^2 + a_2^2),$

where m is the mass of the plate, and $2a_1$ and $2a_2$ are the lengths of the edges.

90

The plate has an angular velocity $\boldsymbol{\omega}$ the line of action of which is the diagonal AC and the magnitude of which is the given constant ω. If α is the angle between $\boldsymbol{\omega}$ and $\mathbf{i}_1$, then

(41.16)
$$\tan \alpha = \frac{a_2}{a_1}$$

and

$$\boldsymbol{\omega} = \omega \mathbf{i}_1 \cos \alpha + \omega \mathbf{i}_2 \sin \alpha.$$

Thus

(41.17) $\qquad \omega_1 = \omega \cos \alpha, \quad \omega_2 = \omega \sin \alpha, \quad \omega_3 = 0.$

Since the coordinate axes are fixed in the body, Euler's Equations (41.9) apply. We substitute in these equations from (41.15) and (41.17), obtaining the relations

$$G_1 = 0, \quad G_2 = 0, \quad G_3 = \tfrac{1}{3}\, m\, (a_1{}^2 - a_2{}^2)\, \omega^2 \sin \alpha \cos \alpha.$$

Thus the moment $\mathbf{G}$ about O of the external forces is normal to the plate and rotates with it. Hence the forces exerted on the shaft by the bearings must be in the plane of the plate. Let us denote these forces by $\mathbf{R}$ and $-\mathbf{R}$, as shown in Figure 48. We must then have

$$2cR = G_3$$

whence we find that

(41.18) $\qquad R = \tfrac{1}{6c}\, m\, (a_1{}^2 - a_2{}^2)\, \omega^2 \sin \alpha \cos \alpha$
$$= \tfrac{1}{6}\, m\omega^2\, \frac{a_1\, a_2\, (a_1{}^2 - a_2{}^2)}{c\,(a_1{}^2 + a_2{}^2)}\,.$$

By Newton's third law (§ 31), the forces exerted on the right and left bearings are $-\mathbf{R}$ and $\mathbf{R}$, with magnitudes R given in Equation (41.18) above.

Example 3. *A gyroscope is mounted so that one point on its axis is fixed. Investigate those motions under gravity in which the axis of the gyroscope makes a constant angle with the vertical.*

A gyroscope is a body with an axis of symmetry, the shape of the body being such that the moment of inertia of the body about its

91

axis of symmetry is large. For example, the disc and shaft in Figure 49 constitute a gyroscope.

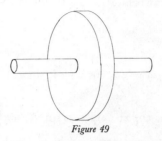

Figure 49

In Figure 50 the line OA is the axis of the gyroscope, the fixed point being at O and the center of mass being at C. We introduce a fixed unit vector $\mathbf{j}$ pointing up from O, and a set of moving orthogonal

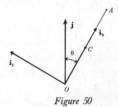

Figure 50

unit vectors $\mathbf{i}_1$, $\mathbf{i}_2$ and $\mathbf{i}_3$ defined as follows: $\mathbf{i}_3$ is along OA; $\mathbf{i}_1$ is in the plane of $\mathbf{j}$ and $\mathbf{i}_3$, as shown; $\mathbf{i}_2$ completes the triad. We note that $\mathbf{i}_2$ is horizontal.

The angle between OA and $\mathbf{j}$ is denoted by θ; it is constant. The plane of $\mathbf{j}$ and $\mathbf{i}_3$ rotates about $\mathbf{j}$ at a rate of p radians per unit time; p is called the precession. The gyroscope spins about its axis at the rate of s radians per unit time; s is called the spin. We denote the mass of the gyroscope by m and the distance OC by l.

The only external forces are the reaction of the pivot support at O and the gravity forces. The former force has no moment about O. The latter forces may be replaced by a single force $-mg\mathbf{j}$ at C. Hence

$$\mathbf{G} = (l\,\mathbf{i}_3) \times (-mg\mathbf{j})\,.$$

92

But

(41.19)
$$\mathbf{j} = \mathbf{i}_1 \sin \theta + \mathbf{i}_3 \cos \theta,$$

whence we get

$$\mathbf{G} = -lmg \sin \theta \, \mathbf{i}_2.$$

Thus

(41.20)
$$G_1 = 0, \quad G_2 = -lmg \sin \theta, \quad G_3 = 0.$$

The angular velocity $\boldsymbol{\omega}$ of the gyroscope is

$$\boldsymbol{\omega} = s\mathbf{i}_3 + p\mathbf{j}.$$

Because of Equation (41.19) we then have

$$\boldsymbol{\omega} = p \sin \theta \mathbf{i}_1 + (s + p \cos \theta) \, \mathbf{i}_3,$$

whence

(41.21)
$$\omega_1 = p \sin \theta, \quad \omega_2 = 0, \quad \omega_3 = s + p \cos \theta.$$

The angular velocity $\boldsymbol{\Omega}$ of the coordinate axes is given by the relation

$$\begin{aligned}\boldsymbol{\Omega} &= p\mathbf{j} \\ &= p \, (\mathbf{i}_1 \sin \theta + \mathbf{i}_3 \cos \theta).\end{aligned}$$

Thus

(41.22)
$$\Omega_1 = p \sin \theta, \quad \Omega_2 = 0, \quad \Omega_3 = p \cos \theta.$$

The coordinate axes associated with $\mathbf{i}_1$, $\mathbf{i}_2$ and $\mathbf{i}_3$ are principal axes of inertia at O, and we have

(41.23)
$$I_1 = I_2, \qquad K_1 = K_2 = K_3 = 0.$$

We now substitute in Euler's equations (41.8) from Equations (41.20), (41.21), (41.22) and (41.23) to obtain the relations

(41.24)
$$I_1 \dot{p} \sin \theta = 0,$$

(41.25)
$$[I_3 s + (I_3 - I_1) \, p \cos \theta] \, p \sin \theta = lmg \sin \theta,$$

(41.26)
$$I_3 \, (\dot{s} - \dot{p} \cos \theta) = 0.$$

One solution of these equations is $\theta = 0$. In this case the axis of the gyroscope is vertical, and the gyroscope is said to be "sleeping". If θ is not equal to zero, then Equations (41.24) and (41.26) yield

$$p = \text{constant}, \qquad s = \text{constant},$$

and Equation (41.25) takes the form

(41.27) $$(I_3 - I_1) \cos \theta \, p^2 + I_3 s p - lmg = 0.$$

This is a relation among the three constants p, s and θ. Hence it appears that we may assign arbitrarily values for two of these constants and there will exist a corresponding motion of the top with θ a constant, provided of course the value of third constant, as obtained from Equation (41.27), is real.

We note from (41.27) that

(41.28) $$s = \frac{lmg}{I_3 p} - \frac{(I_3 - I_1) \, p \cos \theta}{I_3}.$$

The quantities p and θ may be observed readily. The corresponding spin s may be computed by means of this relation. If the precession is small, we note from Equation (41.28) that the spin is large and has the approximate value

$$s = \frac{lmg}{I_3}.$$

42. *The general motion of a rigid body.* We now consider a rigid body moving in a general manner. It may or may not have a fixed point. The motion of its mass center can be determined from Theorem 2 of § 40, which applies to the motion of any system of particles. This theorem yields

(42.1) $$m \frac{d\mathbf{v}_C}{dt} = \mathbf{F},$$

where m is the total mass of the body, $\mathbf{v}_C$ is the velocity of its center of mass, and $\mathbf{F}$ is the sum of the external forces acting on the body. Integration of (42.1) gives the position-vector $\mathbf{x}_C$ of the center of mass C of the body as a function of the time t.

To determine the complete motion of the body it is then only necessary to find the angular velocity of the body about its center of mass.

To do this, we choose the origin O of the coordinate system at the center of mass C of the body. We then consider the body as having a velocity of translation $\mathbf{v}_C$ plus an angular velocity $\boldsymbol{\omega}$ with a line of action through C. The velocity $\mathbf{v}_j$ of the j-th particle is then given by the relations

$$(42.2) \qquad \mathbf{v}_j = \mathbf{v}_C + \frac{d\mathbf{x}_j}{dt} = \mathbf{v}_C + \boldsymbol{\omega} \times \mathbf{x}_j .$$

But by definition the angular momentum $\mathbf{h}$ of the body about the point O is

$$\mathbf{h} = \sum_{j=1}^{N} m_j \mathbf{x}_j \times \mathbf{v}_j,$$

and we then have, just as in § 41,

$$(42.3) \qquad \frac{d\mathbf{h}}{dt} = \mathbf{A} + \mathbf{B} ,$$

where

$$(42.4) \qquad \mathbf{A} = \sum_{j=1}^{N} m_j \frac{d\mathbf{x}_j}{dt} \times \mathbf{v}_j , \qquad \mathbf{B} = \sum_{j=1}^{N} m_j \mathbf{x}_j \times \frac{d\mathbf{v}_j}{dt} .$$

From Equation (42.2) we then have

$$\mathbf{A} = \sum_{j=1}^{N} m_j (\mathbf{v}_j - \mathbf{v}_C) \times \mathbf{v}_j$$
$$= \sum_{j=1}^{N} m_j \mathbf{v}_j \times \mathbf{v}_j - \mathbf{v}_C \times \sum_{j=1}^{N} m_j \mathbf{v}_j$$
$$= 0 - \mathbf{v}_C \times \mathbf{M},$$

where $\mathbf{M}$ is the linear momentum of the body. But $\mathbf{M} = m\mathbf{v}_C$ by Equation (39.2). Thus $\mathbf{A} = O$. Just as in § 41 we find that $\mathbf{B} = \mathbf{G}$, where $\mathbf{G}$ denotes the total moment about O of all the external forces. Thus Equation (42.3) takes the form

$$(42.5) \qquad \frac{d\mathbf{h}}{dt} = \mathbf{G} .$$

We have thus the result: *the rate of change of the angular momentum of a body about its center of mass is equal to the total moment of the external forces about the center of mass.*

We have placed the origin of the coordinate system at the center of mass C of the body. If we choose the coordinate axes to coincide with principal axes of inertia of the body at C, then just as in § 41 we obtain Equations (41.6) and finally Euler's Equations (41.8) from which we can find the unknown quantities ω_1, ω_2 and ω_3 which characterize the rotation of the body about its center of mass.

In conclusion, it should be noted particularly that the equation $d\mathbf{h}/dt = \mathbf{G}$ can be used only in the two following cases: (i) the body has a fixed point and the origin is at this fixed point; (ii) the origin is at the center of mass of the body.

Example 1. *A gyroscope with a constant spin is carried along a horizontal circular path at a constant speed, with its axis tangent to the path of its center of mass. Find the forces exerted on the axle of the gyroscope by the bearings in which the axle turns, neglecting gravity.*

We choose the center of mass of the gyroscope as the origin O of the coordinate system. The path of O is shown in Figure 51; it is a circle

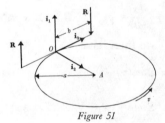

Figure 51

with center A and radius a. We introduce an orthogonal right triad of unit vectors at O, as shown; $\mathbf{i}_1$ points vertically up; $\mathbf{i}_2$ points towards A; $\mathbf{i}_3$ is tangent to the circle and hence lies along the axis of the gyroscope.

Let us suppose that O travels at a speed v in the direction opposite to $\mathbf{i}_3$, and that s is the rate at which the gyroscope spins about its axis, s being positive when it is in the sense of the $90°$ rotation from $\mathbf{i}_1$ to $\mathbf{i}_2$.

The time required for O to go around the circle is $2\pi a/v$. In this time the gyroscope has turned about $\mathbf{i}_1$ through an angle of 2π radians. Hence the angular velocity $\boldsymbol{\omega}$ of the gyroscope is

96

$$\boldsymbol{\omega} = s\mathbf{i}_3 + \frac{2\pi}{2\pi \, a/v}\,\mathbf{i}_1$$

$$= \frac{v}{a}\,\mathbf{i}_1 + s\mathbf{i}_3 \,.$$

Thus

(42.6) $$\omega_1 = \frac{v}{a}\,, \qquad \omega_2 = 0 \,, \qquad \omega_3 = s \,.$$

The angular velocity $\boldsymbol{\Omega}$ of the coordinate axes is

$$\boldsymbol{\Omega} = \frac{v}{a}\,\mathbf{i}_1$$

whence

(42.7) $$\Omega_1 = \frac{v}{a}\,, \qquad \Omega_2 = 0 \,, \qquad \Omega_3 = 0 \,.$$

Also

(42.8) $$I_1 = I_2, \qquad K_1 = K_2 = K_3 = 0 \,.$$

We now substitute in Euler's equations (41.8) from Equations (42.6), (42.7) and (42.8) to obtain the relations

$$G_1 = 0 \,, \qquad G_2 = -I_3\frac{sv}{a}\,, \qquad G_3 = 0 \,.$$

Hence the forces exerted on the gyroscope by the bearings must be in the x_3x_1 plane. If $\mathbf{R}$ and $-\mathbf{R}$ are these forces, and $2b$ is the distance between the bearings, then

$$2bR = I_3\frac{vs}{a}$$

whence

$$R = I_3\frac{vs}{2ab} \,.$$

Problems

1. A particle moves on the curve $x_2 = h \tan kx_1$, $x_3 = 0$, where h and k are constants. The x_2 component of the velocity is constant. Find the acceleration.

97

2. A particle moves with constant speed. Prove that its acceleration is perpendicular to its velocity.

3. A particle moves on an elliptical path with constant speed. At what points is the magnitude of its acceleration (i) a maximum, (ii) a minimum?

4. A particle moves in space. Find the components of its velocity and acceleration along the parametric lines of spherical polar coordinates.

5. A particle moves in space. Its position-vector $\mathbf{x}$ relative to the origin of a fixed set of rectangular cartesian coordinate axes is given in terms of the time t by the relation

$$\mathbf{x} = h(\mathbf{i}_1 \cos t + \mathbf{i}_2 \sin t + \mathbf{i}_3 t),$$

where h is a constant and $\mathbf{i}_1$, $\mathbf{i}_2$ and $\mathbf{i}_3$ are the usual unit vectors in the directions of the coordinate axes. Find the components of the velocity and acceleration in the directions of (i) the coordinate axes mentioned above, (ii) the principal triad of the path of the particle, (iii) the parametric lines of spherical polar coordinates. Find the speed and the magnitude of the acceleration.

6. A particle describes a rhumb line on a sphere in such a way that its longitude increases uniformly. Prove that the resultant acceleration varies as the cosine of the latitude, and that its direction makes with the inner normal an angle equal to the latitude.

7. Two forces $\mathbf{A}$ and $\mathbf{B}$ act at a point. If α is the angle between their lines of action, prove that the magnitude of the resultant $\mathbf{R}$ is given by the relation

$$R^2 = A^2 + B^2 + 2AB \cos \alpha.$$

8. Four forces $\mathbf{A}$, $\mathbf{B}$, $\mathbf{C}$ and $\mathbf{D}$ act at a point O and are in equilibrium, the forces $\mathbf{C}$ and $\mathbf{D}$ being perpendicular and having equal magnitudes. Find C in terms of A, B and the angle α between $\mathbf{A}$ and $\mathbf{B}$.

9. Forces with magnitudes 1, 4, 4 and $2\sqrt{3}$ lb. wt. act at a point. The directions of the first three forces are respectively the directions of the positive axes of x_1, x_2 and x_3. The direction of the fourth force makes equal acute angles with these axes. Find the magnitude and direction of the resultant.

10. A force **F** acts on a particle of mass m. Find the magnitude of the acceleration, given that (i) $F = 6$ poundals, $m = 3$ lb., (ii) $F = 6$ lb. wt., $m = 2$ slugs, (iii) $F = 6$ poundals, $m = 2$ slugs, (iv) $F = 6$ lb. wt., $m = 3$ lb., (v) $F = 5$ dynes, $m = 10$ gm.

11. A particle of mass m is acted upon by a force **F** given by the relation

$$\mathbf{F} = 16\mathbf{p} \sin 2t + \mathbf{q}e^{-t},$$

where **p** and **q** are constant vectors and t is the time. Find the velocity **v** and position-vector **x** of the particle in terms of t, given that **v** $= 0$ and **x** $= 0$ when $t = 0$.

12. A particle of mass m is acted upon by two forces **P** and **Q**. The force **P** acts in the direction of the x_1 axis. The force **Q** makes angles of 45° with the axes of x_2 and x_3. Also $P = p \sin kt$ and $Q = q \cos kt$, where p, q and k are constants and t is the time. At time $t = 0$ the particle has coordinates $(b, 0, 0)$ and is moving towards the origin with a speed p/mk. Find the position-vector **x** of the particle. Prove that the particle moves on an ellipse, and find the center and lengths of the axes of the ellipse.

13. A particle of mass m moves under the action of a force $\mathbf{p}e^{-qt}$ and a resistance $-l\mathbf{v}$, where **p** is a constant vector, q and l are positive constants, t is the time, and **v** is the velocity of the particle. Prove that

$$\mathbf{x}_\infty - \mathbf{x}_0 = \frac{1}{lq}(\mathbf{p} + m q \, \mathbf{u})$$

where **u** is the velocity when $t = 0$, and $\mathbf{x}_0$ and $\mathbf{x}_\infty$ are respectively the position-vectors of the particle when $t = 0$ and when t becomes infinite. Is the above result true when $l = mq$?

14. A particle of mass m moves under the action of a force **p** $\cos qt$ $- k\mathbf{x}$, where **p** is a constant vector, q and k are positive constants, t is the time, and **x** is the position-vector of the particle relative to a fixed point O. When $t = 0$, the particle is at O and has a velocity **u**. Find **x** in terms of t when (i) $k \neq mq^2$, (ii) $k = mq^2$.

15. A particle of mass m is acted upon by a single force $\gamma \, m/x^2$ directed towards a fixed point O, where γ is a constant and x is the

distance from O to the particle. At time $t = 0$ the particle is at a point B and has a velocity of magnitude u in a direction perpendicular to the line OB. Prove that the orbit is (i) an ellipse if $bu^2 < 2\gamma$, (ii) a parabola if $bu^2 = 2\gamma$, (iii) an hyperbola if $bu^2 > 2\gamma$, where $b = OB$.

16. Find the moment of inertia of a circular disk of mass m and radius a about (i) the axis of the disk, (ii) a diameter of the disk. [Answer: (i) $\frac{1}{2}ma^2$; (ii) $\frac{1}{4}ma^2$.]

17. Using the result of Problem 16, find the moment of inertia of a circular cylinder of mass m, length $2l$ and radius a about (i) the axis of the cylinder, (ii) a generator of the cylinder, (iii) a line through the center of the cylinder perpendicular to its axis, (iv) a diameter of one end of the cylinder. [Answer: (i) $\frac{1}{2}ma^2$; (ii) $\frac{3}{2}ma^2$; (iii) $\frac{1}{12} m (4l^2+3a^2)$; (iv) $\frac{1}{12} m (16l^2+3a^2)$.]

18. A circular cylinder has a mass m, length $2l$ and radius a. Rectangular cartesian coordinates are introduced, with origin O at the center of the cylinder, and the x_3 axis coinciding with the axis of the cylinder. Two particles each of mass m' are attached to the cylinder at the points $(0, a, l)$ and $(0, -a, -l)$. Find the moments and products of inertia I_1, I_2, I_3, K_1, K_2, and K_3 for the system consisting of the cylinder and the two particles.

19. A circular disk of mass m and radius a spins with angular speed ω about a line through its center O, making an angle α with its axis. Find the angular momentum of the disk about O.

20. For the system of masses in Problem 18, find the angular momentum about the point O when the system has an angular speed ω about (i) the x_1 axis, (ii) the x_2 axis, (iii) the x_3 axis.

21. A circular cylinder of mass m, length $2l$ and radius a turns freely about its axis which is horizontal. A light inextensible cord is wrapped around the cylinder several times. A constant force F is applied to the end of the cord. If the cylinder starts from rest at time $t = 0$, show that at time t it has turned through the angle Ft^2/ma.

22. The circular cylinder of Problem 21 is again mounted with its axis horizontal, and has a light inextensible cord wrapped around it. A body with a mass m' is attached to the end of the cord. If the cylinder starts from rest at time $t = 0$ show that at time t the cylinder has

100

turned through the angle $\dfrac{mgt^2}{a(m+2m')}$, where g is the acceleration due to gravity.

23. A circular cylinder of mass m, length $2l$ and radius a is placed on a rough plane which makes an angle α with the horizontal, and is then released. Find the distance the cylinder moves down the plane in time t.

24. In Problem 18 there was introduced a system consisting of a circular cylinder of mass m with two attached particles each of mass m'. This system is mounted so it can turn about the axis of the cylinder in two smooth bearings each at a distance c from the center of the cylinder. The system is made to rotate with constant angular speed ω. Find the reactions of the bearings.

25. A circular disk of mass m and radius a turns with constant angular speed ω about an axis through the center O of the disk and making a constant angle α with the axis of the disk. The disk turns in two smooth bearings each at a distance c from the point O. Find the reactions of the bearings.

26. A uniform rod of length $2l$ is free to turn about an axis L perpendicular to it and through its center. The center of the rod moves at constant speed v around a circular track of radius a, the axis L being always tangent to the track. Deduce the equations of motion of system.

CHAPTER IV

PARTIAL DIFFERENTIATION

43. *Scalar and vector fields.* Let V denote a region in space, and let X be a general point in V. Let x_1, x_2, x_3 denote the rectangular cartesian coordinates of X, and let $\mathbf{x}$ denote the position-vector of X. Then

$$\mathbf{x} = x_1\mathbf{i}_1 + x_2\mathbf{i}_2 + x_3\mathbf{i}_3.$$

Let us now consider the case when there is associated with each point in the region V a value of a scalar f. Then we write $f = f(x_1, x_2, x_3)$, or more compactly

$$f = f(\mathbf{x}).$$

The values of f associated with all the points in V constitute a *scalar field*.

Let us now consider the case when there is associated with each point in the region V a value of a vector $\mathbf{a}$. Then we write $\mathbf{a} = \mathbf{a}(x_1, x_2, x_3)$, or more compactly

$$\mathbf{a} = \mathbf{a}(\mathbf{x}).$$

The values of $\mathbf{a}$ associated with the points in V constitute a *vector field*.

It is frequently necessary to consider scalar and vector fields which vary with a parameter, such as the time t. In such cases we write

$$f = f(\mathbf{x}, t), \qquad \mathbf{a} = \mathbf{a}(\mathbf{x}, t).$$

44. *Directional derivatives. The operator del.* Let C be a curve in a region V, as shown in Figure 52. Let X be a general point on C, with position-vector $\mathbf{x}$ as shown, and let s be the arc length of C measured from some fixed point Q on C. It was seen in § 28 that the vector $\dfrac{d\mathbf{x}}{ds}$ is a unit vector tangent to C in the direction of s increasing. This vector is shown in Figure 52.

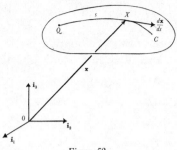

Figure 52

We now introduce a function $f(x_1, x_2, x_3)$ defined everywhere in the region V. Then f is defined at all points on the curve C, and the rate of change of f with respect to the arc length s at the general point X on C is given by the well-known formula of differential calculus,

$$(44.1) \qquad \frac{df}{ds} = \frac{\partial f}{\partial x_1}\frac{dx_1}{ds} + \frac{\partial f}{\partial x_2}\frac{dx_2}{ds} + \frac{\partial f}{\partial x_3}\frac{dx_3}{ds}.$$

Let us now consider all curves through X having the same tangent at X as C has there. For each of these curves the value at X of the right side of Equation (44.1) is the same. Thus at each point X there is a unique value of $\frac{df}{ds}$ associated with each direction. This value is called the *directional derivative* of f.

We now introduce an operator called *del*, which we denote by the symbol ∇ and define by the relation

$$(44.2) \qquad \nabla = \mathbf{i}_1 \frac{\partial}{\partial x_1} + \mathbf{i}_2 \frac{\partial}{\partial x_2} + \mathbf{i}_3 \frac{\partial}{\partial x_3}.$$

If we wish to operate on a function with this operator, we write the symbol denoting the function immediately to the right of the symbol ∇. Thus, if f is a scalar field, then

$$\nabla f = \left(\mathbf{i}_1 \frac{\partial}{\partial x_1} + \mathbf{i}_2 \frac{\partial}{\partial x_2} + \mathbf{i}_3 \frac{\partial}{\partial x_3} \right) f$$

or

$$\nabla f = \mathbf{i}_1 \frac{\partial f}{\partial x_1} + \mathbf{i}_2 \frac{\partial f}{\partial x_2} + \mathbf{i}_3 \frac{\partial f}{\partial x_3}.$$

103

The expression ∇f is often called the gradient of f, and is denoted by grad f.

We note that the right side of Equation (44.1) is equal to the scalar product of ∇f and $d\mathbf{x}/ds$, by Equation (7.2). Thus

$$(44.3) \qquad \frac{df}{ds} = \nabla f \cdot \frac{d\mathbf{x}}{ds},$$

or

$$(44.4) \qquad \frac{df}{ds} = \nabla f \cdot \mathbf{t},$$

where $\mathbf{t}$ is the unit vector in the direction in which the directional derivative is taken. Some theorems will now be proved.

Theorem 1. The component of ∇f in the direction of a unit vector $\mathbf{t}$ is equal to the directional derivative of f in that direction.

Proof. The component of ∇f in the direction of $\mathbf{t}$ is $|\nabla f| \cos \theta$, where θ is the angle between the vectors ∇f and $\mathbf{t}$. But, since $\mathbf{t}$ is a unit vector,

$$|\nabla f| \cos \theta = \nabla f \cdot \mathbf{t}$$

or

$$(44.5) \qquad |\nabla f| \cos \theta = \frac{df}{ds},$$

by Equation (44.4).

Theorem 2. The vector ∇f points in the direction in which df/ds has a maximum value; also, this maximum value is equal to $|\nabla f|$.

Proof. Both parts of this theorem follow from Equation (44.5) which shows that when $\theta = 0$, df/ds attains its maximum value which is $|\nabla f|$.

Theorem 3. The vector field ∇f is normal to the surfaces $f =$ constant.

Proof. Let X be a point on a surface $f =$ constant, and let $\mathbf{t}$ be a unit vector tangent at X to this surface. Then the value of df/ds at X corresponding to the direction of $\mathbf{t}$ vanishes. By Equation (44.4) we then have

$$\nabla f \cdot \mathbf{t} = 0.$$

104

This implies that ∇f is perpendicular to all vectors at X tangent there to the surface $f = $ constant, which completes the proof.

45. *Properties of the operator del.* This operator, which is denoted by the symbol ∇, is defined in the previous section. For convenience we express it in the form

(45.1) $$\nabla = \sum_{r=1}^{3} \mathbf{i}_r \frac{\partial}{\partial x_r}.$$

Then

(45.2) $$\nabla f = \sum_{r=1}^{3} \mathbf{i}_r \frac{\partial f}{\partial x_r}.$$

We shall now prove a number of theorems relating to this operator.

Theorem 1. If f and g are scalar fields, then

(45.3) $$\nabla (f+g) = \nabla f + \nabla g.$$

Proof. Now, by Equation (45.2) we have

$$\nabla(f+g) = \sum_{r=1}^{3} \mathbf{i}_r \frac{\partial}{\partial x_r} (f+g)$$
$$= \sum_{r=1}^{3} \mathbf{i}_r \frac{\partial f}{\partial x_r} + \sum_{r=1}^{3} \mathbf{i}_r \frac{\partial g}{\partial x_r}$$
$$= \nabla f + \nabla g.$$

Theorem 2. If f is a function of a single scalar field u, then

(45.4) $$\nabla f = \frac{df}{du} \nabla u.$$

Proof. By Equation (45.2), we have

$$\nabla f = \sum_{r=1}^{3} \mathbf{i}_r \frac{\partial f}{\partial x_r}.$$

But f is a function of u, which is a function of x_r. Thus

$$\frac{\partial f}{\partial x_r} = \frac{df}{du} \frac{\partial u}{\partial x_r} \qquad (r = 1, 2, 3),$$

so

$$\nabla f = \sum_{r=1}^{3} \mathbf{i}_r \frac{df}{du} \frac{\partial u}{\partial x_r}$$

$$= \frac{df}{du} \sum_{r=1}^{3} \mathbf{i}_r \frac{\partial u}{\partial x_r}$$

$$= \frac{df}{du} \nabla u.$$

Theorem 3.   If f is a function of n scalar fields $u_1, u_2, \cdots, u_n$, then

(45.5)
$$\nabla f = \frac{\partial f}{\partial u_1} \nabla u_1 + \frac{\partial f}{\partial u_2} \nabla u_2 + \cdots + \frac{\partial f}{\partial u_n} \nabla u_n$$

$$= \sum_{s=1}^{n} \frac{\partial f}{\partial u_s} \nabla u_s.$$

Proof.   Since f is a function of the n variables $u_1, u_2, \cdots, u_n$ which are themselves functions of x_1, x_2, x_3 then

$$\frac{\partial f}{\partial x_r} = \sum_{s=1}^{n} \frac{\partial f}{\partial u_s} \frac{\partial u_s}{\partial x_r}.$$

Hence

$$\nabla f = \sum_{r=1}^{3} \mathbf{i}_r \sum_{s=1}^{n} \frac{\partial f}{\partial u_s} \frac{\partial u_s}{\partial x_r}$$

$$= \sum_{s=1}^{n} \sum_{r=1}^{3} \mathbf{i}_r \frac{\partial f}{\partial u_s} \frac{\partial u_s}{\partial x_r}$$

$$= \sum_{s=1}^{n} \frac{\partial f}{\partial u_s} \sum_{r=1}^{3} \mathbf{i}_r \frac{\partial u_s}{\partial x_r}$$

$$= \sum_{s=1}^{n} \frac{\partial f}{\partial u_s} \nabla u_s.$$

As mentioned in the previous section, ∇ operates only on functions written on its immediate right. Thus, if f and g are scalar fields, then

$$f \nabla g = f \sum_{r=1}^{3} \mathbf{i}_r \frac{\partial g}{\partial x_r}$$

$$= \mathbf{i}_1 f \frac{\partial g}{\partial x_1} + \mathbf{i}_2 f \frac{\partial g}{\partial x_2} + \mathbf{i}_3 f \frac{\partial g}{\partial x_3}.$$

Theorem 4. If f and g are scalar fields, then

(45.6) $$\nabla(fg) = f\nabla g + g\nabla f.$$

Proof. We have

$$\nabla(fg) = \sum_{r=1}^{3} \mathbf{i}_r \frac{\partial}{\partial x_r}(fg)$$

$$= \sum_{r=1}^{3} \mathbf{i}_r \left(f\frac{\partial g}{\partial x_r} + g\frac{\partial f}{\partial x_r} \right)$$

$$= f\nabla g + g\nabla f.$$

46. *Some additional operators.* Let $\mathbf{a}$ be any vector field. We first consider the operator $\mathbf{a}\cdot\nabla$. This operator has the obvious meaning

(46.1) $$\mathbf{a}\cdot\nabla = (a_1\mathbf{i}_1 + a_2\mathbf{i}_2 + a_3\mathbf{i}_3)\cdot\left(\mathbf{i}_1\frac{\partial}{\partial x_1} + \mathbf{i}_2\frac{\partial}{\partial x_2} + \mathbf{i}_3\frac{\partial}{\partial x_3} \right)$$

$$= a_1\frac{\partial}{\partial x_1} + a_2\frac{\partial}{\partial x_2} + a_3\frac{\partial}{\partial x_3}$$

$$= \sum_{r=1}^{3} a_r\frac{\partial}{\partial x_r}.$$

This operator is a scalar, and can be applied to a scalar field or to a vector field. Thus, if f and $\mathbf{b}$ are two fields, then

(46.2) $$(\mathbf{a}\cdot\nabla)f = \sum_{r=1}^{3} a_r\frac{\partial f}{\partial x_r}, \quad (\mathbf{a}\cdot\nabla)\mathbf{b} = \sum_{r=1}^{3} a_r\frac{\partial\mathbf{b}}{\partial x_r}.$$

We note that

$$(\mathbf{a}\cdot\nabla)f = \mathbf{a}\cdot\nabla f.$$

The operator $\mathbf{a}\times\nabla$ can be considered similarly. We have

(46.3) $$\mathbf{a}\times\nabla = (a_1\mathbf{i}_1 + a_2\mathbf{i}_2 + a_3\mathbf{i}_3)\times\left(\mathbf{i}_1\frac{\partial}{\partial x_1} + \mathbf{i}_2\frac{\partial}{\partial x_2} + \mathbf{i}_3\frac{\partial}{\partial x_3} \right),$$

or

(46.4) $$\mathbf{a}\times\nabla = \mathbf{i}_1\left(a_2\frac{\partial}{\partial x_3} - a_3\frac{\partial}{\partial x_2} \right) + \mathbf{i}_2\left(a_3\frac{\partial}{\partial x_1} - a_1\frac{\partial}{\partial x_3} \right)$$

$$+ \mathbf{i}_3\left(a_1\frac{\partial}{\partial x_2} - a_2\frac{\partial}{\partial x_1} \right),$$

or

$$
(46.5) \qquad \mathbf{a} \times \nabla = \begin{vmatrix} \mathbf{i}_1 & \mathbf{i}_2 & \mathbf{i}_3 \\ a_1 & a_2 & a_3 \\ \dfrac{\partial}{\partial x_1} & \dfrac{\partial}{\partial x_2} & \dfrac{\partial}{\partial x_3} \end{vmatrix}.
$$

The operator $\mathbf{a} \times \nabla$ is a vector operator. It can be applied to scalar fields. Thus, if f is a scalar field, then

$$
(46.6) \qquad (\mathbf{a} \times \nabla) f = \begin{vmatrix} \mathbf{i}_1 & \mathbf{i}_2 & \mathbf{i}_3 \\ a_1 & a_2 & a_3 \\ \dfrac{\partial f}{\partial x_1} & \dfrac{\partial f}{\partial x_2} & \dfrac{\partial f}{\partial x_3} \end{vmatrix}.
$$

We note that

$$
(\mathbf{a} \times \nabla) f = \mathbf{a} \times \nabla f.
$$

In writing the expressions $(\mathbf{a} \cdot \nabla) f$, $(\mathbf{a} \cdot \nabla) \mathbf{b}$ and $(\mathbf{a} \times \nabla) f$, one must exercise care in the matter of the order in which the symbols appear, since the operator ∇ and all operators constructed from it operate only on the functions on their immediate right. Thus, for example,

$$
(\mathbf{a} \cdot \nabla) \mathbf{b} \neq \mathbf{b}(\mathbf{a} \cdot \nabla).
$$

The left side of this expression is a vector field, while the right side is a vector operator.

We now introduce the operators $\nabla \cdot$ and $\nabla \times$. These operators can be applied to vector fields, the vector portion of the operator ∇ operating on the vector field with scalar or vector multiplication. If $\mathbf{b}$ is a vector field, then

$$
(46.7) \qquad \nabla \cdot \mathbf{b} = \left(\mathbf{i}_1 \frac{\partial}{\partial x_1} + \mathbf{i}_2 \frac{\partial}{\partial x_2} + \mathbf{i}_3 \frac{\partial}{\partial x_3} \right) \cdot \mathbf{b}.
$$

Thus we may write

$$
(46.8) \qquad \nabla \cdot \mathbf{b} = \left(\sum_{r=1}^{3} \mathbf{i}_r \frac{\partial}{\partial x_r} \right) \cdot \mathbf{b} = \sum_{r=1}^{3} \mathbf{i}_r \cdot \frac{\partial \mathbf{b}}{\partial x_r} = \sum_{r=1}^{3} \frac{\partial}{\partial x_r} (\mathbf{i}_r \cdot \mathbf{b}).
$$

But

$$
\mathbf{i}_r \cdot \mathbf{b} = b_r, \qquad (r = 1, 2, 3).
$$

Thus

$$
(46.9) \qquad \nabla \cdot \mathbf{b} = \sum_{r=1}^{3} \frac{\partial b_r}{\partial x_r} = \frac{\partial b_1}{\partial x_1} + \frac{\partial b_2}{\partial x_2} + \frac{\partial b_3}{\partial x_3}.
$$

108

The expression $\nabla \cdot \mathbf{b}$ is often called the divergence of $\mathbf{b}$, and is written div $\mathbf{b}$.

We also have

(46.10) $$\nabla \times \mathbf{b} = \left(\mathbf{i}_1 \frac{\partial}{\partial x_1} + \mathbf{i}_2 \frac{\partial}{\partial x_2} + \mathbf{i}_3 \frac{\partial}{\partial x_3} \right) \times \mathbf{b}.$$

Thus we may write

(46.11) $$\nabla \times \mathbf{b} = \left(\sum_{r=1}^{3} \mathbf{i}_r \frac{\partial}{\partial x_r} \right) \times \mathbf{b} = \sum_{r=1}^{3} \mathbf{i}_r \times \frac{\partial \mathbf{b}}{\partial x_r} = \sum_{r=1}^{3} \frac{\partial}{\partial x_r} (\mathbf{i}_r \times \mathbf{b}).$$

But

$$\mathbf{i}_1 \times \mathbf{b} = \mathbf{i}_1 \times (b_1 \mathbf{i}_1 + b_2 \mathbf{i}_2 + b_3 \mathbf{i}_3)$$
$$= b_2 \mathbf{i}_3 - b_3 \mathbf{i}_2$$

by Equations (8.9). Similarly we have

$$\mathbf{i}_2 \times \mathbf{b} = b_3 \mathbf{i}_1 - b_1 \mathbf{i}_3, \quad \mathbf{i}_3 \times \mathbf{b} = b_1 \mathbf{i}_2 - b_2 \mathbf{i}_1.$$

Hence (46.11) becomes

(46.12) $$\nabla \times \mathbf{b} = \mathbf{i}_1 \left(\frac{\partial b_3}{\partial x_2} - \frac{\partial b_2}{\partial x_3} \right) + \mathbf{i}_2 \left(\frac{\partial b_1}{\partial x_3} - \frac{\partial b_3}{\partial x_1} \right) + \mathbf{i}_3 \left(\frac{\partial b_2}{\partial x_1} - \frac{\partial b_1}{\partial x_2} \right).$$

This can be written conveniently in the form

(46.13) $$\nabla \times \mathbf{b} = \begin{vmatrix} \mathbf{i}_1 & \mathbf{i}_2 & \mathbf{i}_3 \\ \dfrac{\partial}{\partial x_1} & \dfrac{\partial}{\partial x_2} & \dfrac{\partial}{\partial x_3} \\ b_1 & b_2 & b_3 \end{vmatrix}.$$

The expression $\nabla \times \mathbf{b}$ is often called the curl of $\mathbf{b}$ or the rotation of $\mathbf{b}$, and is written curl $\mathbf{b}$ or rot $\mathbf{b}$.

Theorem. 1.   If $\mathbf{a}$ and $\mathbf{b}$ are two vector fields, then

(46.14) $$\nabla \cdot (\mathbf{a} + \mathbf{b}) = \nabla \cdot \mathbf{a} + \nabla \cdot \mathbf{b},$$

(46.15) $$\nabla \times (\mathbf{a} + \mathbf{b}) = \nabla \times \mathbf{a} + \nabla \times \mathbf{b}.$$

Proof of Equation (46.14).   From Equation (46.9), we have

$$\nabla \cdot (\mathbf{a} + \mathbf{b}) = \sum_{r=1}^{3} \frac{\partial}{\partial x_r} (a_r + b_r)$$
$$= \sum_{r=1}^{3} \left(\frac{\partial a_r}{\partial x_r} + \frac{\partial b_r}{\partial x_r} \right)$$
$$= \nabla \cdot \mathbf{a} + \nabla \cdot \mathbf{b}.$$

Proof of Equation (46.15). From (46.13) we have

$$\nabla \times (\mathbf{a}+\mathbf{b}) = \begin{vmatrix} \mathbf{i}_1 & \mathbf{i}_2 & \mathbf{i}_3 \\ \dfrac{\partial}{\partial x_1} & \dfrac{\partial}{\partial x_2} & \dfrac{\partial}{\partial x_3} \\ a_1+b_1 & a_2+b_2 & a_3+b_3 \end{vmatrix}$$

$$= \begin{vmatrix} \mathbf{i}_1 & \mathbf{i}_2 & \mathbf{i}_3 \\ \dfrac{\partial}{\partial x_1} & \dfrac{\partial}{\partial x_2} & \dfrac{\partial}{\partial x_3} \\ a_1 & a_2 & a_3 \end{vmatrix}$$

$$+ \begin{vmatrix} \mathbf{i}_1 & \mathbf{i}_2 & \mathbf{i}_3 \\ \dfrac{\partial}{\partial x_1} & \dfrac{\partial}{\partial x_2} & \dfrac{\partial}{\partial x_3} \\ b_1 & b_2 & b_3 \end{vmatrix}$$

$$= \nabla \times \mathbf{a} + \nabla \times \mathbf{b}.$$

Theorem 2. If $\mathbf{a}$ and $\mathbf{b}$ are two vector fields, then

(46.16) $$(\mathbf{a}\times\nabla)\cdot\mathbf{b} = \mathbf{a}\cdot(\nabla\times\mathbf{b}).$$

Proof. Because of (46.4) we have

(46.17) $$(\mathbf{a}\times\nabla)\cdot\mathbf{b} = \left(a_2\frac{\partial}{\partial x_3} - a_3\frac{\partial}{\partial x_2}\right)(\mathbf{i}_1\cdot\mathbf{b})$$

$$+ \left(a_3\frac{\partial}{\partial x_1} - a_1\frac{\partial}{\partial x_3}\right)(\mathbf{i}_2\cdot\mathbf{b})$$

$$+ \left(a_1\frac{\partial}{\partial x_2} - a_2\frac{\partial}{\partial x_1}\right)(\mathbf{i}_3\cdot\mathbf{b}).$$

But

$$\mathbf{i}_1\cdot\mathbf{b} = b_1, \qquad \mathbf{i}_2\cdot\mathbf{b} = b_2, \qquad \mathbf{i}_3\cdot\mathbf{b} = b_3.$$

Thus (46.17) can be written in the form

$$(\mathbf{a}\times\nabla)\cdot\mathbf{b} = a_1\left(\frac{\partial b_3}{\partial x_2} - \frac{\partial b_2}{\partial x_3}\right) + a_2\left(\frac{\partial b_1}{\partial x_3} - \frac{\partial b_3}{\partial x_1}\right) + a_3\left(\frac{\partial b_2}{\partial x_1} - \frac{\partial b_1}{\partial x_2}\right).$$

Because of (46.12), we see that the right side of this equation is equal to $\mathbf{a}\cdot(\nabla\times\mathbf{b})$.

110

47. *Ivariance of the operator del.* Let us consider two rectangular cartesian coordinate systems with a common origin O. We denote them by the symbols S and S'. For the coordinate system S the coordinates and associated unit vectors will be denoted by x_1, x_2, x_3 and $\mathbf{i}_1$, $\mathbf{i}_2$, $\mathbf{i}_3$, respectively, while for the system S' the corresponding

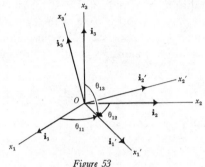

Figure 53

quantities will be denoted by x_1', x_2', x_3' and $\mathbf{i}_1'$, $\mathbf{i}_2'$, $\mathbf{i}_3'$. Figure 53 shows the coordinate axes and the associated unit vectors.

We now introduce the two operators

$$\nabla = \mathbf{i}_1 \frac{\partial}{\partial x_1} + \mathbf{i}_2 \frac{\partial}{\partial x_2} + \mathbf{i}_3 \frac{\partial}{\partial x_3},$$

$$\nabla' = \mathbf{i}_1' \frac{\partial}{\partial x_1'} + \mathbf{i}_2' \frac{\partial}{\partial x_2'} + \mathbf{i}_3' \frac{\partial}{\partial x_3'}.$$

Let f be a scalar field, and let $\mathbf{b}$ be a vector field. We shall now consider proofs of the relations

(47.1) $$\nabla' f = \nabla f,$$

(47.2) $$\nabla' \cdot \mathbf{b} = \nabla \cdot \mathbf{b},$$

(47.3) $$\nabla' \times \mathbf{b} = \nabla \times \mathbf{b}.$$

The implications of these equations are the following. The operator del includes differentiations with respect to the coordinates of the system S and multiplications by the three unit vectors associated with the system S. It thus appears that when del operates on any

111

field, the resultant field is likely to depend on the particular choice of coordinates. However, Equations (47.1), (47.2) and (47.3) state that this is not the case. It is this property of del which is termed "invariance of the operator del".

Before proceeding to a proof of the above three formulas, we shall develop some preliminary formulas. Let us consider the three angles which the x_1' axis makes with the axes of the system S. These are the angles θ_{11}, θ_{12} and θ_{13} in Figure 53. We denote their cosines by a_{11}, a_{12} and a_{13}. These three quantities are the components of $\mathbf{i}_1'$ relative to the system S, and so

$$\mathbf{i}_1' = a_{11}\,\mathbf{i}_1 + a_{12}\,\mathbf{i}_2 + a_{13}\,\mathbf{i}_3 = \sum_{s=1}^{3} a_{1s}\,\mathbf{i}_s.$$

There are similar expressions for $\mathbf{i}_2'$ and $\mathbf{i}_3'$. The three expressions can be written in the compact form

$$(47.4) \qquad \mathbf{i}_r' = \sum_{s=1}^{3} a_{rs}\,\mathbf{i}_s \qquad (r = 1, 2, 3).$$

We note that the constant a_{rs} is the cosine of the angle between the two vectors $\mathbf{i}_r'$ and $\mathbf{i}_s$.

The components of the vector $\mathbf{i}_1$ relative to the system S' are seen to be a_{11}, a_{21} and a_{31}. Thus

$$\mathbf{i}_1 = \sum_{s=1}^{3} a_{s1}\,\mathbf{i}_s'.$$

Proceeding similarly for $\mathbf{i}_2$ and $\mathbf{i}_3$, we obtain the three equations

$$(47.5) \qquad \mathbf{i}_r = \sum_{s=1}^{3} a_{sr}\,\mathbf{i}_s' \qquad (r = 1, 2, 3).$$

Throughout the remainder of this section we will adopt the convention that latin subscripts range over the values 1, 2 and 3, as in the above equations.

We now introduce a set of nine quantities called the Kronecker delta. This set is denoted by the symbol δ_{rs}, and is defined by the equation

$$(47.6) \qquad \begin{aligned} \delta_{rs} &= 1 \text{ if } r = s \\ &= 0 \text{ if } r \neq s. \end{aligned}$$

112

Thus $\delta_{11} = \delta_{22} = \delta_{33} = 1$ and $\delta_{23} = \delta_{31} = \delta_{12} = \delta_{32} = \delta_{13} = \delta_{21} = 0$. Since $\mathbf{i}_1$, $\mathbf{i}_2$ and $\mathbf{i}_3$ are unit orthogonal vectors, they satisfy the nine relations (7.3). These nine relations can now be written compactly in the form

$$(47.7) \qquad \mathbf{i}_r \cdot \mathbf{i}_s = \delta_{rs}.$$

We also have the nine relations

$$(47.8) \qquad \mathbf{i}_r' \cdot \mathbf{i}_s' = \delta_{rs}.$$

Let us now substitute in Equation (47.8) from (47.4). This gives the relation

$$\delta_{rs} = \left(\sum_{t=1}^{3} a_{rt} \mathbf{i}_t \right) \cdot \left(\sum_{u=1}^{3} a_{su} \mathbf{i}_u \right)$$
$$= \sum_{t=1}^{3} \sum_{u=1}^{3} a_{rt} a_{su} \mathbf{i}_t \cdot \mathbf{i}_u.$$

But by (47.7) we have $\mathbf{i}_t \cdot \mathbf{i}_u = \delta_{tu}$ so

$$(47.9) \qquad \delta_{rs} = \sum_{t=1}^{3} \sum_{u=1}^{3} a_{rt} a_{su} \delta_{tu} = \sum_{t=1}^{3} a_{rt} \sum_{u=1}^{3} a_{su} \delta_{tu}.$$

The last summation here is

$$\sum_{u=1}^{3} a_{su} \delta_{tu} = a_{s1} \delta_{t1} + a_{s2} \delta_{t2} + a_{s3} \delta_{t3}.$$

The right side reduces to a_{s1} when $t = 1$, to a_{s2} when $t = 2$, and to a_{s3} when $t = 3$. Thus we may write

$$(47.10) \qquad \sum_{u=1}^{3} a_{su} \delta_{tu} = a_{st},$$

and so (47.9) reduces to the relations

$$(47.11) \qquad \delta_{rs} = \sum_{t=1}^{3} a_{rt} a_{st}.$$

The nine equations in (47.11) are called the *orthogonality conditions*. We could also run through the above derivation of (47.11) but with the roles of the primed and unprimed quantities interchanged. This would entail substituting in Equations (47.7) from (47.5). In this way we would obtain the orthogonality conditions in the form

$$(47.12) \qquad \delta_{rs} = \sum_{t=1}^{3} a_{tr} a_{ts}.$$

Let **b** be any vector field with components b_r relative to the system S, and with components b_r' relative to the system S'. Then

$$(47.13) \qquad \mathbf{b} = \sum_{r=1}^{3} b_r \mathbf{i}_r = \sum_{s=1}^{3} b_s' \mathbf{i}_s'.$$

We now substitute here for $\mathbf{i}_r$ from (47.5), obtaining the relation

$$\sum_{r=1}^{3} b_s' \mathbf{i}_s' = \sum_{r=1}^{3} b_r \sum_{s=1}^{3} a_{sr} \mathbf{i}_s'$$

$$= \sum_{s=1}^{3} \sum_{r=1}^{3} b_r a_{sr} \mathbf{i}_s'.$$

Hence we must have

$$(47.14) \qquad b_s' = \sum_{r=1}^{3} a_{sr} b_r.$$

If in an analogous fashion we substitute in Equation (47.13) for $\mathbf{i}_s'$ from (47.4), we obtain the relations

$$(47.15) \qquad b_s = \sum_{r=1}^{3} a_{rs} b_r'.$$

Equations (47.14) and (47.15) are the equations of transformation of the components of a vector field **b**.

If we choose $\mathbf{b} = \mathbf{x}$, where as usual $\mathbf{x}$ is the position-vector of a general point X with coordinates x_r relative to the system S and coordinates x_r' relative to the system S', then Equations (47.14) and (47.15) yield

$$(47.16) \qquad x_s' = \sum_{r=1}^{3} a_{sr} x_r, \qquad x_s = \sum_{r=1}^{3} a_{rs} x_r'.$$

These are the equations of transformation from a set of rectangular cartesian coordinates to a second set whose axes are obtained from those of the first set by a rotation about the origin. From Equations (47.16) we have the relations

114

$$(47.17) \qquad \frac{\partial x'_s}{\partial x_r} = a_{sr}, \qquad \frac{\partial x_s}{\partial x'_r} = a_{rs}.$$

We are now in a position to turn to proofs of Equations (47.1), (47.2) and (47.3).

Proof of Equation (47.1). This equation reads

$$\nabla' f = \nabla f.$$

Now

$$(47.18) \qquad \nabla' f = \sum_{r=1}^{3} \mathbf{i'}_r \frac{\partial f}{\partial x'_r},$$

and

$$\frac{\partial f}{\partial x''} = \sum_{t=1}^{3} \frac{\partial f}{\partial x_t} \frac{\partial x_t}{\partial x'_r}.$$

Because of this relation and (47.4) we can write (47.18) in the form

$$(47.19) \qquad \nabla' f = \sum_{r=1}^{3} \sum_{s=1}^{3} \sum_{t=1}^{3} a_{rs} \mathbf{i}_s \frac{\partial f}{\partial x_t} \frac{\partial x_t}{\partial x'_r}.$$

But, from Equations (47.17) we have

$$\frac{\partial x_t}{\partial x'_r} = a_{rt}.$$

Thus (47.19) becomes

$$\nabla' f = \sum_{r=1}^{3} \sum_{s=1}^{3} \sum_{t=1}^{3} a_{rs} a_{rt} \mathbf{i}_s \frac{\partial f}{\partial x_t}$$

$$= \sum_{s=1}^{3} \sum_{t=1}^{3} \mathbf{i}_s \frac{\partial f}{\partial x_t} \sum_{r=1}^{3} a_{rs} a_{rt}.$$

Because of the orthogonality conditions (47.12), the last summation here is equal to δ_{st}. Thus

$$\nabla' f = \sum_{s=1}^{3} \sum_{t=1}^{3} \mathbf{i}_s \frac{\partial f}{\partial x_t} \delta_{st}$$

$$= \sum_{s=1}^{3} \mathbf{i}_s \sum_{t=1}^{3} \frac{\partial f}{\partial x_t} \delta_{st}.$$

The last summation here reduces to $\partial f / \partial x_1$ when $s = 1$, to $\partial f / \partial x_2$ when $s = 2$, and to $\partial f / \partial x_3$ when $s = 3$. Thus

(47.20)
$$\sum_{t=1}^{3} \frac{\partial f}{\partial x_t} \delta_{st} = \frac{\partial f}{\partial x_s},$$

and so

$$\nabla' f = \sum_{s=1}^{3} \mathbf{j}_s \frac{\partial f}{\partial x_s} = \nabla f.$$

The truth of Equation (47.1) also follows from Theorem 2 of § 44, as this theorem states that ∇f points in the direction in which the directional derivative of f has a maximum value, and that the magnitude of ∇f is equal to this maximum value. This theorem then implies that both the direction and magnitude of ∇f are independent of the coordinate system.

Proof of Equation (47.2). This equation reads

$$\nabla' \cdot \mathbf{b} = \nabla \cdot \mathbf{b}.$$

Now

$$\nabla' \cdot \mathbf{b} = \sum_{s=1}^{3} \frac{\partial b'_s}{\partial x'_s}.$$

Because of (47.14) we then have

$$\nabla' \cdot \mathbf{b} = \sum_{s=1}^{3} \sum_{r=1}^{3} \frac{\partial}{\partial x'_s} (a_{sr} b_r)$$

$$= \sum_{s=1}^{3} \sum_{r=1}^{3} a_{sr} \frac{\partial b_r}{\partial x'_s}$$

$$= \sum_{s=1}^{3} \sum_{r=1}^{3} a_{sr} \sum_{t=1}^{3} \frac{\partial b_r}{\partial x_t} \frac{\partial x_t}{\partial x'_s}.$$

But by Equations (47.17), the last partial derivative here is equal to a_{st}. Thus

$$\nabla' \cdot \mathbf{b} = \sum_{s=1}^{3} \sum_{r=1}^{3} \sum_{t=1}^{3} a_{sr} a_{st} \frac{\partial b_r}{\partial x_t}$$

$$= \sum_{r=1}^{3} \sum_{t=1}^{3} \frac{\partial b_r}{\partial x_t} \sum_{s=1}^{3} a_{sr} a_{st}.$$

Because of the orthogonality conditions (47.12) the last summation here reduces to δ_{rt}. Thus

116

$$\nabla' \cdot \mathbf{b} = \sum_{r=1}^{3} \sum_{t=1}^{3} \frac{\partial b_r}{\partial x_t} \delta_{rt}$$

$$= \sum_{r=1}^{3} \frac{\partial b_r}{\partial x_r},$$

by a repetition of the arguments leading up to Equations (47.10) and (47.20). This completes the proof.

Proof of Equation (47.3). This is left as an exercise for the reader (Problem 13 at the end of the present chapter).

48. *Differentiation formulas.* We shall consider here a group of well-known formulas involving the operator del. If f is a scalar field, $\mathbf{a}$ and $\mathbf{b}$ are vector fields, and $\mathbf{x}$ is the usual position-vector of a general point X, these formulas are the following:

(48.1) $\quad \nabla \cdot (f\mathbf{a}) = f(\nabla \cdot \mathbf{a}) + (\nabla f) \cdot \mathbf{a}$,

(48.2) $\quad \nabla \times (f\mathbf{a}) = f(\nabla \times \mathbf{a}) + (\nabla f) \times \mathbf{a}$,

(48.3) $\quad \nabla \cdot (\mathbf{a} \times \mathbf{b}) = \mathbf{b} \cdot (\nabla \times \mathbf{a}) - \mathbf{a} \cdot (\nabla \times \mathbf{b})$,

(48.4) $\quad \nabla \times (\mathbf{a} \times \mathbf{b}) = \mathbf{a}(\nabla \cdot \mathbf{b}) + (\mathbf{b} \cdot \nabla)\mathbf{a} - \mathbf{b}(\nabla \cdot \mathbf{a}) - (\mathbf{a} \cdot \nabla)\mathbf{b}$,

(48.5) $\quad \nabla(\mathbf{a} \cdot \mathbf{b}) = (\mathbf{a} \cdot \nabla)\mathbf{b} + (\mathbf{b} \cdot \nabla)\mathbf{a} + \mathbf{a} \times (\nabla \times \mathbf{b}) + \mathbf{b} \times (\nabla \times \mathbf{a})$,

(48.6) $\quad \nabla \times (\nabla f) = 0$,

(48.7) $\quad \nabla \cdot (\nabla \times \mathbf{a}) = 0$,

(48.8) $\quad \nabla \times (\nabla \times \mathbf{a}) = \nabla(\nabla \cdot \mathbf{a}) - (\nabla \cdot \nabla)\mathbf{a}$,

(48.9) $\quad \nabla \cdot \mathbf{x} = 3$,

(48.10) $\quad \nabla \times \mathbf{x} = 0$.

(48.11) $\quad (\mathbf{a} \cdot \nabla)\mathbf{x} = \mathbf{a}$.

Direct proofs of all eleven of these formulas follow similar lines. We shall present here only proofs of (48.1), (48.3), (48.5) and (48.8). The proofs of the remaining formulas are left as exercises for the reader (Problems 14, 15 and 16 at the end of the present chapter).

Proof of Equation (48.1). Because of Equation (46.8), which gives some equivalent forms for $\nabla \cdot \mathbf{b}$, we have

117

$$\nabla \cdot (f\mathbf{a}) = \sum_{r=1}^{3} \mathbf{i}_r \cdot \frac{\partial}{\partial x_r} (f\mathbf{a})$$

$$= \sum_{r=1}^{3} \mathbf{i}_r \cdot \left(f \frac{\partial \mathbf{a}}{\partial x_r} + \frac{\partial f}{\partial x_r} \mathbf{a} \right)$$

$$= f \sum_{r=1}^{3} \mathbf{i}_r \cdot \frac{\partial \mathbf{a}}{\partial x_r} + \sum_{r=1}^{3} \mathbf{i}_r \frac{\partial f}{\partial x_r} \cdot \mathbf{a}$$

$$= f(\nabla \cdot \mathbf{a}) + (\nabla f) \cdot \mathbf{a}.$$

Proof of Equation (48.3). Because of Equation (46.8) we have

$$\nabla \cdot (\mathbf{a} \times \mathbf{b}) = \sum_{r=1}^{3} \mathbf{i}_r \cdot \frac{\partial}{\partial x_r} (\mathbf{a} \times \mathbf{b})$$

$$= \sum_{r=1}^{3} \mathbf{i}_r \cdot \left(\frac{\partial \mathbf{a}}{\partial x_r} \times \mathbf{b} \right) + \sum_{r=1}^{3} \mathbf{i}_r \cdot \left(\mathbf{a} \times \frac{\partial \mathbf{b}}{\partial x_r} \right).$$

Because of the permutation theorem for scalar triple products (Theorem 1 of § 9), we can write this last equation in the form

$$\nabla \cdot (\mathbf{a} \times \mathbf{b}) = \sum_{r=1}^{3} \mathbf{b} \cdot \left(\mathbf{i}_r \times \frac{\partial \mathbf{a}}{\partial x_r} \right) - \sum_{r=1}^{3} \mathbf{a} \cdot \left(\mathbf{i}_r \times \frac{\partial \mathbf{b}}{\partial x_r} \right)$$

$$= \mathbf{b} \cdot \sum_{r=1}^{3} \mathbf{i}_r \times \frac{\partial \mathbf{a}}{\partial x_r} - \mathbf{a} \cdot \sum_{r=1}^{3} \mathbf{i}_r \times \frac{\partial \mathbf{b}}{\partial x_r}$$

$$= \mathbf{b} \cdot (\nabla \times \mathbf{a}) - \mathbf{a} \cdot (\nabla \times \mathbf{b}).$$

Proof of Equation (48.5). Because of Equation (46.11) we have

$$\mathbf{a} \times (\nabla \times \mathbf{b}) = \mathbf{a} \times \sum_{r=1}^{3} \mathbf{i}_r \times \frac{\partial \mathbf{b}}{\partial x_r}.$$

We now apply to the right side of this equation the identity (9.3) for vector triple products, obtaining

$$(48.12) \quad \mathbf{a} \times (\nabla \times \mathbf{b}) = \sum_{r=1}^{3} \mathbf{i}_r \left(\mathbf{a} \cdot \frac{\partial \mathbf{b}}{\partial x_r} \right) - \sum_{r=1}^{3} \frac{\partial \mathbf{b}}{\partial x_r} (\mathbf{a} \cdot \mathbf{i}_r)$$

$$= \sum_{r=1}^{3} \mathbf{i}_r \left(\mathbf{a} \cdot \frac{\partial \mathbf{b}}{\partial x_r} \right) - \sum_{r=1}^{3} a_r \frac{\partial \mathbf{b}}{\partial x_r}$$

$$= \sum_{r=1}^{3} \mathbf{i}_r \left(\mathbf{a} \cdot \frac{\partial \mathbf{b}}{\partial x_r} \right) - (\mathbf{a} \cdot \nabla) \mathbf{b}.$$

Similarly, by an interchange of **a** and **b** we have

$$(48.13) \qquad \mathbf{b} \times (\nabla \times \mathbf{a}) = \sum_{r=1}^{3} \mathbf{i}_r \left(\frac{\partial \mathbf{a}}{\partial x_r} \cdot \mathbf{b} \right) - (\mathbf{b} \cdot \nabla) \, \mathbf{a}.$$

Addition of (48.12) and (48.13) yields

$$\mathbf{a} \times (\nabla \times \mathbf{b}) + \mathbf{b} \times (\nabla \times \mathbf{a}) = \sum_{r=1}^{3} \mathbf{i}_r \frac{\partial}{\partial x_r} (\mathbf{a} \cdot \mathbf{b}) - (\mathbf{a} \cdot \nabla) \, \mathbf{b} - (\mathbf{b} \cdot \nabla \mathbf{a})$$
$$= \nabla (\mathbf{a} \cdot \mathbf{b}) - (\mathbf{a} \cdot \nabla) \mathbf{b} - (\mathbf{b} \cdot \nabla) \, \mathbf{a}.$$

If the last two terms here are taken to the left side of the equation, (48.5) results.

In addition to this manner of proving formulas (48.1)–(48.11), there is another manner of proof which applies to some of these formulas, and which is quite expeditious. We mention it here because it affords one an opportunity to acquire additional facility in manipulations involving the operator del. This manner of proof consists in applying to expressions involving del the permutation theorem for scalar triple products (Theorem 1 of § 9), and the identity (9.3) for vector triple products which is

$$(48.14) \qquad \mathbf{a} \times (\mathbf{b} \times \mathbf{c}) = \mathbf{b}(\mathbf{a} \cdot \mathbf{c}) - \mathbf{c}(\mathbf{a} \cdot \mathbf{b}).$$

Of course, when such an application is made, a symbol denoting a scalar or vector field must never be moved from one side of del to the other, since del operates only on those quantities on its right. Also, when such application is made, the resulting expression must have the same scalar or vector character as the original expression.

For example, let us prove Equation (48.8) in this way. If we apply the identity (48.14) formally to $\nabla \times (\nabla \times \mathbf{a})$, we obtain the difference of two terms. The first term must be one of the following:

$$(48.15) \qquad \nabla (\nabla \cdot \mathbf{a}), \quad \nabla (\mathbf{a} \cdot \nabla), \quad (\nabla \cdot \mathbf{a}) \nabla, \quad (\mathbf{a} \cdot \nabla) \nabla.$$

Now, in the expression $\nabla \times (\nabla \times \mathbf{a})$, the symbol **a** appears to the right of both symbols ∇. Hence we must select from the terms in (48.15) the one with this same property. Hence we select $\nabla (\nabla \cdot \mathbf{a})$. As a check, we note that $\nabla \times (\nabla \times \mathbf{a})$ is a vector, and that the only term in (48.15) which is a vector is $\nabla (\nabla \cdot \mathbf{a})$. In a similar fashion

119

we find that the term corresponding to the second term on the right side of (48.14) is $(\bigtriangledown \cdot \bigtriangledown) \mathbf{a}$. Thus

$$\bigtriangledown \times (\bigtriangledown \mathbf{a}) = \bigtriangledown (\bigtriangledown \cdot \mathbf{a}) - (\bigtriangledown \cdot \bigtriangledown) \mathbf{a}.$$

We note that the operator $\bigtriangledown \cdot \bigtriangledown$ satisfies the relation

$$\bigtriangledown \cdot \bigtriangledown = \frac{\partial^2}{(\partial x_1)^2} + \frac{\partial^2}{(\partial x_2)^2} + \frac{\partial^2}{(\partial x_3)^2}.$$

This operator is called the Laplacian operator, and is denoted in many books by the symbol $\bigtriangledown^2$.

As a second example, let us prove Equation (48.3) by application of the permutation theorem for scalar triple products. To do this, it is convenient to introduce an operator $\bigtriangledown_a$ which is just the operator del with the added restriction that the partical differentiation is to be applied to no vector field other than $\mathbf{a}$. The operator $\bigtriangledown_b$ is defined similarly. Equation (12.4) states the differentiation rule for vector products. Because of this rule we have

(48.16) $\qquad \bigtriangledown \cdot (\mathbf{a} \times \mathbf{b}) = \bigtriangledown_a \cdot (\mathbf{a} \times \mathbf{b}) + \bigtriangledown_b \cdot (\mathbf{a} \times \mathbf{b}).$

We now apply the permutation theorem for scalar triple products to the first term on the right side of Equation (48.16), remembering that $\mathbf{a}$ must always remain on the right side of $\bigtriangledown_a$, and that $\mathbf{b}$ need not do so. We then get $\mathbf{b} \cdot (\bigtriangledown_a \times \mathbf{a})$. If the second term on the right side of Equation (48.16) is treated analogously, we obtain the relation

$$\bigtriangledown \cdot (\mathbf{a} \times \mathbf{b}) = \mathbf{b} \cdot (\bigtriangledown_a \times \mathbf{a}) - \mathbf{a} \cdot (\bigtriangledown_b \times \mathbf{b}).$$

But

$$\bigtriangledown_a \times \mathbf{a} = \bigtriangledown \times \mathbf{a}, \qquad \bigtriangledown_b \times \mathbf{b} = \bigtriangledown \times \mathbf{b}.$$

Thus Equation (48.3) is proved.

49. *Curvilinear coordinates.* Let us write down the three equations

(49.1) $\quad z_1 = f_1(x_1, x_2, x_3), \quad z_2 = f_2(x_1, x_2, x_3), \quad z_3 = f_3(x_1, x_2, x_3),$

where $f_1(x_1, x_2, x_3)$, $f_2(x_1, x_2, x_3)$ and $f_3(x_1, x_2, x_3)$ are any functions which are single valued and differentiable throughout some region V. These equations prescribe for any point X with rectangular cartesian

120

coordinates x_1, x_2 and x_3 a new set of coordinates z_1, z_2 and z_3. These new coordinates are called curvilinear coordinates, and Equations (49.1) are equations of transformation of coordinates.

We now propose to compute, in terms of quantities pertaining to curvilinear coordinates only, the expressions ∇f, $\nabla \cdot \mathbf{b}$ and $\nabla \times \mathbf{b}$, where f and $\mathbf{b}$ denote respectively a scalar and a vector field. With this goal in mind, we shall devote the rest of this section to some preliminary considerations, and shall complete the final computations in the next section.

The Jacobian of the transformation (49.1) is the determinant

$$
(49.2) \qquad I' = \begin{vmatrix} \dfrac{\partial z_1}{\partial x_1} & \dfrac{\partial z_1}{\partial x_2} & \dfrac{\partial z_1}{\partial x_3} \\[2mm] \dfrac{\partial z_2}{\partial x_1} & \dfrac{\partial z_2}{\partial x_2} & \dfrac{\partial z_2}{\partial x_3} \\[2mm] \dfrac{\partial z_3}{\partial x_1} & \dfrac{\partial z_3}{\partial x_2} & \dfrac{\partial z_3}{\partial x_3} \end{vmatrix}
$$

We shall consider only the case when I' does not vanish anywhere in V, so that Equations (49.1) may be solved[1] for x_1, x_2 and x_3 to yield the relations

$$(49.3) \quad x_1 = g_1(z_1, z_2, z_3), \quad x_2 = g_2(z_1, z_2, z_3), \quad x_3 = g_3(z_1, z_2, z_3).$$

Let us write down the equation

$$z_1 = f_1(x_1, x_2, x_3) = \text{constant.}$$

The locus of this equation is a surface. If we vary the constant in this equation, we get a family of surfaces called the parametric surfaces of z_1. Similarly, we have parametric surfaces of z_2 and z_3. Let us now consider the curves of intersection of the parametric surfaces of z_2 and z_3. Along each of these curves z_2 and z_3 are constant, and z_1 alone varies. These curves are called the parametric lines of z_1. Simi-

---

[1] See almost any book on Advanced Calculus; for example, I. S. Sokolnikoff, Advanced Calculus, McGraw-Hill Book Co., New York, 1939, pp. 430–438.

larly, we have parametric lines of z_2 and z_3. For example, in the case of cylindrical coordinates r, θ, x_3, the parametric lines of r, θ and x_3 are respectively horizontal straight lines cutting the x_3 axis, horizontal circles with centers on the x_3 axis, and vertical straight lines.

Let X be a general point in a region V. Through X there passes a parametric line of each of the curvilinear coordinates z_1, z_2, z_3. We now introduce three unit vectors $\mathbf{k}_1$, $\mathbf{k}_2$ and $\mathbf{k}_3$ with origins at X, defined as follows: $\mathbf{k}_1$ is tangent at X to the parametric line of z_1, and points in the direction of z_1 increasing; $\mathbf{k}_2$ and $\mathbf{k}_3$ are defined analogously with respect to the parametric lines of z_2 and z_3. Figure 54

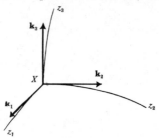

Figure 54

shows these parametric lines and associated unit vectors. In the case of cylindrical coordinates, the associated unit vectors $\mathbf{k}_1$, $\mathbf{k}_2$ and $\mathbf{k}_3$ were introduced in § 30.

In the remainder of the present section we shall consider only the case when the three vectors $\mathbf{k}_1$, $\mathbf{k}_2$ and $\mathbf{k}_3$ are mutually perpendicular. The curvilinear coordinates are then said to be *orthogonal*. We shall also require that $\mathbf{k}_1$, $\mathbf{k}_2$ and $\mathbf{k}_3$ form a *right-handed triad*, the term „right-handed" being as defined in § 6.

The distance ds between two adjacent points is given by the relation

$$(49.4) \qquad (ds)^2 = (dx_1)^2 + (dx_2)^2 + (dx_3)^2 = \sum_{r=1}^{3} (dx_r)^2,$$

where dx_1, dx_2 and dx_3 are the infinitesimal differences between the rectangular cartesian coordinates of the two points. From Equations (49.3) we have

122

$$dx_r = \frac{\partial x_r}{\partial z_1} dz_1 + \frac{\partial x_r}{\partial z_2} dz_2 + \frac{\partial x_r}{\partial z_3} dz_3 \qquad (r = 1, 2, 3).$$

Substitution from these relations in (49.4) then yields for $(ds)^2$ a homogeneous quadratic expression in the quantities dz_1, dz_2 and dz_3. Because the coordinate system z_1, z_2, z_3 is orthogonal, it turns out that no terms involving products of these differentials appear in this quadratic expression, and we can then write

(49.5) $$(ds)^2 = (h_1\, dz_1)^2 + (h_2\, dz_2)^2 + (h_3\, dz_3)^2,$$

where h_1, h_2 and h_3 are known positive functions of z_1, z_2 and z_3. The right side of (49.5) is called the *fundamental quadratic form*, or the *metric form*.

Les s_1, s_2 and s_3 denote the arc lengths of the three parametric lines in Figure 54. From (49.5) we then have

(49.6) $$ds_1 = h_1\, dz_1, \quad ds_2 = h_2\, dz_2, \quad ds_3 = h_3\, dz_3.$$

Let us consider z_1. It is a scalar field. We shall now consider ∇z_1. Because of Theorems 2 and 3 of § 44 we see that

(i) ∇z_1, being normal to the surface $z_1 = $ constant, has the same direction as $\mathbf{k}_1$,

(ii) $|\nabla z_1|$ is equal to the maximum value of the directional derivative dz_1/ds,

(iii) this maximum value arises when the directional derivative is taken in the direction of $\mathbf{k}_1$, and is hence equal to dz_1/ds_1.

Because of (ii), (iii) and Equation (49.6) it follows that $|\nabla z_1| = 1/h_1$, and because of (i) we then have $\nabla z_1 = \mathbf{k}_1/h_1$. Similar observations regarding z_2 and z_3 then permit us to write

(49.7) $$\mathbf{k}_1 = h_1 \nabla z_1, \quad \mathbf{k}_2 = h_2 \nabla z_2, \quad \mathbf{k}_3 = h_3 \nabla z_3.$$

From these equations we get the relation

$$\mathbf{k}_1 \cdot (\mathbf{k}_2 \times \mathbf{k}_3) = h_1 h_2 h_3 \nabla z_1 \cdot (\nabla z_2 \times \nabla z_3).$$

But the left side of this equation is equal to one since $\mathbf{k}_1$, $\mathbf{k}_2$ and $\mathbf{k}_3$ form a right-handed orthogonal triad of unit vectors. Thus

$$(49.8) \qquad \nabla z_1 \cdot (\nabla z_2 \times \nabla z_3) = \frac{1}{h_1 h_2 h_3}.$$

50. *The expressions* ∇f, $\nabla \cdot \mathbf{b}$ *and* $\nabla \times \mathbf{b}$ *in curvilinear coordinates.*
We consider first the expression ∇f. Now f is a function of z_1, z_2 and z_3. Hence by Equantion (45.5) we have

$$\nabla f = \frac{\partial f}{\partial z_1} \nabla z_1 + \frac{\partial f}{\partial z_2} \nabla z_2 + \frac{\partial f}{\partial z_3} \nabla z_3.$$

Because of Equation (49.7) we may then write this relation in the form

$$(50.1) \qquad \nabla f = \frac{1}{h_1} \frac{\partial f}{\partial z_1} \mathbf{k}_1 + \frac{1}{h_2} \frac{\partial f}{\partial z_2} \mathbf{k}_2 + \frac{1}{h_3} \frac{\partial f}{\partial z_3} \mathbf{k}_3,$$

or

$$(50.2) \qquad \nabla f = \sum_{r=1}^{3} \frac{1}{h_r} \frac{\partial f}{\partial z_r} \mathbf{k}_r.$$

We now turn to $\nabla \cdot \mathbf{b}$. We first express $\mathbf{b}$ as a linear function of the unit vectors $\mathbf{k}_1$, $\mathbf{k}_2$ and $\mathbf{k}_3$, in the form

$$(50.3) \qquad \mathbf{b} = b_1 \mathbf{k}_1 + b_2 \mathbf{k}_2 + b_3 \mathbf{k}_3.$$

It should be noted that b_1, b_2 and b_3 are here the orthogonal projections of $\mathbf{b}$ on the lines of action of the unit vectors $\mathbf{k}_1$, $\mathbf{k}_2$ and $\mathbf{k}_3$, respectively. In order to deduce conveniently the desired expression for $\nabla \cdot \mathbf{b}$, we now make a rather unusual step. Since

$$\mathbf{k}_1 = \mathbf{k}_2 \times \mathbf{k}_3, \quad \mathbf{k}_2 = \mathbf{k}_3 \times \mathbf{k}_1, \quad \mathbf{k}_3 = \mathbf{k}_1 \times \mathbf{k}_2,$$

then substitution from Equations (49.7) yields

$$\mathbf{k}_1 = h_2 h_3 \, \nabla z_2 \times \nabla z_3,$$
$$\mathbf{k}_2 = h_3 h_1 \, \nabla z_3 \times \nabla z_1,$$
$$\mathbf{k}_3 = h_1 h_2 \, \nabla z_1 \times \nabla z_2.$$

We now substitute from these expressions in Equation (50.3), and operate on the resultant expression with the operator $\nabla \cdot$ to obtain the relation

124

$$(50.4) \quad \nabla \cdot \mathbf{b} = \nabla \cdot (b_1 h_2 h_3 \, \nabla z_2 \times \nabla z_3) + \nabla \cdot (b_2 h_3 h_1 \, \nabla z_3 \times \nabla z_1)$$
$$+ \nabla \cdot (b_3 h_1 h_2 \, \nabla z_1 \times \nabla z_2).$$

For the first of the three terms on the right side of (50.4) we can write, because of relation (48.1),

$$(50.5) \quad \nabla \cdot (b_1 h_2 h_3 \, \nabla z_2 \times \nabla z_3) = \nabla (b_1 h_2 h_3) \cdot (\nabla z_2 \times \nabla z_3)$$
$$+ b_1 h_2 h_3 \, \nabla \cdot (\nabla z_2 \times \nabla z_3).$$

But because of Equation (45.5) we have

$$\nabla (b_1 h_2 h_3) = \frac{\partial}{\partial z_1} (b_1 h_2 h_3) \, \nabla z_1 + \frac{\partial}{\partial z_2} (b_1 h_2 h_3) \, \nabla z_2 + \frac{\partial}{\partial z_3} (b_1 h_2 h_3) \, \nabla z_3.$$

Thus, since ∇z_1, ∇z_2 and ∇z_3 are mutually perpendicular, we obtain

$$\nabla (b_1 h_2 h_3) \cdot (\nabla z_2 \times \nabla z_3) = \frac{\partial}{\partial z_1} (b_1 h_2 h_3) \, \nabla z_1 \cdot (\nabla z_2 \times \nabla z_3)$$

or, by Equation (49.8),

$$(50.6) \quad \nabla (b_1 h_2 h_3) \cdot (\nabla z_2 \times \nabla z_3) = \frac{1}{h_1 h_2 h_3} \frac{\partial}{\partial z_1} (b_1 h_2 h_3).$$

Also, because of Equation (48.3) we have

$$(50.7) \quad \nabla \cdot (\nabla z_2 \times \nabla z_3) = \nabla z_3 \cdot (\nabla \times \nabla z_2) - \nabla z_2 \cdot (\nabla \times \nabla z_3) = 0$$

because of Equation (48.6). The Equations (50.6) and (50.7) now permit us to write (50.5) in the form

$$\nabla \cdot (b_1 h_2 h_3 \, \nabla z_2 \times \nabla z_3) = \frac{1}{h_1 h_2 h_3} \frac{\partial}{\partial z_1} (b_1 h_2 h_3).$$

This relation and two similar relations involving the second and third terms on the right side of Equation (50.4) then permit us to write (50.4) in the form

$$(50.8) \quad \nabla \cdot \mathbf{b} = \frac{1}{h_1 h_2 h_3} \left[\frac{\partial}{\partial z_1} (b_1 h_2 h_3) + \frac{\partial}{\partial z_2} (b_2 h_3 h_1) + \frac{\partial}{\partial z_3} (b_3 h_1 h_2) \right].$$

We note that if the curvilinear coordinates happen to be rectangular cartesian coordinates, then $h_1 = h_2 = h_3 = 1$ and (50.8) reduces to (46.9), as expected.

Finally, we turn to the expression $\nabla \times \mathbf{b}$. Because of Equations (49.7) and (50.3) we have

$$\nabla \times \mathbf{b} = \nabla \times (b_1 \, \mathbf{k}_1 + b_2 \, \mathbf{k}_2 + b_3 \, \mathbf{k}_3),$$

or

$$(50.9) \qquad \nabla \times \mathbf{b} = \nabla \times (b_1 h_1 \, \nabla z_1) + \nabla \times (b_2 h_2 \, \nabla z_2) \\ + \nabla \times (b_3 h_3 \, \nabla z_3).$$

For the first term on the right side we can then write

$$(50.10) \qquad \nabla \times (b_1 h_1 \, \nabla z_1) = \nabla \, (b_1 h_1) \times \nabla z_1 + b_1 h_1 \, (\nabla \times \nabla z_1),$$

because of Equation (48.2). But $\nabla \times \nabla z_1 = 0$ by Equation (48.6), and by Equation (45.5) we have

$$\nabla \, (b_1 h_1) \times \nabla z_1 = \left[\frac{\partial}{\partial z_1} \, (b_1 h_1) \nabla z_1 + \frac{\partial}{\partial z_2} \, (b_1 h_1) \, \nabla z_2 \right. \\ \left. + \frac{\partial}{\partial z_3} \, (b_1 h_1) \, \nabla z_3 \right] \times \nabla z_1.$$

Now Equations (49.7) yield

$$\nabla z_1 \times \nabla z_1 = 0,$$
$$\nabla z_2 \times \nabla z_1 = \frac{1}{h_2 h_1} \, \mathbf{k}_2 \times \mathbf{k}_1 = - \frac{1}{h_2 h_1} \, \mathbf{k}_3,$$
$$\nabla z_3 \times \nabla z_1 = \frac{1}{h_3 h_1} \, \mathbf{k}_3 \times \mathbf{k}_1 = \frac{1}{h_3 h_1} \, \mathbf{k}_2.$$

Thus Equation (50.10) reduces to

$$\nabla \times (b_1 h_1 \, \nabla z_1) = \frac{\mathbf{k}_2}{h_3 h_1} \, \frac{\partial}{\partial z_3} \, (b_1 h_1) - \frac{\mathbf{k}_3}{h_2 h_1} \, \frac{\partial}{\partial z_2} \, (b_1 h_1).$$

This relation and two similar relations involving the second and third terms on the right side of Equation (50.9) permit us to write Equation (50.9) in the form

$$(50.11) \qquad \nabla \times \mathbf{b} = \frac{\mathbf{k}_1}{h_2 h_3} \left[\frac{\partial}{\partial z_2} \, (b_3 h_3) - \frac{\partial}{\partial z_3} \, (b_2 h_2) \right] \\ + \frac{\mathbf{k}_2}{h_3 h_1} \left[\frac{\partial}{\partial z_3} \, (b_1 h_1) - \frac{\partial}{\partial z_1} \, (b_3 h_3) \right] \\ + \frac{\mathbf{k}_3}{h_1 h_2} \left[\frac{\partial}{\partial z_1} \, (b_2 h_2) - \frac{\partial}{\partial z_2} \, (b_1 h_1) \right].$$

We note that if the curvilinear coordinates happen to be rectangular cartesian coordinates, then (50.11) reduces to (46.12), as expected.

Problems

1. If $f = (x_1)^2 x_2 + (x_2)^2 x_3 - x_1 x_2 x_3$, find the directional derivative of f at the point $A(1,-4,8)$ in the direction of the position-vector **a** of A.

2. If $f = x_1 \sin(\pi x_2) + x_3 \tan(\pi x_2)$, find the directional derivative of f at the point $A(1, 0, -2)$ in the direction of the vector drawn from A to the point $B(3, -3,4)$.

3. Find a unit vector normal to the surface $x_2 x_3 - x_3 x_1 + x_1 x_2 - 1 = 0$ at the point $A(1, 2, -1)$.

4. Two surfaces $x_1 x_2 - (x_3)^2 + 15 = 0$ and $(x_2)^2 - 3x_3 + 5 = 0$ intersect in a curve C. At the point $A(3,-2,3)$ on C find (i) the angle between the normals to the two surfaces, (ii) a unit vector tangent to C.

5. If $f = (x_1)^2 + 2(x_2)^2 + 2(x_3)^2$, find the maximum value of the directional derivative of f at the point $(1, -2, -4)$.

6. If $\mathbf{x} = x_1 \mathbf{i}_1 + x_2 \mathbf{i}_2 + x_3 \mathbf{i}_3$, prove that $\nabla x = \mathbf{x}/x$, and that

$$\nabla . x^n = n x^{n-2} \mathbf{x},$$

where n is a constant.

7. Find ∇r and $\nabla \theta$, where r and θ are the usual plane polar coordinates. Also, find the magnitudes and directions of ∇r and $\nabla \theta$.

8. If $f = r^3 - \cos^2 \theta$, where r and θ are plane polar coordinates, find ∇f in terms of r, θ and the unit vectors $\mathbf{i}_1$ and $\mathbf{i}_2$ associated with the corresponding rectangular cartesian coordinates.

9. If f and g are scalar fields, prove that

$$\nabla (f/g) = g^{-2} (g \nabla f - f \nabla g).$$

10. If $f = (x_1)^2 + x_3 \sqrt{(x_1)^2 + (x_2)^2}$ and $g = x_1 x_2 x_3$, find at the point $A(3, 4, 5)$ the expressions $\nabla(fg)$ and $\nabla(f/g)$. Note Theorem 4 of §45, and Problem 9 above.

11. If $f = x_1 x_2 x_3$, $\mathbf{a} = x_1 \mathbf{i}_1 - x_2 \mathbf{i}_2$ and $\mathbf{b} = x_3 x_1 \mathbf{i}_2 - x_1 x_2 \mathbf{i}_3$, compute the following: (i) $(\mathbf{a} \cdot \nabla) f$, (ii) $(\mathbf{a} \cdot \nabla) \mathbf{b}$, (iii) $(\mathbf{a} \times \nabla) f$, (iv) $(\mathbf{a} \times \nabla) \cdot \mathbf{b}$,

(v) $(\mathbf{a} \times \nabla) \times \mathbf{b}$, (vi) $\nabla \cdot \mathbf{b}$, (vii) $\nabla \times \mathbf{b}$, (viii) $\mathbf{a} \cdot (\nabla \times \mathbf{b})$.

12. Let S and S' be two rectangular cartesian coordinate systems. The axes of S can be moved into coincidence with the axes of S' by a positive rotation of $\frac{1}{4}\pi$ radians about the x_3 axis, followed by a second positive rotation of $\frac{1}{4}\pi$ about the bisector of the angle between the positive axes of x_1 and x_2. (i) Express the coordinates of S' in terms of the coordinates of S, and conversely. (ii) If $f = x_2x_3 + x_3x_1$ and $\mathbf{b} = (x_1 + x_2)\,\mathbf{i}_1 + (x_1 - x_2)\,\mathbf{i}_2 + x_3\mathbf{i}_3$, express f and $\mathbf{b}$ in terms of quantities pertaining to the system S'.

13. Prove Equation (47.3).

14. Starting from Equations (46.8) and (46.11), verify Equations (48.2), (48.4), (48.6), (48.7), (48.8), (48.9), (48.10) and (48.11).

15. Using the identity (48.14), verify Equations (48.4) and (48.5).

16. Using the permutation theorem for scalar triple products, verify Equation (48.7).

17. If $\mathbf{a}$ is a constant vector, prove that $\nabla (\mathbf{a} \cdot \mathbf{x}) = \mathbf{a}$.

18. Prove that $\mathbf{a} \times (\nabla \times \mathbf{x}) = 0$.

19. If $\mathbf{a}$ is a constant vector, prove that $\nabla \times (\mathbf{a} \times \mathbf{x}) = 2\mathbf{a}$.

20. Prove that
$$\nabla (\mathbf{a} \cdot \mathbf{b}) = \mathbf{a}(\nabla \cdot \mathbf{b}) + \mathbf{b}(\nabla \cdot \mathbf{a}) + (\mathbf{a} \times \nabla) \times \mathbf{b} + (\mathbf{b} \times \nabla) \times \mathbf{a}.$$

21. Prove that
$$\mathbf{a} \times (\nabla \times \mathbf{b}) - (\mathbf{a} \times \nabla) \times \mathbf{b} = \mathbf{a}(\nabla \cdot \mathbf{b}) - (\mathbf{a} \cdot \nabla)\mathbf{b}.$$

22. Prove that
$$(\mathbf{a} \cdot \nabla)\mathbf{a} = \tfrac{1}{2}\nabla a^2 - \mathbf{a} \times (\nabla \times \mathbf{a}).$$

23. Prove that
$$\mathbf{a}(\nabla \cdot \mathbf{a}) = \tfrac{1}{2}\nabla a^2 - (\mathbf{a} \times \nabla) \times \mathbf{a}.$$

24. If $f(x_1, x_2, x_3)$ is a homogeneous polynomial of degree n, prove that $(\mathbf{x} \cdot \nabla)f = nf$.

25. Prove that if $\mathbf{a}$ is a constant vector, then
$$(\mathbf{a} \times \nabla) \cdot (\mathbf{b} \times \mathbf{c}) = (\mathbf{a} \cdot \mathbf{b})(\nabla \cdot \mathbf{c}) + (\mathbf{c} \cdot \nabla)(\mathbf{a} \cdot \mathbf{b})$$
$$- (\mathbf{a} \cdot \mathbf{c})(\nabla \cdot \mathbf{b}) - (\mathbf{b} \cdot \nabla)(\mathbf{a} \cdot \mathbf{c}).$$

26. If r, θ, z are cylindrical coordinates, describe their parametric surfaces and show that
$$(ds)^2 := (dr)^2 + r^2(d\theta)^2 + (dz)^2.$$

27. If r, θ, φ are spherical polar coordinates, describe the parametric surfaces and lines, and show that

$$(ds)^2 = (dr)^2 + r^2(d\theta)^2 + r^2 \sin^2\theta \, (d\varphi)^2.$$

28. Prove that for the transformation from rectangular cartesian coordinates to orthogonal curvilinear coordinates z_1, z_2, z_3 for which the metric form is as given in Equation (49.5), the Jacobian I satisfies the relation $h_1 h_2 h_3 I = 1$.

29. Express Equation (50.11) in terms of a determinant.

30. Write out the expressions ∇f, $\nabla \cdot \mathbf{b}$ and $\nabla \times \mathbf{b}$ in the case of cylindrical coordinates r, θ, z.

31. Write out the expressions ∇f, $\nabla \cdot \mathbf{b}$ and $\nabla \times \mathbf{b}$ in the case of spherical polar coordinates.

32. By setting $\mathbf{b} = \nabla f$ in Equation (50.8), deduce an expression for $\nabla^2 f$ in terms of general orthogonal curvilinear coordinates.

33. Show that, in cylindrical coordinates r, θ, z, we have

$$\nabla^2 f = \frac{\partial^2 f}{\partial r^2} + \frac{1}{r^2}\frac{\partial^2 f}{\partial \theta^2} + \frac{\partial^2 f}{\partial z^2} + \frac{1}{r}\frac{\partial f}{\partial r}.$$

34. Solve the differential equation $\nabla^2 f = 0$ when f is a function only of the cylindrical coordinate r.

35. Show that, in spherical polar coordinates r, θ, φ, we have

$$\nabla^2 f = \frac{\partial^2 f}{\partial r^2} + \frac{1}{r^2}\frac{\partial^2 f}{\partial \theta^2} + \frac{1}{r^2\sin^2\theta}\frac{\partial^2 f}{\partial \varphi^2} + \frac{2}{r}\frac{\partial f}{\partial r} + \frac{\cot\theta}{r^2}\frac{\partial f}{\partial \theta}.$$

36. Solve the differential equation $\nabla^2 f = 0$ when f is a function only of the spherical polar coordinate r.

37. If $\mathbf{k}_1$, $\mathbf{k}_2$ and $\mathbf{k}_3$ are the unit vectors associated with the spherical polar coordinates r, θ and φ, prove that

$$\frac{\partial \mathbf{k}_1}{\partial r} = 0, \qquad \frac{\partial \mathbf{k}_1}{\partial \theta} = \mathbf{k}_2, \qquad \frac{\partial \mathbf{k}_1}{\partial \varphi} = \mathbf{k}_3 \sin\theta,$$

$$\frac{\partial \mathbf{k}_2}{\partial r} = 0, \qquad \frac{\partial \mathbf{k}_2}{\partial \theta} = -\mathbf{k}_1, \qquad \frac{\partial \mathbf{k}_2}{\partial \varphi} = \mathbf{k}_3 \cos\theta,$$

$$\frac{\partial \mathbf{k}_3}{\partial r} = 0, \qquad \frac{\partial \mathbf{k}_3}{\partial \theta} = 0, \qquad \frac{\partial \mathbf{k}_3}{\partial \varphi} = -\mathbf{k}_1 \sin\theta - \mathbf{k}_2 \cos\theta.$$

Note: the corresponding problem in the case of plane polar coordinates is worked out in Chapter III, § 30.

CHAPTER V

INTEGRATION

51. *Line integrals.* A curve is called a *regular arc* it can be represented in some rectangular cartesian coordinate system by the equation

$$\mathbf{x} = x_1(u)\mathbf{i}_1 + x_2(u)\mathbf{i}_2 + x_3(u)\mathbf{i}_3,$$

where $\mathbf{x}$ is the position-vector of a general point X on the curve, u is a parameter with the range $\alpha \leqslant u \leqslant \beta$, and for this range of u the functions $x_1(u)$, $x_2(u)$ and $x_3(u)$ are continuous with continuous first derivatives. A curve which consists of a finite number of regular arcs joined end to end, and which does not intersect itself, is called a *regular curve*. Throughout this chapter we shall consider only regular curves, and shall refer to them simply as curves.

Let us consider a curve C with terminal points A and B, as shown in Figure 55. Let $f(x_1, x_2, x_3)$ be a function which is single valued and

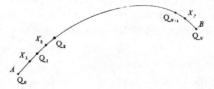

Figure 55

continuous on the curve C. We divide C into N parts by the $N+1$ points $Q_0, Q_1, Q_2, \cdots, Q_N$, as shown. The length of the line segment $Q_{p-1}Q_p$ $(p = 1, 2, \cdots, N)$ is denoted by Δs_p. Let X_p be a point on the arc $Q_{p-1}Q_p$, and let its coordinates be (x_{p1}, x_{p2}, x_{p3}). The line integral of f over C is then defined to be

$$(51.1) \qquad \lim_{\substack{N \to \infty \\ \Delta s_p \to 0}} \sum_{p=1}^{N} f(x_{p1}, x_{p2}, x_{p3}) \, \Delta s_p = \int_C f \, ds.$$

This limit is independent of the manner in which the curve C is divided into parts, since f is continuous and single valued on C. If $f = 1$

130

everywhere on C, then Equation (51.1) defines the arc length of C. Let X be a general point on the curve C, as shown in Figure 56.

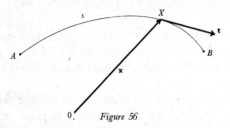

Figure 56

Let s denote the arc length of C measured from the end A of C. The vector $d\mathbf{x}/ds$ was seen in § 28 to be a unit vector tangent to C in the direction of s increasing. Denoting this vector by $\mathbf{t}$, we have

$$(51.2) \qquad \mathbf{t} = \frac{d\mathbf{x}}{ds}.$$

Let $\mathbf{b}(x_1, x_2, x_3)$ be a vector field defined over C. The orthogonal projection of $\mathbf{b}$ on the unit tangent vector $\mathbf{t}$ is called the tangential component of $\mathbf{b}$. If we denote it by b_t, we have

$$(51.3) \qquad b_t = \mathbf{b} \cdot \mathbf{t}.$$

The line integral of $\mathbf{b}$ over C is defined to be

$$(51.4) \qquad \int_C b_t \, ds = \int_C \mathbf{b} \cdot \mathbf{t} \, ds.$$

Because of (51.2), we have

$$(51.5) \qquad \mathbf{t} \, ds = d\mathbf{x} = \mathbf{i}_1 dx_1 + \mathbf{i}_2 dx_2 + \mathbf{i}_3 dx_3.$$

Thus

$$(51.6) \qquad \int_C b_t \, ds = \int_C \mathbf{b} \cdot d\mathbf{x} = \int_C (b_1 dx_1 + b_2 dx_2 + b_3 dx_3).$$

We may also consider line integrals over C with integrands which are vectors. The integration of vectors was defined in §13. Following this definition, we have

$$(51.7) \qquad \int_C \mathbf{b} \, ds = \mathbf{i}_1 \int_C b_1 ds + \mathbf{i}_2 \int_C b_2 ds + \mathbf{i}_3 \int_C b_3 ds,$$

131

(51.8) $$\int_C \mathbf{b} \times \mathbf{t} \, ds = \int_C \mathbf{b} \times d\mathbf{x}$$
$$= \mathbf{i}_1 \int_C (b_2 dx_3 - b_3 dx_2) + \mathbf{i}_2 \int_C (b_3 dx_1 - b_1 dx_3) + \mathbf{i}_3 \int_C (b_1 dx_2 - b_2 dx_1).$$

To apply the above considerations to two-dimensional problems involving line integrals along curves in the $x_1 x_2$ plane, it is only necessary to set $b_3 = x_3 = 0$ in the above formulas. A few examples will now be worked out.

Example 1. Let $f = (x_1)^2 + (x_2)^3$, and let us evalute the line integral of f along the straight line $x_2 = 2x_1$ in the $x_1 x_2$ plane from the origin to the point $B(2,4)$. This problem is two-dimensional. There are several ways of solving this problem, since a curve may be represented parametrically in many different ways. We present here two solutions.

(i) The curve C can be represented by the equations

$$x_1 = u, \quad x_2 = 2u, \quad 0 \leqslant u \leqslant 2.$$

Thus

$$d\mathbf{x} = \mathbf{i}_1 dx_1 + \mathbf{i}_2 dx_2 = (\mathbf{i}_1 + 2\mathbf{i}_2) \, du,$$
$$ds = |d\mathbf{x}| = \sqrt{5} \, du.$$

Also, $f = u^2 + 8u^3$, whence

$$\int_C f \, ds = \int_0^2 (u^2 + 8u^3) \, \sqrt{5} \, du = \frac{104\sqrt{5}}{3}.$$

(ii) On C we have

$$\dot{x}_2 = 2x_1, \quad f = (x_1)^2 + 8(x_1)^3,$$
$$ds = \sqrt{1 + \left(\frac{dx_2}{dx_1}\right)^2} \, dx_1 = \sqrt{5} \, dx_1.$$

Thus

$$\int_C f \, ds = \int_0^2 [(x_1)^2 + 8(x_1)^3] \, \sqrt{5} \, dx_1 = \frac{104\sqrt{5}}{3}.$$

Example 2. Let $\mathbf{b} = x_2 \mathbf{i}_1 + (x_3 + x_1)^2 \mathbf{i}_2 + x_1 \mathbf{i}_3$, and let us evaluate the line integral of $\mathbf{b}$ over the curve C in Example 1 above. We present two solutions.

132

(i)   We have

(51.9) $\mathbf{b} \cdot d\mathbf{x} = b_1 dx_1 + b_2 dx_2 + b_3 dx_3$

$$= x_2 dx_1 + (x_3 + x_1)^2 \, dx_2 + x_1 dx_3$$

$$= \left[x_2 + (x_3 + x_1)^2 \frac{dx_2}{dx_1} + x_1 \frac{dx_3}{dx_1} \right] dx_1 .$$

But on C we have $x_2 = 2x_1$, $x_3 = 0$, so

$$\int_C \mathbf{b} \cdot d\mathbf{x} = \int_0^2 [2x_1 + 2(x_1)^2] \, dx_1 = \tfrac{28}{3} .$$

(ii)   From (51.9) we have

$$\mathbf{b} \cdot d\mathbf{x} = \left[x_2 \frac{dx_1}{dx_2} + (x_3 + x_1)^2 + x_1 \frac{dx_3}{dx_2} \right] dx_2 .$$

But on C we have $x_1 = \tfrac{1}{2} x_2$, $x_3 = 0$, so

$$\int_C \mathbf{b} \cdot d\mathbf{x} = \int_0^4 [\tfrac{1}{2} x_2 + \tfrac{1}{4} (x_2)^2] \, dx_2 = \tfrac{28}{3} .$$

Example 3.   Let $\mathbf{b} = a^2 x_1 \mathbf{i}_1 + a x_2 x_3 \mathbf{i}_2 + x_1 (x_3)^2 \, \mathbf{i}_3$ where a is a constant, and let us evalute the line integral of $\mathbf{b}$ along the curve C in Figure 57

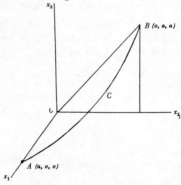

Figure 57

from the point A to the point B, the curve C being a portion of the intersection of the cylinder $(x_1)^2 + (x_2)^2 = a^2$ and the plane $x_1 + x_3 = a$.

133

Now

$$\mathbf{b} \cdot d\mathbf{x} = \left(b_1 + b_2 \frac{dx_2}{dx_1} + b_3 \frac{dx_3}{dx_1} \right) dx_1$$

$$= \left[a^2 x_1 + a x_2 x_3 \frac{dx_2}{dx_1} + x_1 (x_3)^2 \frac{dx_3}{dx_1} \right] dx_1.$$

But on C we have

$$(x_2)^2 = a^2 - (x_1)^2, \qquad x_3 = a - x_1 \qquad (a \geqslant x_1 \geqslant 0),$$

$$\frac{dx_2}{dx_1} = -\frac{x_1}{x_2}, \qquad \frac{dx_3}{dx_1} = -1.$$

Thus

$$\int_C \mathbf{b} \cdot d\mathbf{x} = \int_a^0 [a^2 x_1 - a(a - x_1)x_1 - x_1 (a - x_1)^2] \, dx_1 = -\tfrac{1}{4} a^4.$$

52. *Surface integrals.* A *regular surface element* is defined to be a portion of a surface which, for some orientation of the coordinate axes can be projected onto a region S' in the $x_1 x_2$ plane enclosed by a regular closed curve, and which can be represented by the equation $x_3 = g(x_1, x_2)$, where $g(x_1, x_2)$ is continuous and has continuous first derivatives in S'. In this chapter we shall consider only surfaces composed of a finite number of regular surface elements.

Let us consider a surface S bounded by a closed curve C, as shown in Figure 58. Let $f(x_1, x_2, x_3)$ be a function which is single valued and

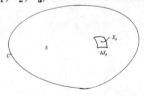

Figure 58

continuous on S. We divide the region S into N parts with areas ΔS_p $(p = 1, 2, \cdots, N)$. Let X_p be a point on the element of area ΔS_p, as shown, and let its coordinates be (x_{p1}, x_{p2}, x_{p3}). The surface integral of f over S is defined to be

134

$$(52.1) \qquad \lim_{\substack{N \to \infty \\ \Delta S_p \to 0}} \sum_{p=1}^{N} f(x_{p1}, x_{p2}, x_{p3}) \, \Delta S_p = \int_S f \, dS.$$

This limit is independent of the manner in which S is divided into parts, since f is continuous and single valued throughout the region S. If $f = 1$, then Equation (52.1) yields the surface area of S.

Let us suppose that S is a regular surface element, as shown in Figure 59. To evaluate the surface integral in Equation (52.1), we let X be

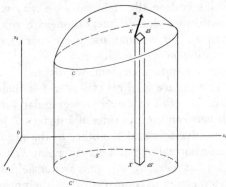

Figure 59

a general point on S and let dS be an element of area at X. We now project S onto the region S' in the $x_1 x_2$ plane, X and dS projecting into X' and dS', respectively. Let $\mathbf{n}$ be the unit vector normal at X to the surface S, making an acute angle with the x_3 axis. Then

$$dS' = n_3 \, dS.$$

Let the equation of the surface S be

$$(52.2) \qquad x_3 - g(x_1, x_2) = 0.$$

Denoting the left side of this equation by G, we have by Theorems 2 and 3 of § 44,

$$\mathbf{n} \, |\nabla G| = \nabla G = \frac{\partial G}{\partial x_1} \mathbf{i}_1 + \frac{\partial G}{\partial x_2} \mathbf{i}_2 + \frac{\partial G}{\partial x_3} \mathbf{i}_3$$

$$= -\frac{\partial x_3}{\partial x_1} \mathbf{i}_1 - \frac{\partial x_3}{\partial x_2} \mathbf{i}_2 + \mathbf{i}_3.$$

135

Thus

(52.3)
$$n_3 = \left[1 + \left(\frac{\partial x_3}{\partial x_1} \right)^2 + \left(\frac{\partial x_3}{\partial x_2} \right)^2 \right]^{-\frac{1}{2}}.$$

We then have

(52.4)
$$\int_S f \, dS = \int_{S'} f \left[x_1, x_2, g(x_1, x_2) \right] \left[1 + \left(\frac{\partial g}{\partial x_1} \right)^2 + \left(\frac{\partial g}{\partial x_2} \right)^2 \right]^{\frac{1}{2}} dS'.$$

To evaluate the integral on the right side, we may write $dS' = dx_1 \, dx_2$, and then perform a double integration with respect to x_1 and x_2 over the region S'. Or we may use polar coordinates r and θ in the $x_1 x_2$ plane, writing $dS' = r \, dr \, d\theta$.

If S is not a regular surface element, we divide it into regular surface elements. The surface integral of f over S is then found as the sum of the surface integrals of f over these regular surface elements.

To distinguish between the two sides of a surface S, let us designate one side as the positive side and the other as the negative side. Let **n** be the unit vector normal to S at a general point X, and lying on the positive side of S. Let $\mathbf{b}(x_1, x_2, x_3)$ be a vector field defined over S. The orthogonal projection of **b** on **n** is called the normal component of **b**. If we denote it by b_n, we have

(52.5)
$$b_n = \mathbf{b} \cdot \mathbf{n}.$$

The surface integral of **b** over S is defined to be

(52.6)
$$\int_S b_n \, dS = \int_S \mathbf{b} \cdot \mathbf{n} \, dS.$$

It is often convenient to introduce an infinitesimal vector $d\mathbf{S}$ defined by the relation

(52.7)
$$d\mathbf{S} = \mathbf{n} \, dS,$$

so Equation (52.6) may take the form

(52.8)
$$\int_S b_n \, dS = \int_S \mathbf{b} \cdot d\mathbf{S}.$$

It is sometimes necessary to consider surface integrals with integrands which are vectors. For example, we have, following the definition of integration of vectors in § 13,

136

$$(52.9) \qquad \int_S \mathbf{b}\, dS = \mathbf{i}_1 \int_S b_1 dS + \mathbf{i}_2 \int_S b_2 dS + \mathbf{i}_3 \int_S b_3 dS,$$

$$(52.10) \qquad \int_S \mathbf{b} \times \mathbf{n}\, dS = \mathbf{i}_1 \int_S (b_2 n_3 - b_3 n_2)\, dS + \mathbf{i}_2 \int_S (b_3 n_1 - b_1 n_3)\, dS$$
$$+ \mathbf{i}_3 \int_S (b_1 n_2 - b_2 n_1)\, dS.$$

We shall now work out some examples.

Example 1. Let $f = (x_1)^2 + 2x_2 + x_3 - 1$, and let us evaluate the surface integral of f over a region S consisting of that part of the plane $2x_1 + 2x_2 + x_3 = 2$ lying in the first octant.

The region S is shown in Figure 60. It is a regular plane element.

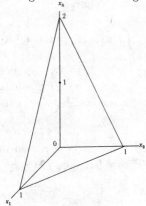

Figure 60

We have
$$\frac{\partial x_3}{\partial x_1} = -2, \qquad \frac{\partial x_3}{\partial x_2} = -2$$

whence (52.3) yields $n_3 = 1/3$. Thus $dS = 3\, dx_1\, dx_2$, and so
$$\int_S f dS = \int_S 3f\, dx_1\, dx_2.$$

But on S, we have
$$x_3 = 2 - 2x_1 - 2x_2,$$
$$f = (x_1)^2 + 2x_2 + (2 - 2x_1 - 2x_2) - 1$$
$$= (x_1 - 1)^2.$$

137

Thus, if S' denotes the projection of S on the x_1x_2 plane, we have

$$\int_S f dS = 3\int_{S'} (x_1 - 1)^2 dx_1 dx_2 = 3\int_0^1 \int_0^{1-x_1} (x_1 - 1)^2 dx_2 dx_1 = \frac{3}{4}.$$

Example 2.   If $\mathbf{b} = x_2\mathbf{i}_1 + x_3\mathbf{i}_2$, evaluate the surface integral of $\mathbf{b}$ over the region S in Example 1, the origin being on the negative side of S.

We have

$$n_1 = \tfrac{2}{3}, \quad n_2 = \tfrac{2}{3}, \quad n_3 = \tfrac{1}{3},$$
$$b_n = b_1 n_1 + b_2 n_2 + b_3 n_3 = \tfrac{2}{3}(x_2 + x_3),$$
$$dS = 3 dx_1\, dx_2.$$

Thus

$$\int_S b_n dS = 2 \int_S (x_2 + x_3) dx_1\, dx_2.$$

But on S we have $x_3 = 2 - 2x_1 - 2x_2$, whence

$$\int_S b_n dS = 2 \int_{S'} (2 - 2x_1 - x_2) dx_1\, dx_2 = 2 \int_0^1 \int_0^{1-x_2} (2 - 2x_1 - x_2) dx_1\, dx_2 = 1.$$

53. *Triple integrals.*   Let V be a region in space enclosed by a surface S as shown in Figure 61. Let $f(x_1, x_2, x_3)$ be a function which is

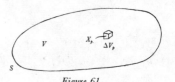

Figure 61

single valued and continuous throughout V. We divide V into N parts with volumes ΔV_p $(p = 1, 2, \cdots, N)$. Let X_p be a point in the element of volume ΔV_p, as shown, and let its coordinates be (x_{p1}, x_{p2}, x_{p3}). The triple integral of f over V is defined to be

$$(53.1) \qquad \lim_{\substack{N \to \infty \\ \Delta V_p \to 0}} \sum_{p=1}^{N} f(x_{p1}, x_{p2}, x_{p3})\, \Delta V_p = \int_V f dV.$$

This limit is independent of the manner in which V is divided into parts, since f is single valued and continuous in V.

We may also consider triple integrals with integrands which are vectors. Thus, if $\mathbf{b}$ is a vector field which is single valued and continuous in V, we have, following the definition of integration of vectors in § 13,

$$(53.2) \qquad \int_V \mathbf{b}\, dV = \mathbf{i}_1 \int_V b_1 dV + \mathbf{i}_2 \int_V b_2 dV + \mathbf{i}_3 \int_V b_3 dV.$$

To evalute triple integrals, one may divide the region V into elements by means of three systems of planes parallel to the coordinate planes. The value of the integral is then found by the performance of three integrations with respect to the rectangular cartesian coordinates x_1, x_2 and x_3. Or we may divide V using parametric surfaces of a curvilinear coordinate system, in which case we evaluate the triple integral by performing three integrations with respect to the three curvilinear coordinates. Since most readers will have had considerable experience in evaluating triple integrals in connection with elementary calculus, no example need be given here.

Problems

1. If $\mathbf{x}$ is the prosition-vector of a general point on a circle C of radius a, and $\mathbf{t}$ is the unit tangent vector to C, evaluate $\int_C \mathbf{t} \cdot d\mathbf{x}$.

2. If $f = (x_1)^2 - (x_2)^2$, evaluate the line integral of f along the line $x_1 + 2x_2 = 2$ from the point $A(0,1)$ to the point $B(2,0)$.

3. Evaluate the line integral in Problem 2 when the curve C consists of (i) the two line segments AD and DB, where D has coordinates $(1,1)$, (ii) the two line segments AO and OB, where O is the origin.

4. If $f = 81x_1 - 9$, evaluate the line integral of f along the curve $(x_2)^2 = (x_1)^3$ from the origin to the point $(1,1)$.

5. If $f = x_2 x_3 + x_3 x_1 + x_1 x_2$, evaluate the line integral of f from the origin O to the point $B(1,2,3)$ along the path consisting of (i) the line segment OB; (ii) the three line segments OD, DE and EB, where D and E have coordinates $(1,0,0)$ and $(1,2,0)$, respectively.

6. If $f = x_1 + x_2 + x_3$, evaluate the line integral of f along the curve

$$\mathbf{x} = a \cos u \, \mathbf{i}_1 + a \sin u \, \mathbf{i}_2 + a \, u \cot \alpha \, \mathbf{i}_3, \quad (0 \leqslant u \leqslant \tfrac{1}{2}\pi),$$

where a and α are constants.

7. If $\mathbf{b} = (x_1 - x_2)\mathbf{i}_1 + x_2\mathbf{i}_2$, evaluate the line integral of $\mathbf{b}$ along the following curves: (i) the path in Problem 2 above, (ii) the two paths in Problem 3 above, (iii) the path in Problem 4 above.

8. If $\mathbf{b} = 2x_1x_2\mathbf{i}_1 + [(x_1)^2 - (x_2)^2]\mathbf{i}_2$, evaluate the line integral of $\mathbf{b}$ from the point $A(0,0)$ to the point $B(1,1)$ along the following curves: (i) $x_2 = x_1$, (ii) $(x_1)^2 = x_2$, (iii) $x_1 = (x_2)^2$.

9. If $\mathbf{b}$ is as given in Problem 8, evaluate the line integral of $\mathbf{b}$ from the point $A(a, 0)$ to the point $B(0,a)$ along the circle $(x_1)^2 + (x_2)^2 = a^2$, using the polar angle θ as the parameter varying along the curve.

10. Evaluate the line integral in Example 3 of § 51, using for the curve C the parametric representation

$$\mathbf{x} = a \cos u \, \mathbf{i}_1 + a \sin u \, \mathbf{i}_2 + a(1 - \cos u) \, \mathbf{i}_3, \quad (0 \leqslant u \leqslant \tfrac{1}{2}\pi).$$

11. If $\mathbf{b} = x_2\mathbf{i}_1 + x_3\mathbf{i}_2 - x_1\mathbf{i}_3$, evaluate the line integral of $\mathbf{b}$ along the curve in Problem 6.

12. If C is the curve in Problem 6, evaluate the following:

$$\text{(i)} \int_C \mathbf{x} \, ds, \qquad \text{(ii)} \int_C \mathbf{x} \times \mathbf{t} \, ds.$$

13. If $f = x_1 + x_3$, evaluate the surface integral of f over the region S consisting of the triangle cut from the plane $6x_1 + 3x_2 + 2x_3 = 6$ by the three planes $x_1 = 0$, $x_2 = 0$, $x_1 + x_2 = 1$.

14. If $\mathbf{b} = x_1\mathbf{i}_1 + (x_2)^2\mathbf{i}_3$, evaluate the surface integral of $\mathbf{b}$ over the region S in Problem 13, the origin being on the negative side of S.

15. If $f = (x_1)^2 + (x_2)^2$, evaluate its surface integral over the region S consisting of the part of the surface $x_3 = 2 - (x_1)^2 - (x_2)^2$ in the first octant. Use polar coordinates in the x_1x_2 plane.

16. Find the area of the region S in Problem 15.

17. If $\mathbf{b} = (x_1)^2\mathbf{i}_1 + x_3\mathbf{i}_3$, evaluate the surface integral of $\mathbf{b}$ over the region S of Problem 15, the origin being on the positive side of S.

54. *Green's theorem in the plane.* This theorem is as follows. Let S be a closed region in the x_1x_2 plane bounded by a curve C, as shown in

140

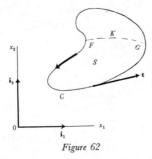

Figure 62

Figure 62, and let **b** be a vector field continuous and with continuous first derivatives in the region S. Then

(54.1)
$$\int_S \mathbf{i}_3 \cdot (\nabla \times \mathbf{b})\, dS = \int_C \mathbf{b} \cdot \mathbf{t}\, ds,$$

where the integration over C is carried out in the positive direction, that is, in that direction of travel around C in which the interior of S lies on the left. This direction is indicated by the arrow on C in Figure 62. In Equation (54.1), $\mathbf{i}_3$ is as usual a unit vector which forms with $\mathbf{i}_1$ and $\mathbf{i}_2$ a right handed triad, and $\mathbf{t}$ is a unit vector tangent to C in the positive direction.

Equation (54.1) is often written in the form

(54.2)
$$\int_S \left(\frac{\partial b_1}{\partial x_2} - \frac{\partial b_2}{\partial x_1} \right) dS = -\int_C (b_1 dx_1 + b_2 dx_2).$$

We first prove that

(54.3)
$$\int_S \frac{\partial b_1}{\partial x_2}\, dS = -\int_C b_1 dx_1,$$

in the case when C can be cut by a line parallel to the x_2 axis in two points at most. Figure 63 illustrates the situation. On C there are two points D and E where the tangent to C is parallel to the x_2 axis. Let d and e be the abscissas of D and E, respectively. These points divide C into two parts C' and C''. At a general point $X(x_1, x_2)$ in S we introduce an element of area lying in a strip parallel to the x_2 axis, the left edge of the strip cutting C' and C'' at the points $X'(x_1, x_2')$ and $X''(x_1, x_2'')$, as shown. Then

141

$$\int_S \frac{\partial b_1}{\partial x_2}\, dS = \int_d^e \int_{x_2''}^{x_2'} \frac{\partial b_1}{\partial x_2}\, dx_2\, dx_1$$

$$= \int_d^e \left[b_1(x_1, x_2) \right]_{x_2''}^{x_2'} dx_1$$

$$= \int_d^e b_1(x_1, x_2')\, dx_1 - \int_d^e b_1(x_1, x_2'')\, dx_1$$

$$= -\int_e^d b_1(x_1, x_2')\, dx_1 - \int_d^e b_1(x_1, x_2'')\, dx_1$$

$$= -\int_C b_1 dx_1.$$

Let us now consider the case when C can be cut by a line parallel to the x_2 axis in more than two points, such as the case of the curve C in Figure 62. Here we have only to join the points F and G where there are tangents parallel to the x_2 axis by a curve K which is contained

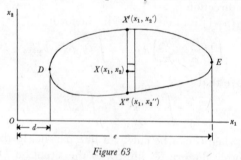

Figure 63

in S and which cannot be cut by a line parallel to the x_2 axis in more than one point. The curve K divides S into two portions for both of which the above proof of (54.3) holds. Hence, is we apply (54.3) to both portions, and add, the two line integrals over K cancel, and we hence establish (54.3) for the entire region S. In a similar fashion we can prove Equation (54.3) for the case when several curves such as

142

K are required. And we can do likewise when S is multiply connected, that is, S has holes in it and C then consists of several isolated parts.

In an analogous fashion we can prove that

$$(54.4) \qquad \int_S \frac{\partial b_2}{\partial x_1} \, dS = \int_C b_2 \, dx_2.$$

Subtraction of (54.4) from (54.3) then yields (54.2). This completes the proof.

55. Green's theorem in space.

This theorem is as follows. Let V be a closed region bounded by a surface S, and let $\mathbf{b}$ be a vector field continuous and with continuous first derivatives in V. Then

$$(55.1) \qquad \int_V \triangledown \cdot \mathbf{b} \, dV = \int_S \mathbf{b} \cdot \mathbf{n} \, dS,$$

where $\mathbf{n}$ is the unit outer normal vector to S.

This theorem is also called the divergence theorem, and can be written in the form

$$(55.2) \qquad \int_V \left(\frac{\partial b_1}{\partial x_1} + \frac{\partial b_2}{\partial x_2} + \frac{\partial b_3}{\partial x_3} \right) dV = \int_S (b_1 n_1 + b_2 n_2 + b_3 n_3) \, dS.$$

We shall first prove that

$$(55.3) \qquad \int_V \frac{\partial b_3}{\partial x_3} \, dV = \int_S b_3 n_3 \, dS,$$

in the case when S can be cut by a line parallel to the x_3 axis in two points at most. Figure 64 illustrates the situation, T being the projection of S on the $x_1 x_2$ plane. On S there is a curve C consisting of points where the tangent plane to S is parallel to the x_3 axis. The curve C cuts S into two portions S' and S''. At a point $X(x_1, x_2, x_3)$ in V we introduce an element of volume lying in a prism parallel to the x_3 axis, the vertical line through X meeting S' and S'' at the points X' (x_1, x_2, x_3') and $X''(x_1, x_2, x_3'')$, as shown. Thus

$$(55.4) \qquad \int\limits_V \frac{\partial b_3}{\partial x_3} \, dV = \iint\limits_T \int\limits_{x_3''}^{x_3'} \frac{\partial b_3}{\partial x_3} \, dx_3 \, dx_2 \, dx_1$$

$$= \iint\limits_T [b_3(x_1, x_2, x'_3) - b_3(x_1, x_2, x_3')'] \, dx_2 \, dx_1.$$

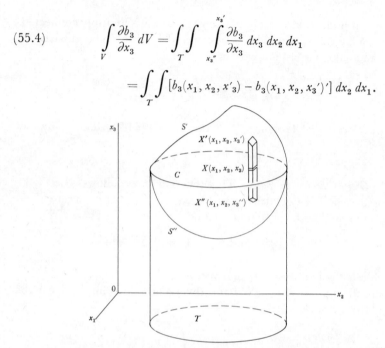

Figure 64

Let $\mathbf{n'}$ be the unit outer normal vector at X', and let dS' be the area of of the element cut from S' by the vertical prism. Let us define $\mathbf{n''}$ and dS'' at X'' similarly. Then we have

$$dx_2 \, dx_1 = n_3' \, dS' = -n_3'' \, dS'',$$

and so we may write (55.4) in the form

$$\int\limits_V \frac{\partial b_3}{\partial x_3} \, dV = \int\limits_{S'} b_3(x_1, x_2, x_3')n_3'dS' + \int\limits_{S''} b_3(x_1, x_2, x_3'')n_3''dS'' = \int\limits_S b_3 n_3 dS.$$

Let us now consider the case when S can be cut by a vertical line in more than two points. In such cases we can always divide V into a number of regions $V_1, V_2, \cdots$ by cutting V by a number of surfaces $K_1, K_2, \cdots$ so chosen that the boundary of each of the regions V_1,

144

$V_2, \cdots$ can be cut by a vertical line in two points at most. The above proof of (55.3) then applies to the regions $V_1, V_2, \cdots$. If we apply (55.3) to $V_1, V_2, \cdots$ and add, the surface integrals over $K_1, K_2, \cdots$ cancel, and we hence establish (55.3) for the entire region V.

In a manner similar to the above we can prove that

$$(55.5). \quad \int_V \frac{\partial b_2}{\partial x_2} \, dV = \int_S b_2 n_2 \, dS, \qquad \int_V \frac{\partial b_3}{\partial x_3} \, dV = \int_S b_3 n_3 \, dS.$$

Addition of Equations (55.3) and (55.5) then yields (55.2). This completes the proof.

If f is a scalar field with continuous second order derivatives, then we can set $\mathbf{b} = \nabla f$ and substitute in Equation (55.1) to obtain

$$\int_V \nabla \cdot (\nabla f) \, dV = \int_S \nabla f \cdot \mathbf{n} \, dS,$$

or

$$(55.6) \qquad \int_V (\nabla \cdot \nabla) f \, dV = \int_S \frac{df}{dn} \, dS,$$

where $\nabla \cdot \nabla$ is the familiar Laplacian operator, often denoted by ∇^2, and df/dn is the directional derivative of f in the direction of the outer normal to the surface S.

56. *The symmetric form of green's theorem.* Let f and g be scalar fields with continuous second derivatives in a closed region V bounded by a surface S. We may then apply Green's theorem as stated in Equation (55.1), but with the vector $\mathbf{b}$ replaced by $f \nabla g$. This yields

$$(56.1) \qquad \int_V \nabla \cdot (f \nabla g) \, dV = \int_S f \nabla g \cdot \mathbf{n} \, dS.$$

But

$$\nabla \cdot (f \nabla g) = f (\nabla \cdot \nabla) g + \nabla f \cdot \nabla g$$
$$= f \nabla^2 g + \nabla f \cdot \nabla g,$$

because of Equation (48.1). Also, $\nabla g \cdot \mathbf{n}$ is equal to the directional derivative dg/dn of g in the direction of the outer normal $\mathbf{n}$ to S. Thus Equation (56.1) becomes

$$(56.2) \qquad \int_V (f \nabla^2 g + \nabla f \cdot \nabla g)\, dV = \int_S f \frac{dg}{dn}\, dS.$$

Similarly, by an interchange of f and g in the above, we obtain

$$(56.3) \qquad \int_V (g \nabla^2 f + \nabla g \cdot \nabla f)\, dV = \int_S g \frac{df}{dn}\, dS.$$

Subtraction of (56.3) from (56.2) then yields

$$(56.4) \qquad \int_V (f \nabla^2 g - g \nabla^2 f)\, dV = \int_S \left(f \frac{dg}{dn} - g \frac{df}{dn} \right) dS.$$

This equation is called *the symmetric form of Green's theorem*.

57. *Stokes's theorem.* This theorem is as follows. Let S be a closed region on a surface, the boundary of S being a curve C. We choose a positive side for S, and let **n** be the unit vector normal to S on the positive side. The positive direction on C is defined to be that in which an observer on the positive side of S would travel to have the interior of S on his left. Let **t** be the unit vector tangent to C in the positive direction, and let **b** be a vector field with continuous first derivatives in the closed region S. Then Stokes's theorem states that

$$(57.1) \qquad \int_S \mathbf{n} \cdot (\nabla \times \mathbf{b})\, dS = \int_C \mathbf{b} \cdot \mathbf{t}\, ds,$$

where the integration around C is carried out in the positive direction.

This theorem can also be written in the form

$$(57.2) \qquad \int_S \left[n_1 \left(\frac{\partial b_3}{\partial x_2} - \frac{\partial b_2}{\partial x_3} \right) + n_2 \left(\frac{\partial b_1}{\partial x_3} - \frac{\partial b_3}{\partial x_1} \right) + n_3 \left(\frac{\partial b_2}{\partial x_1} - \frac{\partial b_1}{\partial x_2} \right) \right] dS$$
$$= \int_C (b_1 dx_1 + b_2 dx_2 + b_3 dx_3).$$

We shall first prove that

$$(57.3) \qquad \int_S \mathbf{n} \cdot (\nabla \times b_1 \mathbf{i}_1)\, dS = \int_C b_1\, dx_1,$$

in the case when S is a regular surface element and the positive side of

146

S is that side on which the unit normal vector **n** points in the direction of increasing x_3. Figure 65 illustrates the situation, and shows the

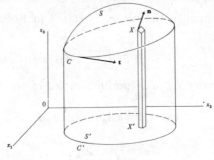

Figure 65

unit tangent vector **t** of C and also the region S' in the x_1x_2 plane into which S projects.

Now

(57.4) $$\int_S \mathbf{n} \cdot (\nabla \times b_1 \mathbf{i}_1)\, dS = \int_S \mathbf{n} \cdot \left(\mathbf{i}_2 \frac{\partial b_1}{\partial x_3} - \mathbf{i}_3 \frac{\partial b_1}{\partial x_2} \right) dS.$$

Let the equation of the surface S be $x_3 = g(x_1, x_2)$. Then on S, we have

$$b_1[x_1, x_2, x_3(x_1, x_2)] = c_1(x_1, x_2),$$

(57.5) $$\frac{\partial c_1}{\partial x_2} = \frac{\partial b_1}{\partial x_2} + \frac{\partial b_1}{\partial x_3} \frac{\partial x_3}{\partial x_2}.$$

We now substitute from this equation for $\partial b_1 / \partial x_2$ in Equation (57.4) to obtain the relation

(57.6) $$\int_S \mathbf{n} \cdot (\nabla \times b_1 \mathbf{i}_1)\, dS = -\int_S \mathbf{n} \cdot \mathbf{i}_3 \frac{\partial c_1}{\partial x_2}\, dS + \int_S \mathbf{n} \cdot \left(\mathbf{i}_2 + \mathbf{i}_3 \frac{\partial x_3}{\partial x_2} \right) \frac{\partial b_1}{\partial x_3}\, dS$$

$$= -I_1 + I_2,$$

where I_1 and I_2 denote the two integrals on the right side of this equation.

Let us consider I_1. We have $\mathbf{n} \cdot \mathbf{i}_3\, dS = n_3\, dS = dS'$, where dS' is the projection of dS on the x_1x_2 plane. Since c_1 is a function of x_1 and x_2 only, we can then write

147

$$I_1 = -\int_{S'} \frac{\partial c_1}{\partial x_2} \, dS'.$$

By Green's theorem in the plane, as stated in Equation (54.2), we then have

$$(57.7) \qquad I_1 = \int_{C'} c_1(x_1, x_2) dx_1 = \int_{C'} b_1[x_1, x_2, x_3(x_1, x_2)] dx_1 = \int_C b_1 dx_1.$$

We now consider I_2. The position-vector of the general point X on S is

$$\mathbf{x} = x_1 \mathbf{i}_1 + x_2 \mathbf{i}_2 + x_3(x_1, x_2) \mathbf{i}_3.$$

Hence

$$\frac{\partial \mathbf{x}}{\partial x_2} = \mathbf{i}_2 + \frac{\partial x_3}{\partial x_2} \mathbf{i}_3,$$

and so

$$(57.8) \qquad I_2 = \int_S \mathbf{n} \cdot \frac{\partial \mathbf{x}}{\partial x_2} \frac{\partial b_1}{\partial x_3} \, dS.$$

But the vector $\partial \mathbf{x} / \partial x_2$ is tangent at X to the curve of intersection of S and a plane parallel to the $x_2 x_3$ plane. Hence this vector is tangent to S and is then perpendicular to the unit normal vector $\mathbf{n}$, so that

$$\mathbf{n} \cdot \frac{\partial \mathbf{x}}{\partial x_2} = 0.$$

Thus Equation (57.8) yields $I_2 = 0$, and from Equations (57.6) and (57.7) we can then conclude that Equation (57.1) is true.

When the positive side of S is chosen so that the unit normal vector $\mathbf{n}$ points in the direction of decreasing x_3, the proof of Equation (57.3) is similar to the above, the only differences in the proofs being that in the present case n_3 is negative and the direction of integration around the curve C is opposite that in the above proof.

When the surface S is not a regular surface element, we divide it into a number of regular surface elements $S_1, S_2, \cdots$ by a number of curves $L_1, L_2, \cdots$. The above proof of (57.3) then applies to the regions $S_1, S_2, \cdots$. If we apply (57.3) to these regions, and add, the line integrals over $L_1, L_2, \cdots$ cancel, and we hence establish Equation (57.3) for the entire region S.

In a manner similar to the above we can prove that

$$(57.9) \qquad \int_S \mathbf{n} \cdot (\nabla \times b_2 \mathbf{i}_2) dS = \int_C b_2 dx_2, \quad \int_S \mathbf{n} \cdot (\nabla \times b_3 \mathbf{i}_3) dS = \int_C b_3 dx_3.$$

Addition of Equations (57.3) and (57.9) then yields (57.1). This completes the proof.

58. *Integration formulas.* Green's theorem in space and Stokes's theorem were considered in §§ 55 and 57, respectively. These theorems are integration formulas which we may write in the form

$$(58.1) \qquad \int_V \nabla \cdot \mathbf{b} \, dV = \int_S \mathbf{n} \cdot \mathbf{b} \, dS,$$

$$(58.2) \qquad \int_S (\mathbf{n} \times \nabla) \cdot \mathbf{b} \, dS = \int_C \mathbf{t} \cdot \mathbf{b} \, ds.$$

Both of these theorems involve a vector field **b**; Equation (58.1) presents a transformation from a triple integral to a surface integral, while (58.2) presents a transformation from a surface integral to a line integral. We shall now introduce four other integration formulas, which we shall state as two theorems.

Theorem 1. Let V be a closed region in space bounded by a surface S with the unit outer normal vector **n**, as in the case of Green's theorem in space. Let f and **b** be two fields with continuous first derivatives in V. Then

$$(58.3) \qquad \int_V \nabla f \, dV = \int_S \mathbf{n} f \, dS,$$

$$(58.4) \qquad \int_V \nabla \times \mathbf{b} \, dV = \int_S \mathbf{n} \times \mathbf{b} \, dS.$$

Theorem 2. Let S be a closed region lying on a surface and bounded by a curve C, **n** being the unit positive normal vector to S and **t** being the unit positive tangent vector to C, as in the case of Stokes's theorem. Let f and **b** be two fields with continuous first derivatives in S. Then

$$(58.5) \qquad \int_S (\mathbf{n} \times \nabla) f \, dS = \int_C \mathbf{t} f \, ds,$$

149

$$(58.6) \qquad \int_S (\mathbf{n} \times \nabla) \times \mathbf{b} \, dS = \int_C \mathbf{t} \times \mathbf{b} \, ds.$$

Proof of Equation (58.3). Let $\mathbf{c}$ be a constant vector field. If in Equation (58.1) we set $\mathbf{b} = f\mathbf{c}$, we obtain

$$(58.7) \qquad \int_V \nabla \cdot (f\mathbf{c}) \, dV = \int_S \mathbf{n} \cdot f\mathbf{c} \, dS.$$

But we have

$$\nabla \cdot (f\mathbf{c}) = \nabla f \cdot \mathbf{c},$$

by Equation (48.1), since $\mathbf{c}$ is a constant vector. Thus Equation (58.7) may be written in the form

$$\mathbf{c} \cdot \left[\int_V \nabla f \, dV - \int_S \mathbf{n} f \, dS \right] = 0.$$

Since $\mathbf{c}$ is an arbitrary constant vector, the expression in the square brackets must vanish, whence Equation (58.3) is proved.

Proof of Equation (58.4). We again introduce the constant vector field $\mathbf{c}$, but in Equation (58.1) we replace $\mathbf{b}$ by $\mathbf{b} \times \mathbf{c}$ to obtain the relation

$$(58.8) \qquad \int_V \nabla \cdot (\mathbf{b} \times \mathbf{c}) \, dV = \int_S \mathbf{n} \cdot (\mathbf{b} \times \mathbf{c}) \, dS.$$

Since $\mathbf{c}$ is a constant vector, we have by the permutation theorem for scalar triple products the relations

$$\nabla \cdot (\mathbf{b} \times \mathbf{c}) = \mathbf{c} \cdot (\nabla \times \mathbf{b}), \quad \mathbf{n} \cdot (\mathbf{b} \times \mathbf{c}) = \mathbf{c} \cdot (\mathbf{n} \times \mathbf{b}.)$$

Thus Equation (58.8) may be written in the form

$$\mathbf{c} \cdot \left[\int_V \nabla \times \mathbf{b} \, dV - \int_S \mathbf{n} \times \mathbf{b} \, dS \right] = 0.$$

Since $\mathbf{c}$ is an arbitrary constant vector, we conclude that (58.4) is true.

Proofs of Equations (58.5) and (58.6). To prove these two equations we replace $\mathbf{b}$ in Equation (58.2) first by $f\mathbf{c}$ and then by $\mathbf{b} \times \mathbf{c}$, where $\mathbf{c}$ is a constant vector field. The procedure then follows that in the previous two proofs. The details are left as exercises for the reader (Problem 11 at the end of this chapter).

The six integration formulas (58.1)–(58.6) may be written compactly in the form

$$(58.9) \qquad \int_V \nabla * T \, dV = \int_S \mathbf{n} * T \, dS,$$

$$(58.10) \qquad \int_S (\mathbf{n} \times \nabla) * T \, dS = \int_C \mathbf{t} * T \, ds,$$

where T can denote a scalar field or a vector field, and the asterisk has the following meanings: if T is a scalar field, it denotes the multiplication of a vector and a scalar; and if T denotes a vector field, it denotes either scalar or vector multiplication. Thus, for example, if T denotes a vector field $\mathbf{b}$ and the asterisk denotes scalar multiplication, then Equation (58.10) becomes (58.2).

59. *Irrotational vectors.* A vector field $\mathbf{b}(x_1, x_2, x_3)$ is said to be irrotational in a region V in space if everywhere in V we have

$$(59.1) \qquad \nabla \times \mathbf{b} = 0.$$

Let φ be any scalar field with continuous second derivatives; and let us write $\mathbf{b} = \nabla \varphi$. Then

$$\nabla \times \mathbf{b} = \nabla \times \nabla \varphi = 0,$$

so a vector $\mathbf{b}$ defined as the gradient of a scalar field is irrotational.

We shall now show that an irrotational vector field $\mathbf{b}$ has the following properties:

(i) Its integral around every reducible circuit in V vanishes.

(ii) When V is simply connected, $\mathbf{b}$ is the gradient of a scalar field.

To verify the first property, we consider a general circuit in V which is reducible, that is, it can be contracted to a point without leaving V. Let S be a surface entirely in V and bounded by C. If we assume that $\mathbf{b}$ has continuous first derivatives, then Stokes's theorem (57.1) yields

$$\int_C \mathbf{b} \cdot \mathbf{t} \, ds = \int_S \mathbf{n} \cdot (\nabla \times \mathbf{b}) \, dS = 0$$

by Equation (59.1).

151

To verify the second property, we let X be a general point in V, and let X_0 be a given point. We also let C' and C'' be any two paths in V from X_0 to X, as shown in Figure 66. Because of property (i)

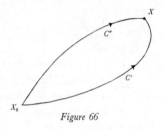

Figure 66

above, the line integral of $\mathbf{b}$ from X_0 to X is the same for paths C' and C'' and hence has the same value for all paths in V from X_0 to X. Thus, if we write

(59.2) $$\varphi = \int_{X_0}^{X} \mathbf{b} \cdot d\mathbf{x},$$

then φ depends only on the coordinates (x_1, x_2, x_3) of X. Differentiation of Equation (59.2) yields $d\varphi = \mathbf{b} \cdot d\mathbf{x}$, or

(59.3) $$\frac{d\varphi}{ds} = \mathbf{b} \cdot \frac{d\mathbf{x}}{ds}.$$

But $d\varphi/ds$ is the directional derivative of φ, and by Equation (44.3) is equal to $\nabla\varphi \cdot (d\mathbf{x}/ds)$. Thus Equation (59.3) may be written in the form

$$(\nabla\varphi - \mathbf{b}) \cdot \frac{d\mathbf{x}}{ds} = 0.$$

Since $d\mathbf{x}/ds$ is an arbitrary vector, then

(59.4) $$\mathbf{b} = \nabla\varphi.$$

This completes the proof.

The function φ is called a scalar potential function.

60. *Solenoidal vectors.* A vector field $\mathbf{b}(x_1, x_2, x_3)$ is said to be solenoidal in a region V in space if everywhere in V we have

(60.1) $$\nabla \cdot \mathbf{b} = 0.$$

152

Let $\boldsymbol{\varphi}$ be any vector field with continuous second derivatives, and let us write $\mathbf{b} = \nabla \times \boldsymbol{\varphi}$. Then

$$\nabla \cdot \mathbf{b} = \nabla \cdot (\nabla \times \boldsymbol{\varphi}) = 0.$$

We shall now show that, if $\mathbf{b}$ is any solenoidal vector field, there exists a vector field $\boldsymbol{\varphi}$ such that $\mathbf{b} = \nabla \times \boldsymbol{\varphi}$.

To prove the proposition, we must solve the scalar equations

$$(60.2) \qquad b_1 = \frac{\partial \varphi_3}{\partial x_2} - \frac{\partial \varphi_2}{\partial x_3},$$

$$(60.3) \qquad b_2 = \frac{\partial \varphi_1}{\partial x_3} - \frac{\partial \varphi_3}{\partial x_1},$$

$$(60.4) \qquad b_3 = \frac{\partial \varphi_2}{\partial x_1} - \frac{\partial \varphi_1}{\partial x_2},$$

for φ_1, φ_2 and φ_3, where b_1, b_2 and b_3 are given functions subject to the condition

$$(60.5) \qquad \frac{\partial b_1}{\partial x_1} + \frac{\partial b_2}{\partial x_2} + \frac{\partial b_3}{\partial x_3} = 0.$$

Let us choose $\varphi_1 = 0$. Then we have from Equations (60.3) and (60.4) by partial integrations with respect to x_1,

$$(60.6) \qquad \varphi_2 = \int_{a_1}^{x_1} b_3 dx_1 + \psi_2(x_2, x_3),$$

$$(60.7) \qquad \varphi_3 = - \int_{a_1}^{x_1} b_2 dx_1 + \psi_3(x_2, x_3),$$

where a_1 is a constant and ψ_2 and ψ_3 are arbitrary functions of x_2 and x_3. To satisfy Equation (60.2) we must have

$$b_1 = - \int_{a_1}^{x_1} \left(\frac{\partial b_2}{\partial x_2} + \frac{\partial b_3}{\partial x_3} \right) dx_1 + \frac{\partial \psi_3}{\partial x_2} - \frac{\partial \psi_2}{\partial x_3}.$$

Because of Equation (60.5) we can then write

$$b_1 = \int_{a_1}^{x_1} \frac{\partial b_1}{\partial x_1} dx_1 + \frac{\partial \psi_3}{\partial x_2} - \frac{\partial \psi_2}{\partial x_3}$$

$$= b_1(x_1, x_2, x_3) - b_1(a_1, x_2, x_3) + \frac{\partial \psi_3}{\partial x_2} - \frac{\partial \psi_2}{\partial x_3}.$$

153

This equation is satisfied if we choose $\psi_2 = 0$,

$$\psi_3 = \int\limits_{a_2}^{x_2} b_1(a_1, x_2, x_3) \, dx_2,$$

where a_2 is a constant. The final result is then

$$\varphi_1 = 0, \qquad \varphi_2 = \int\limits_{a_1}^{x_1} b_3(x_1, x_2, x_3) \, dx_1,$$

$$\varphi_3 = -\int\limits_{a_1}^{x_1} b_2(x_1, x_2, x_3) \, dx_1 + \int\limits_{a_2}^{x_2} b_1(a_1, x_2, x_3) \, dx_2,$$

where all integrations are partial integrations, and a_1 and a_2 are constants. The function $\boldsymbol{\varphi}$ is called a vector potential function.

In the above proof, several arbitrary selections have been made. This indicates that a given solenoidal vector field $\mathbf{b}$ does not possess a unique vector potential function. In order to see this more clearly, we let $\boldsymbol{\varphi}$ be one vector potential function corresponding to the solenoidal vector field $\mathbf{b}$, and let f be any scalar field. Then

$$\nabla \times (\boldsymbol{\varphi} + \nabla f) = \nabla \times \boldsymbol{\varphi} + \nabla \times \nabla f = \nabla \times \boldsymbol{\varphi} = \mathbf{b}.$$

Thus, $\boldsymbol{\varphi} + \nabla f$ is also a vector potential function corresponding to the field $\mathbf{b}$.

If $\mathbf{b}$ is any vector field having continuous second derivatives in a region V, then $\mathbf{b}$ can be expressed as the sum of an irrotational vector and a solenoidal vector. The proof of this will not be given here.

Problems

1. Let C be a closed curve in the $x_1 x_2$ plane. Prove that the area A of the region S enclosed by C is given by the relation

$$A = \tfrac{1}{2} \int\limits_{C} (x_1 \, dx_2 - x_2 \, dx_1)$$

where the integration over C is carried out in the direction of travel around C in which the interior of S is on the left.

2. If $\mathbf{x}$ is the position-vector of a general point X on a closed surface

154

S, and $\mathbf{n}$ is the unit outer normal vector to S, prove that the volume V of the region enclosed by S is given by the relation

$$V = \tfrac{1}{3} \int_S \mathbf{n} \cdot \mathbf{x} \, dS.$$

3. If S is a closed surface with a unit outer normal vector $\mathbf{n}$, prove that

$$\int_S \mathbf{n} \times \mathbf{x} \, dS = 0.$$

4. If V is a region bounded by a surface S, and $\mathbf{n}$ is the unit outer normal vector to S, prove that

$$I_3 = \tfrac{1}{4} \int_S [(x_1)^2 + (x_2)^2] \, (x_1 \mathbf{i}_1 + x_2 \mathbf{i}_2) \cdot \mathbf{n} \, dS,$$

where I_3 is the moment of inertia of V about the x_3 axis.

5. If $\mathbf{b}$ has continuous first derivatives in a closed region V bounded by a surface S, prove that

$$\int_S \mathbf{n} \cdot (\nabla \times \mathbf{b}) \, dS = 0.$$

6. If $\mathbf{b} = a_1 (x_1)^2 \mathbf{i}_1 + a_2 (x_2)^2 \mathbf{i}_2 + a_3 (x_3)^2 \mathbf{i}_3$, where a_1, a_2 and a_3 are constants, evaluate the surface integral of $\mathbf{b}$ over the sphere through the origin with center at the point $A(a_1, a_2, a_3)$.

7. If $\mathbf{b} = (x_1)^2 \mathbf{i}_1 + x_1 x_2 \mathbf{i}_2 + x_3 \mathbf{i}_3$, evaluate the surface integral of $\mathbf{b}$ over the cube bounded by the planes $x_1 = 2$, $x_2 = 2$, $x_3 = 2$ and the coordinate planes.

8. If $\mathbf{b} = [(x_1)^2 - x_2] \, \mathbf{i}_1 + [2(x_1)^2 + 3x_2] \, \mathbf{i}_2 - 2x_1 x_3 \, \mathbf{i}_3$, evaluate the surface integral of $\mathbf{b}$ over the sphere S with center at the point E $(1, 0, 2)$ and passing through the point $F(3, -2, 1)$.

9. If C is any closed curve, prove that $\int_C d\mathbf{x} = 0$.

10. Let C be the circle with the equations $(x_1)^2 + (x_2)^2 = 4$, $x_3 = 0$, and let

$$\mathbf{b} = [(x_1)^2 + x_2] \, \mathbf{i}_1 + [(x_1)^2 + x_3] \, \mathbf{i}_2 + x_2 \mathbf{i}_3.$$

Evaluate the line integral of $\mathbf{b}$ around C in the direction indicated by

155

the fingers of the right hand when the thumb points in the direction of the positive x_3 axis.

11. Prove Equations (58.5) and (58.6).

12. A vector field $\mathbf{b}$ has continuous first derivatives in a closed region V. On the bounding surface S of V, $\mathbf{b}$ is normal to S. Prove that

$$\int_V \nabla \times \mathbf{b}\, dV = 0.$$

13. If f and $\mathbf{b}$ are fields with continuous first derivatives in a region V bounded by a surface S, prove that

$$\int_S f\mathbf{n} \times \mathbf{b}\, dS = \int_V f\nabla \times \mathbf{b}\, dV + \int_V \nabla f \times \mathbf{b}\, dV.$$

14. If $\mathbf{b}$ and $\mathbf{c}$ are irrotational vector fields, prove that $\mathbf{b} \times \mathbf{c}$ is solenoidal.

15. If $\mathbf{b} = x_2 x_3 \mathbf{i}_1 + x_3 x_1 \mathbf{i}_2 + x_1 x_2 \mathbf{i}_3$, show that $\mathbf{b}$ is solenoidal, and find its vector potential.

16. Show that the vector field

$$\frac{x_1 \mathbf{i}_1 + x_2 \mathbf{i}_2}{(x_1)^2 + (x_2)^2}$$

is solenoidal in any region which does not contain the origin.

17. If r, θ and z are cylindrical coordinates, show that $\nabla\theta$ and $\nabla \ln r$ are solenoidal vectors, and find their vector potentials.

18. If $\nabla \cdot \mathbf{b} = \Phi$ and $\nabla \times \mathbf{b} = \mathbf{f}$, prove that

$$\nabla^2 b_1 = \frac{\partial \Phi}{\partial x_1} - \frac{\partial f_3}{\partial x_2} + \frac{\partial f_2}{\partial x_3},$$

and derive similar equations involving b_2 and b_3.

Chapter VI

TENSOR ANALYSIS

61. *Introduction.* Tensors are mathematical or physical concepts which have certain specific laws of transformation when there is a change in the coordinate system. As we shall see, vectors are just one of the many types of tensors.

Tensor analysis is a study of tensors. It has many applications. One of these is in the field of classical differential geometry of the curve and surface in our ordinary space, as well as the more significant generalizations of this geometry to spaces of higher dimensionality; this generalization is often referred to as Riemannian geometry. Another application is to mathematical physics. Here tensor analysis permits us to express easily in terms of curvilinear coordinates the fundamental equations of the various subjects such as hydrodynamics, elasticity, electricity and magnetism. It also aids in the formulation of the natural laws of mathematical physics, since such laws when expressed in terms of tensors are independent of any one particular coordinate system.

62. *Transformation of coordinates.* Let us consider a set of curvilinear coordinates which we denote by the symbols z^1, z^2 and z^3. We use the supercripts to agree with a convention to be introduced later. We shall also refer to these coordinates by writing z^r ($r = 1, 2, 3$).

Let us write

$$(62.1) \qquad z'^r = f^r(z^1, z^2, z^3),$$

where the three functions f^r ($r = 1, 2, 3$) are single valued and differentiable for some range of values of z^1, z^2 and z^3. These equations represent a coordinate transformation to new curvilinear coordinates z'^1, z'^2 and z'^3. The Jacobian J' of a transformation such as

157

this one was defined in § 49. We express it conveniently here by writing

$$(62.2) \qquad I' = \left| \frac{\partial z''}{\partial z^s} \right|,$$

the ranges for r and s being 1, 2, 3. We assume that I' does not vanish, whence, as mentioned in § 49, Equations (62.1) may be solved to yield

$$(62.3) \qquad z^r = g^r(z'^1, z'^2, z'^3).$$

From Equation (62.1) we have

$$(62.4) \qquad dz''^r = \sum_{s=1}^{3} \frac{\partial z''^r}{\partial z^s} \, dz^s \qquad (\text{r} = 1, 2, 3).$$

We now introduce two conventions, as follows:

Range convention. A small latin suffix which occurs just once in a term is understood to assume all the values 1, 2, 3.

Summation convention. A small latin suffix which occurs just twice in a term implies summation with respect to that suffix over the range 1, 2, 3.

Because of these conventions, we may now write Equations (62.4) in the form

$$(62.5) \qquad dz''^r = \frac{\partial z''^r}{\partial z^s} \, dz^s,$$

the repeated suffix s implying the summation. In this equation, the suffix r is called a free suffix, since we obtain from (62.5) a different equation for each value of r; on the other hand, the suffix s in (62.5) is called a dummy suffix, since a change of both of the suffixes s into any other latin suffix does not alter Equation (62.5).

The Kronecker delta δ_{rs} was introduced in § 47. We shall require it in the present chapter, but shall find it convenient to denote it by the symbol δ^r_s, so we have

$$(62.6) \qquad \begin{aligned} \delta^r_s &= 1 \qquad \text{if } r = s \\ &= 0 \qquad \text{if } r \neq s. \end{aligned}$$

158

We note the identity

$$(62.7) \qquad \delta_t^r = \frac{\partial z^r}{\partial z'^s} \frac{\partial z'^s}{\partial z^t},$$

which is true because its right side is equal to $\partial z^r / \partial z^t$, which, because of the independence of the coordinates z^r, satisfies the relations

$$\frac{\partial z^r}{\partial z^t} = 1 \qquad \text{if } r = t,$$
$$= 0 \qquad \text{if } r \neq t.$$

Of course the primed and unprimed coordinates in Equation (62.7) can be interchanged.

Throughout this section we have considered three curvilinear coordinates z^1, z^2, z^3 in space. The considerations here can be applied equally well to the case of two curvilinear coordinates z^1, z^2 on a surface, the only modifications being in the range and summation conventions above, where it becomes necessary to assume that latin suffixes have the range 1, 2. This same modification, when applied to the rest of this chapter, yields results applicable to two-dimensional problems. In an analogous manner, by the assumption that latin suffixes have the range 1, 2, $\cdots$, N, where N is any positive integer, the results in this chapter can be generalized to yield the Riemannian geometry of the N-dimensional Riemannian space. There are many excellent books on this subject.[1]

63. *Contravariant vectors and tensors.* Let X be a general point in space with curvilinear coordinates z^r. Let A^r denote a set of three quantities associated with the point X, such as for example components of a velocity. We now introduce a second curvilinear coordinate system relative to which the coordinates of X are z'', and denote the transforms of A^r by A'^r. We then make the definition: *a set of quantities A^r associated with a point X is said to be the components of a contravariant vector if they transform, on change of coordinates, according to the equation*

---

[1] See, for example: J. L. Synge and A. Schild, Tensor calculus, University of Toronto Press, Toronto, 1949.

159

$$(63.1) \qquad A'^r = \frac{\partial z'^r}{\partial z^s} A^s,$$

where the partial derivatives are evaluated at X.

Because of Equation (62.5) we see that the quantities dz^s are the components of a contravariant vector. Also, we shall see later on that when the transformation is from rectangular cartesian coordinates to rectangular cartesian coordinates, the components of a vector as defined in § 6 have the law of transformation (63.1) and are hence also the components of a contravariant vector.

We shall now define contravariant tensors. Let A^{rs} be a set of nine quantities associated with the point X with curvilinear coordinates z^r, and let A^{rs} transform into A'^{rs} when the coordinates are transformed to z'^r. We then have the definition: *a set of quantities A^{rs} is called the components of a contravariant tensor of the second order if they transform according to the equation*

$$(63.2) \qquad A'^{rs} = \frac{\partial z'^r}{\partial z^t} \frac{\partial z'^s}{\partial z^u} A^{tu}.$$

Contravariant tensors of higher order are defined analogously. Contravariant vectors are often called contravariant tensors of the first order.

64. *Covariant vectors and tensors.* The definition of covariant vectors is as follows: *a set of three quantities A_r associated with a point X is said to be the components of a covariant vector if they transform on change of coordinates, according to the equation*

$$(64.1) \qquad A'_r = \frac{\partial z^s}{\partial z'^r} A_s.$$

As an example, let us consider a function $\Phi(z^1, z^2, z^3)$. We have

$$(64.2) \qquad \frac{\partial \Phi}{\partial z'^r} = \frac{\partial \Phi}{\partial z^s} \frac{\partial z^s}{\partial z'^r},$$

whence we note that the three expressions $\partial \Phi / \partial z^r$ are the components of a covariant vector.

The definition of a covariant tensor of order two is as follows:

160

a set of nine quantities A_{rs} is said to be the components of a covariant tensor of order two if they transform according to the equation

$$(64.3) \qquad A'_{rs} = \frac{\partial z^t}{\partial z'^r} \frac{\partial z^u}{\partial z'^s} A_{tu}.$$

Covariant tensors of higher order are defined analogously. Covariant vectors are often called covariant tensors of order one.

In § 63 we have used superscripts in writing symbols denoting contravariant tensors, and in the present section we have used subscripts in writing symbols denoting covariant character. This convention will be followed throughout the present chapter.

65. *Mixed tensors. Invariants.* We can also define tensors whose law of transformation involves a combination of both contravariant and covariant properties. Such tensors are called mixed tensors. Thus, for example, *a set of twenty-seven quantities A'_{st} is said to be the components of a mixed tensor of the third order with one contravariant suffix and two covariant suffixes if they transform according to the equation*

$$(65.1) \qquad A'^{r}_{st} = \frac{\partial z'^r}{\partial z^u} \frac{\partial z^v}{\partial z'^s} \frac{\partial z^w}{\partial z'^t} A^{u}_{vw}.$$

It should be noted that (65.1) represents twenty-seven equations, and that the right side of each of these equations consists of the sum of twenty-seven terms.

A single quantity A is said to be an *invarinat* if it transforms according to the equation

$$A' = A.$$

Invariants may be called contravariant tensors of order zero, or covariant tensors of order zero. An example of an invariant is the temperature in a fluid.

We shall now prove that the Kronecker delta δ^r_s has the tensor character indicated by its suffixes, that is, that it is a mixed tensor of the second order. We must establish the equation

$$(65.2) \qquad \delta'^{r}_{s} = \frac{\partial z'^r}{\partial z^t} \frac{\partial z^u}{\partial z'^s} \delta^t_u.$$

161

Now

$$\frac{\partial z^u}{\partial z'^s}\,\delta_u^t = \frac{\partial z^1}{\partial z'^s}\,\delta_1^t + \frac{\partial z^2}{\partial z'^s}\,\delta_2^t + \frac{\partial z^3}{\partial z'^s}\,\delta_3^t\,.$$

When t is given the values 1, 2 and 3, the right side of this relation reduces respectively to the expressions

$$\frac{\partial z^1}{\partial z'^s},\qquad \frac{\partial z^3}{\partial z'^s},\qquad \frac{\partial z^2}{\partial z'^s}\,.$$

Thus we may write

$$\frac{\partial z^u}{\partial z'^s}\,\delta_u^t = \frac{\partial z^t}{\partial z'^s},$$

and so the right side of Equation (65.2) reduces to

$$\frac{\partial z'^r}{\partial z^t}\,\frac{\partial z^t}{\partial z'^s}\,.$$

But this is equal to the left side of Equation (65.2) because of Equation (62.7).

66. *Addition and multiplication of tensors.* If we have two tensors of the same order and type, their sum is defined to be the set of quantities obtained by the addition of corresponding components of the two tensors. Thus the sum of the tensors A_{st}^r and B_{st}^r is a set of twenty-seven quantities C_{st}^r given by the relations

(66.1) $$C_{st}^r = A_{st}^r + B_{st}^r\,.$$

It is easily proved that the sum of two tensors is a tensor of the same order and type as the two tensors added.

There are two products of tensors, called the outer product and the inner product. The outer product of two tensors is defined to be the set of quantities obtained by multiplication of each component of the first tensor by each component of the second tensor. Thus, for example, the outer product of the tensors A_s^r and B_{st}^r is the set of 243 quantities C_{tuv}^{rs} given by the relations

(66.2) $$C_{tuv}^{rs} = A_t^r B_{uv}^s\,.$$

In writing this equation, we have been careful to keep each particular

162

suffix at the same level on both sides of the equation. When this convention if followed, it is easily proved that the outer product of two tensors has the tensor character indicated by the number and positions of its suffixes. Thus, for example, in Equation (66.2), C_{tuv}^{rs} is a mixed tensor of the fifth order, with two contravariant suffixes and three covariant suffixes.

We now introduce an operation called contraction. It consists in identifying a superscript and a subscript of a tensor. Thus, for example, if from the tensor A_{st}^{r} we form the set of quantities B_t defined by the relation

$$(66.3) \qquad\qquad B_t = A_{rt}^{r},$$

we are performing a contraction. We note that each component of B_t is equal to the sum of three components of A_{st}^{r}. It is easily proved that contraction of a tensor yields a tensor Thus, for example, B_t in Equation (66.3) is a covariant vector. It should be noted that we do not perform contractions by identifying suffixes at the same level, since such operations do not yield tensors, in general. For example, if A_s^{r} is a tensor, A_{ss}^{r} is not a tensor, in general.

We now define the inner product of two tensors. To obtain it, we form an outer product of the two tensors and then perform a contraction involving a superscript of one tensor and a subscript of the other tensor. Thus, for example, an inner product of two tensors A_s^{r} and B_{rs} is the set of quantities C_{st} given by the relation

$$C_{st} = A_s^{r} B_{rt}.$$

Of course the inner product of two tensors is not unique. Since outer multiplication and contraction of tensors both yield tensors, the inner multiplication of tensors also yields tensors.

67. *Some properties of tensors.* One of the most important properties of tensors is the following: *if a tensor equation is true for one coordinate system, it is true for all coordinate systems.* To prove this, let us consider, for example, a tensor having components A_{st}^{r} for a specific coordinate system z^{r}, and let us suppose that

(67.1) $$A^r_{st} = 0.$$

Let z'' be any other coordinate system, and let A''^r_{st} denote the components of this tensor for the coordinate system z''. We must show that

(67.2) $$A''^r_{st} = 0.$$

By the laws of tensor transformation we have

$$A'^r_{st} = \frac{\partial z'^r}{\partial z'^u} \frac{\partial z^v}{\partial z'^s} \frac{\partial z^w}{\partial z'^t} A^u_{vw} = 0,$$

by Equation (67.1). The proof is similar in the case of other tensor equations.

Now let A^r_{st} and B^r_{st} denote the components of two tensors for a specific coordinate system z_r, and let us suppose that

$$A^r_{st} = B^r_{st}.$$

Then, by the previous section, $A^r_{st} - B^r_{st}$ is a tensor which vanishes for the coordinate system z', and hence for any other coordinate system z'' we have

$$A''^r_{st} = B''^r_{st}.$$

Tensors also have the property of being *transitive*. To explain this property, we introduce three coordinate systems z', z'' and z'''. The property of being transitive is then the following: if a certain set of quantities is a tensor for the transformation from coordinates z' to z'', and is a tensor of the same order and type for the transformation from coordinates z'' to z''', then for the overall transformation from the coordinates z' to z''' the set of quantities is a tensor of this same order and type. It is easily proved that a tensor of any order or type is transitive.

68. *Tests for tensor character*. We shall now demonstrate by some examples a useful test for establishing the tensor character of a set of quantities.

Example 1. Let A^{rs} be a set of nine quantities such that $A^{rs}X_s$ is a contravariant vector, where X_r is an arbitrary covariant vector.

164

We shall now prove that A^{rs} is a contravariant tensor of the second order. Since $A^{rs}X_s$ is a contravariant vector, we have

(68.1) $$A'^{rs}X'_s = \frac{\partial z'^r}{\partial z^t} A^{tu}X_u.$$

But X_u is a covariant vector, so

(68.2) $$X_u = \frac{\partial z'^v}{\partial z^u} X'_v.$$

We now rewrite Equation (68.1), replacing the dummy suffix s on the left side by v, and substituting for X_u on the right side from (68.2), to obtain the relation

$$A'^{rv}X'_v = \frac{\partial z'^r}{\partial z^t} A^{tu} \frac{\partial z'^v}{\partial z^u} X'_v,$$

or

(68.3) $$\left(A'^{rv} - \frac{\partial z'^r}{\partial z^t} \frac{\partial z'^v}{\partial z^u} A^{tu}\right)X'_v = 0.$$

Since X_r is arbitrary, so is X'_v. Hence the expressions in the brackets in Equations (68.3) vanish, whence we conclude that A^{rs} is a contravariant tensor of the second order.

Example 2. Let A_{rs} be a set of quantities such that $A_{rs}X^rX^s$ is an invariant, where X^r is an arbitrary contravariant vector. We shall now prove that A_{rs} is a covariant tensor of the second order provided it is symmetric in all coordinate systems, that is, provided we have for every coordinate system relations of the form $A_{rs} = A_{sr}$. We proceed much as in Example 1. Since $A_{rs}X^rX^s$ is an invarint, we have

(68.3) $$A'_{rs}X'^rX'^s = A_{rs}X^rX^s.$$

Since X^r is a contravariant vector we can express the X^r and X^s in this equation in terms of X''^t, obtaining

$$A'_{rs}X'^rX'^s = A_{rs}\frac{\partial z^r}{\partial z'^t}\frac{\partial z^s}{\partial z'^u} X''^tX'^u.$$

We now replace the dummy suffixes r and s on the left side by t and u, whence we obtain the equation

(68.4) $$b_{tu}X''^tX'^u = 0,$$

165

where

(68.5)
$$b_{tu} = A'_{tu} - \frac{\partial z^r}{\partial z'^t} \frac{\partial z^s}{\partial z'^u} A_{rs}.$$

Equation (68.4) can be written in the form

(68.6)
$$b_{11} (X'^1)^2 + b_{22} (X'^2)^2 + b_{33} (X'^3)^2 + (b_{23} + b_{32}) X'^2 X'^3$$
$$+ (b_{31} + b_{13}) X'^3 X'^1 + (b_{12} + b_{21}) X'^1 X'^2 = 0.$$

Since X^r is arbitrary, so are the three quantities X''. Hence the coefficients in Equation (68.6) must vanish, which leads to the equation

(68.7)
$$b_{tu} + b_{ut} = 0.$$

From (68.5) we then have

$$A'_{tu} + A'_{ut} = \frac{\partial z^r}{\partial z'^t} \frac{\partial z^s}{\partial z'^u} A_{rs} + \frac{\partial z^r}{\partial z'^u} \frac{\partial z^s}{\partial z'^t} A_{rs}.$$

In the last term on the right side, we interchange the dummy suffixes r and s, obtaining the relation

(68.8)
$$A'_{tu} + A'_{ut} = \frac{\partial z^r}{\partial z'^t} \frac{\partial z^s}{\partial z'^u} (A_{rs} + A_{sr}).$$

Since we are given that $A_{rs} = A_{sr}$, $A'_{tu} = A'_{ut}$, then Equation (68.8) reduces to the form

$$A'_{tu} = \frac{\partial z^r}{\partial z'^t} \frac{\partial z^s}{\partial z'^u} A_{rs},$$

which establishes the tensor character of the set of quantities A_{rs}.

69. *The metric tensor.* Let x_r be the three rectangular cartesian coordinates. Then the distance ds between two adjacent points is given by the relation

(69.1)
$$(ds)^2 = (dx_1)^2 + (dx_2)^2 + (dx_3)^2 = dx_r dx_r.$$

If we introduce curvilinear coordinates z^r defined by relations $z^r = f^r(x_1, x_2, x_3)$ or $x_r = g_r(z^1, z^2, z^3)$, then

$$dx_r = \frac{\partial x_r}{\partial z^s} dz^s,$$

and substitution in Equation (69.1) yields an expression of the form

166

$$(69.2) \qquad (ds)^2 = b_{11}(dz^1)^2 + b_{22}(dz^2)^2 + b_{33}(dz^3)^2 + b_{23}dz^2dz^3$$
$$+ b_{31}dz^3dz^1 + b_{12}dz^1dz^2,$$

where b_{rs} are six functions of z^1, z^2, z^3. We now define nine quantities g_{rs} by the relations

$$b_{11} = g_{11}, \quad b_{22} = g_{22}, \quad b_{33} = g_{33},$$

$$(69.3)$$

$$\tfrac{1}{2}b_{23} = g_{23} = g_{32}, \quad \tfrac{1}{2}b_{31} = g_{31} = g_{13}, \quad \tfrac{1}{2}b_{12} = g_{12} = g_{21}.$$

We may now express (69.2) in the form

$$(ds)^2 = g_{11}(dz^1)^2 + g_{22}(dz^2)^2 + g_{33}(dz^3)^2 + (g_{23}+g_{32})\ dz^2dz^3$$
$$+ (g_{31}+g_{13})\ dz^3dz^1 + (g_{12}+g_{21})\ dz^1dz^2,$$

or

$$(69.4) \qquad\qquad\qquad (ds)^2 = g_{rs}dz^rdz^s.$$

Let us observe the right side of this equation. It is an invariant, since ds is an invariant; also dz^t is an arbitrary contravariant vector; also, from Equations (69.3) defining g_{rs}, we see that g_{rs} is symmetric. Hence, by the test for tensor character presented in Example 2 of § 68 we can conclude that g_{rs} *is a covariant tensor of the second order*. It is called the *metric tensor*.

70. *The conjugate tensor.* Let g denote the determinant whose elements are the components of the metric tensor. Then

$$(70.1) \qquad\qquad\qquad g = |g_{rs}|.$$

In the expanded form of this determinant, the coefficient of any one element g_{rs} is called the cofactor of g_{rs}. We denote it by the symbol $\triangle^{rs}$. We note in passing that the minor of g_{rs} is equal to

$$(-1)^{r+s}\ \triangle^{rs}.$$

We shall now prove that

$$(70.2) \qquad\qquad\qquad g_{rs}\ \triangle^{rt} = g\ \delta_s^t,$$

$$(70.3) \qquad\qquad\qquad g_{sr}\ \triangle^{tr} = g\ \delta_s^t.$$

Proof of Equation (70.2). Let us suppose that, when we write the determinant $|g_{rs}|$, the subscript r varies over the rows, while the subscript s varies over the columns. We now consider Equation (70.2) when $s = t = 1$. The right side is equal to g. The left side is

$$g_{r1}\Delta^{r1} = g_{11}\,\Delta^{11} + g_{21}\,\Delta^{21} + g_{31}\,\Delta^{31},$$

which is just the expansion of the determinant g by elements of the first column. The proof of Equation (70.2) when $r = s = 2$ and $r = s = 3$ is similar. Now let us consider Equation (70.2) when $s = 2$ and $t = 1$. The right side is equal to zero. The left side is

$$g_{r2}\,\Delta^{r1} = g_{12}\,\Delta^{11} + g_{22}\,\Delta^{21} + g_{32}\,\Delta^{31},$$

which is just the expansion of a determinant obtained from g by a replacement of the elements of the first column by those of the second column; in this determinant the first two columns are identical, and so the value of the determinant is zero. The proof of Equation (70.2) in all other cases when r and s differ is similar.

Proof of Equation (70.3). This proof is quite similar to the proof of (70.3), differing from it only in that the various expansions of determinants are by elements of rows rather than columns.

We now define the conjugate tensor g^{rs} by the relation

$$(70.4) \qquad\qquad g^{rs} = \frac{\Delta^{rs}}{g}.$$

Then Equations (70.2) and (70.3) yield the expressions

$$(70.5) \qquad\qquad g_{rs}g^{rt} = \delta_s^t,$$

$$(70.6) \qquad\qquad g_{sr}g^{tr} = \delta_s^t.$$

We shall now prove that g^{rs} is a contravariant tensor of the second order. Even though Equation (70.5) indicates that $g_{rs}g^{rt}$ is a mixed tensor of the second order, and g_{rs} had known tensor character, we cannot make any direct deductions from this as to the tensor character of g^{rt}, since we cannot assign g_{rs} arbitrarily without changing g^{rs}. Let X^r be an arbitrary contravariant vector. If we write

$$g_{sr}X^s = Y_r,$$

then Y_r is an arbitrary covariant vector. Hence we have

$$g^{pr}Y_r = g^{pr}g_{sr}X^s = \delta^p_s X^s = X^p,$$

and so $g^{pr}Y_r$ is a contravariant vector, Y_r being an arbitrary covariant vector. Thus, by the test for tensor character presented in Example 1 of § 68, we can conclude that g^{pr} is a contravariant tensor of the second order.

71. *Lowering and raising of suffixes.* In order to avoid ambiguity in certain steps to follow, we shall adopt the convention of placing but one suffix in any one vertical line. We shall use dots to denote vacant spaces in the rows of suffixes. Thus, for example, we might write $A^r_{.s}$ to denote a mixed tensor of the second order. Other examples are $B_{r.t}^{.s}$, $C_{..t}^{rs}$.

If we form inner products of any given tensor with the metric tensor or the conjugate tensor, we obtain a number of new tensors. It is customary to use the same principal letter in writing these tensors. For example, from a contravariant tensor A^{rs}, we can generate another second order tensor $A^r_{.s}$ as follows:

$$A^r_{.s} = g_{st} A^{rt}.$$

In appearance, this new tensor differs from the original one only in that the suffix in the second position has dropped from the upper level to the lower one. We say that we have lowered a suffix. Other tensors obtained from A^{rs} by this lowering process are the following:

$$A_r^{.s} = g_{rt}A^{ts}, \quad A_{rs} = g_{rt}g_{su} A^{tu}.$$

In an analogous fashion, the inner multiplication of a tensor by the conjugate tensor results in a raising of a suffix. Thus for example, from a given tensor B_{rs} we can generate other tensors by this raising process, as follows:

$$B^r_{.s} = g^{rt} B_{ts}, \quad B_r^{.s} = g^{st} B_{rt}, \quad B^{rs} = g^{rt}g^{su} B_{tu}.$$

If a certain subscript is raised, and is then lowered, it is easily seen that the final tensor is the same as the original one. The convention of writing no two suffixes in any one vertical line was introduced solely to ensure this property.

72. *Magnitude of a vector. Angle between two vectors.* Let A^r be a contravariant vector. Its magnitude A is defined by the relation

$$(72.1) \qquad A = \sqrt{g_{rs}A^rA^s}.$$

From this relation it readily follows that

$$(72.2) \qquad A = \sqrt{A_sA^s} = \sqrt{g^{rs}A_rA_s}.$$

A unit vector is one whose magnitude is equal to one. We note that, if the coordinates are rectangular cartesian, then $g_{rs} = \delta_{rs}$, and (72.1) then reduces to the familiar form

$$(72.3) \qquad A = \sqrt{(A^1)^2+(A^2)^2+(A^3)^2}.$$

Let X^r and Y^r be two unit vectors at a point. The angle θ between them is defined by the relation

$$(72.4) \qquad \cos\theta = g_{rs}X^rY^s.$$

If the coordinates are rectangular cartesian, this equation reduces to the familiar form

$$(72.5) \qquad \cos\theta = X^1Y^1+X^2Y^2+X^3Y^3.$$

73. *Geodesics.* The parametric equations of a curve C may be written in the form

$$(73.1) \qquad z^r = f^r(s),$$

the arc length s of the curve being used as the parameter. Because of Equation (62.5) we see that dz^r/ds are the components of a contravariant vector. We denote it by p^r, so

$$(73.2) \qquad p^r = \frac{dz^r}{ds}.$$

Further, by a definition of the previous section, the magnitude p of this vector is given by the relation

170

$$p^2 = g_{mn}p^mp^n = g_{mn}\frac{dz^m}{ds}\frac{dz^n}{ds} = \frac{(ds)^2}{(ds)^2} = 1.$$

Thus p^r is a unit vector. It is called the unit tangent vector of the curve C.

A geodesic may be defined as the curve of shortest length joining two points. In our three-dimensional space, the geodesics are straight lines. If we consider surfaces, which are of course two-dimensional spaces, the geodesics are not necessarily straight lines. For example, in the case of a spherical surface, the geodesics are the great circles, that is, those circles on the sphere whose centers coincide with the center of the sphere.

Let X and Y be two points. The distance L between them, measured along some curve, is given by the line integral

$$(73.3) \qquad L = \int_X^Y ds = \int_X^Y \sqrt{g_{mn}\,dz^m dz^n} = \int_X^Y \sqrt{w}\,ds,$$

where

$$(73.4 \qquad\qquad w = g_{mn}\,p^m\,p^n.$$

According to the Calculus of Variations, L is an extremum if the path joining X and Y is such that

$$(73.5) \qquad\qquad \frac{d}{ds}\left(\frac{\partial w}{\partial p^r}\right) - \frac{\partial w}{\partial z^r} = 0.$$

The actual derivation of these equations is beyond the scope of this book.

Now w is a function of p^r and g_{mn} which are known functions of z^s. Thus $w = w(z^1, z^2, z^3, p^1, p^2, p^3)$. The two partial derivatives in Equation (73.5) are computed as though the quantities p^r and z^s are independent. Thus

$$\begin{aligned}
\frac{\partial w}{\partial p^r} &= g_{mn}\,\delta_r^m p^n + g_{mn}p^m\,\delta_r^n \\
&= g_{rn}p^n + g_{mr}p^m = g_{rn}p^n + g_{rm}p^m \\
&= g_{rn}p^n + g_{rn}p^n = 2g_{rn}p^n,
\end{aligned}$$

171

$$\frac{d}{ds}\left(\frac{\partial w}{\partial p^r}\right) = 2g_{rn}\frac{dp^n}{ds} + 2\frac{\partial g_{rn}}{dz^m}p^mp^n,$$

$$\frac{\partial w}{\partial z^r} = \frac{\partial g_{mn}}{\partial z^r}p^mp^n.$$

Hence equations (73.5) become

(73.6) $$g_{rn}\frac{dp^n}{ds} + \frac{\partial g_{rn}}{\partial z^m}p^mp^n - \tfrac{1}{2}\frac{\partial g_{mn}}{\partial z^r}p^mp^n = 0.$$

But, by an interchange of the dummy suffixes m and n we have

(73.7) $$\frac{\partial g_{rn}}{\partial z^m}p^mp^n = \frac{\partial g_{rm}}{\partial z^n}p^np^n.$$

Substituting for one half of the middle term in Equation (73.6) from Equation (73.7), we then obtain the relation

(73.8) $$g_{rn}\frac{dp^n}{ds} + [mn, r]p^mp^n = 0,$$

where

(73.9) $$[mn, r] = \tfrac{1}{2}\left(\frac{\partial g_{rm}}{\partial z^n} + \frac{\partial g_{rn}}{\partial z^m} - \frac{\partial g_{mn}}{\partial z^r}\right).$$

The quantities $[mn,r]$ are the Christoffel symbols of the first kind. We note that

(73.10) $$[mn,r] = [nm,r].$$

If we multiply Equation (73.8) by g^{rt}, we obtain

(73.11) $$g^{rt}\,g_{rn}\frac{dp^n}{ds} + F^t_{mn}\,p^mp^n = 0,$$

where

(73.12) $$F^t_{mn} = g^{tr}[mn,r].$$

The quantities F^t_{mn} are the Christoffel symbols of the second kind. We note that

(73.13) $$F^t_{mn} = F^t_{nm}.$$

The first term in Equation (73.11) reduces to

$$\delta^t_n\frac{dp^n}{ds} = \frac{dp^t}{ds} = \frac{d^2z^t}{ds^2}.$$

Thus we may write the differential equations of a geodesic in the form

$$(73.14) \qquad \frac{d^2 z^t}{ds^2} + F^t_{mn} \frac{dz^m}{ds} \frac{dz^n}{ds} = 0.$$

74. *Transformation of the Christoffel symbols.* Let z' and z'' be two sets of curvilinear coordinates. In terms of these coordinates the equations of the geodesics are

$$(74.1) \qquad \frac{d^2 z^r}{ds^2} + F^r_{mn} \frac{dz^m}{ds} \frac{dz^n}{ds} = 0,$$

and

$$(74.2) \qquad \frac{d^2 z'^s}{ds^2} + F'^s_{pq} \frac{dz'^p}{ds} \frac{d' z^q}{ds} = 0.$$

But

$$\frac{dz^r}{ds} = \frac{\partial z^r}{\partial z'^p} \frac{dz'^p}{ds},$$

$$\frac{d^2 z^r}{ds^2} = \frac{\partial z^r}{\partial z'^p} \frac{d^2 z'^p}{ds^2} + \frac{\partial^2 z^r}{\partial z'^p \partial z'^q} \frac{dz'^p}{ds} \frac{dz'^q}{ds}.$$

Substitution in Equation (74.1) then yields

$$\frac{\partial z^r}{\partial z'^p} \frac{d^2 z'^p}{ds^2} + \left(\frac{\partial^2 z^r}{\partial z'^p \partial z'^q} \right.$$

$$+ \left. F^r_{mn} \frac{\partial z^m}{\partial z'^p} \frac{\partial z^n}{\partial z'^q} \right) \frac{dz'^p}{ds} \frac{dz'^q}{ds} = 0.$$

We now multiply this equation by $\partial z'^s / \partial z^r$, obtaining the relation

$$\frac{d^2 z'^s}{ds^2} + \left(\frac{\partial z'^s}{\partial z^r} \frac{\partial^2 z^r}{\partial z'^p \partial z'^q} + F^r_{mn} \frac{\partial z'^s}{\partial z^r} \frac{\partial z^m}{\partial z'^p} \frac{\partial z^n}{\partial z'^q} \right) \frac{dz'^p}{ds} \frac{dz'^q}{ds} = 0.$$

Comparison of this equation with (74.2) then yields

$$(74.3) \qquad F'^s_{pq} = \frac{\partial z'^s}{\partial z^r} \frac{\partial z^m}{\partial z'^p} \frac{\partial z^n}{\partial z'^q} F^r_{mn} + \frac{\partial z'^s}{\partial z^r} \frac{\partial^2 z^r}{\partial z'^p \partial z'^q}.$$

This is the equation of transformation of the Christoffel symbols of the second kind. We note that these symbols are not tensors, but would be if the last term on the right side were missing.

173

75. *Absolute differentiation*.   Let A_p be a covariant vector defined over a curve C with equations $z^r = f^r(u)$, u being a parameter on C. Then $A_p = A_p(u)$. The absolute derivative of A_p along C is

$$(75.1) \qquad \frac{\delta A_p}{\delta u} = \frac{dA_p}{du} - F^s_{pq} A_s \frac{dz^q}{du}.$$

We shall now prove that $\delta A_p / \delta u$ is a covariant vector.   We have

$$(75.2) \qquad \frac{\delta A'_p}{\delta u} = \frac{dA'_p}{du} - F'^s_{pq} A'_s \frac{dz'^q}{du}.$$

Now

$$(75.3) \qquad \frac{dA'_p}{du} = \frac{d}{du}\left(\frac{\partial z_r}{\partial z'^p} A_r \right)$$

$$= \frac{\partial z^r}{\partial z'^p} \frac{dA_r}{du} + \frac{\partial^2 z^r}{\partial z'^p \, \partial z'^q} \frac{dz'^q}{du} A_r.$$

Also, because of Equation (74.3), the second term on the right side of Equation (75.2) satisfies the relation

$$F'^s_{pq} A'_s \frac{dz'^q}{du} = \frac{\partial z'^s}{\partial z^r} \frac{\partial z^m}{\partial z'^p} \frac{\partial z^n}{\partial z'^q} F^r_{mn} A'_s \frac{dz'^q}{du}$$

$$+ \frac{\partial z'^s}{\partial z^r} \frac{\partial^2 z^r}{\partial z'^p \, \partial z'^q} A'_s \frac{dz'^q}{du}$$

$$(75.4) \qquad = \frac{\partial z^m}{\partial z'^p} F^r_{mn} A_r \frac{dz^n}{du} + \frac{\partial^2 z^r}{\partial z'^p \, \partial z'^q} A_r \frac{dz'^q}{du}.$$

Substitution from Equations (75.3) and (75.4) in (75.2) then yields

$$\frac{\delta A'_p}{\delta u} = \frac{\partial z^m}{\partial z'^p} \left(\frac{dA_m}{du} - F^r_{mn} A_r \frac{dz^n}{du} \right)$$

$$= \frac{\partial z^m}{\partial z'^p} \frac{\delta A_m}{\delta u}.$$

This completes the proof.

The covariant vector A_r is said to be propagated parallelly along C if

$$(75.5) \qquad \frac{\delta A_r}{\delta u} = 0.$$

174

In this case the components A_r satisfy first order differential equations, and can hence be assigned arbitrarily at any one point on C. When the space is three dimensional and the coordinates are rectangular cartesian, Equations (75.5) reduce to $dA_r/du = 0$, so that A_r are constant along C.

If A^r is a contravariant vector defined on a curve C, its absolute derivative along C is

$$(75.6) \qquad \frac{\delta A^r}{\delta u} = \frac{dA^r}{du} + F^r_{mn} A^m \frac{dz^n}{du}.$$

We could prove that $\delta A^r/\delta u$ is a contravariant vector in a manner similar to that used above for $\delta A_r/\delta u$. However, it is more convenient to proceed as follows. Let B_r be any vector propagated parallelly along C. Then

$$\frac{dB_r}{du} = F^m_{rn} B_m \frac{dz^n}{du}.$$

But $A^m B_m$ is an invariant, and hence so is

$$\begin{aligned}
\frac{d}{du}(A^r B_r) &= \frac{dA^r}{du} B_r + A^r \frac{dB_r}{du} \\
&= \frac{dA^r}{du} B_r + A^r F^m_{rn} B_m \frac{dz^n}{du} \\
&= \left(\frac{dA^m}{du} + F^m_{rn} A^r \frac{dz^n}{du} \right) B^m.
\end{aligned}$$

Since B_m can be assigned arbitrarily at any one point, the coefficient of B_m here, which is $\delta A^m/\delta u$, is then a contravariant vector.

The contravariant vector A^r is said to be propagated parallelly along C if

$$\frac{\delta A^r}{\delta u} = 0.$$

Let A^{mn}, $A^m_{.n}$ and A_{mn} be any second order tensors. Their absolute derivatives along a curve C are

$$(75.7) \qquad \frac{\delta A^{mn}}{\delta u} = \frac{dA^{mn}}{du} + F^m_{pq} A^{pn} \frac{dz^q}{du} + F^n_{pq} A^{mp} \frac{dz^q}{du},$$

(75.8) $$\frac{\delta A^{m}_{\cdot n}}{\delta u} = \frac{dA^{m}_{\cdot n}}{du} + F^{m}_{pq} A^{p}_{\cdot n} \frac{dz^{q}}{du} - F^{p}_{nq} A^{m}_{\cdot p} \frac{dz^{q}}{du},$$

(75.9) $$\frac{\delta A_{mn}}{\delta u} = \frac{dA_{mn}}{du} - F^{p}_{mq} A_{pn} \frac{dz^{q}}{du} - F^{p}_{nq} A_{mp} \frac{dz^{q}}{du}.$$

The patterns exhibited by the suffixes in these equations should be noted. Just as in the case of the absolute derivatives of the vectors, each of the above three absolute derivatives has the same tensor characters as the original tensor. We can prove this in a manner similar to that used above. For example in the case of $\delta A^{m}_{\cdot n}/\delta u$, we form the invariant $A^{m}_{\cdot n} X_{m} Y^{n}$, where X_{m} and Y^{n} are any vectors propagated parallelly along C.

The absolute derivative of any tensor of higher order is defined similarly, and has the tensor character of the original tensor. For example, we have

$$\frac{\delta A^{r}_{st}}{\delta u} = \frac{dA^{r}_{st}}{ds} + F^{r}_{pq} A^{p}_{\cdot st} \frac{dz^{q}}{dt} - F^{p}_{sq} A^{r}_{\cdot pt} \frac{dz^{q}}{dt} - F^{p}_{tq} A^{r}_{\cdot sp} \frac{dz^{q}}{dt}.$$

If A is an invariant, we make the definition

(75.10) $$\frac{\delta A}{\delta u} = \frac{dA}{du}.$$

It can be proved in a direct manner that

(75.11) $$\frac{\delta g_{mn}}{\delta u} = 0, \quad \frac{\delta}{\delta u} \delta^{m}_{n} = 0, \quad \frac{\delta g^{mn}}{\delta u} = 0.$$

The proofs of these are left as exercises for the reader (Problem 28 at the end of this chapter).

The rule for the absolute derivative of a product of two tensors is the same as for the ordinary derivative of a product. Thus, for example

(75.12) $$\frac{\delta}{\delta u} (A^{r}_{\cdot s} B_{t}) = \frac{\delta A^{r}_{\cdot s}}{\delta u} B_{t} + A^{r}_{\cdot s} \frac{\delta B_{t}}{\delta u}.$$

This can be proved in a direct manner which is somewhat lengthy. It can also be proved concisely by the use of special coordinates called Riemannian coordinates.

176

76. *Covariant derivatives.* Let A_r be a covariant vector defined over some region V in space, and let C be a curve in V. If u is a parameter on C, then

$$\frac{\delta A_p}{\delta u} = \frac{dA_p}{du} - F^s_{pq}\, A_s\, \frac{dz^q}{du} = \left(\frac{\partial A_p}{\partial z^q} - F^s_{pq}\, A_s \right) \frac{dz^q}{du}.$$

The expression on the right side is a covariant vector, and dz^q/du is a contravariant vector which may be assigned arbitrarily. Hence the coefficient of dz^q/du is a covariant tensor of the second order. We denote it by $A_{p|q}$ and call it the covariant derivative of A_p, so we have

$$(76.1) \qquad\qquad A_{p|q} = \frac{\partial A_p}{\partial z^q} - F^s_{pq}\, A_s.$$

In a similar manner we can arrive at the covariant derivatives of tensors of all orders and types. We have, for example,

$$(76.2) \qquad\qquad A^p_{\cdot|q} = \frac{\partial A^p}{\partial z^q} + F^p_{rq}\, A^r,$$

$$(76.3) \qquad A^p_{\cdot qr|s} = \frac{\partial}{\partial z^s}\, A^p_{\cdot qr} + F^p_{ts}\, A^t_{\cdot qr} - F^t_{qs}\, A^p_{\cdot tr} - F^t_{rs}\, A^p_{\cdot qt}.$$

These two covariant derivatives have the tensor character indicated by their suffixes.

Of course, we have from Equations (75.10) and (75.11),

$$(76.4) \qquad\qquad A_{|q} = \frac{\partial A}{\partial z^q},$$

$$(76.5) \qquad g_{mn|q} = 0, \quad \delta^m_{n|q} = 0, \quad g^{mn}_{\cdot\cdot|q} = 0.$$

Because of these relations, the operation of raising and lowering suffixes can be permuted with the operation of taking the covariant derivative. Thus, for example, we have

$$g_{rs}\, A^s_{\cdot|t} = (g_{rs}\, A^s)_{|t} = A_{r|t}.$$

It can be shown that covariant differentiation has the same product rule as ordinary differentiation.

77. *The curvature tensor.* Now

$$(77.1) \qquad\qquad A_{r|m} = \frac{\partial A_r}{\partial z^m} - F^p_{rm}\, A_p.$$

177

Since $A_{r|m}$ is a covariant tensor of the second order, then

(77.2) $\qquad A_{r|mn} = (A_{r|m})_{|n} = \dfrac{\partial}{\partial z^n}(A_{r|m}) - F_{rn}^q A_{q|m} - F_{mn}^q A_{r|q}.$

By use of Equations (77.1) and (77.2), we can arrive after a straightforward but lengthy calculation at the relation

(77.3) $\qquad\qquad A_{r|mn} - A_{r|nm} = R_{.rmn}^s A_s,$

where

(77.4) $\qquad R_{.rmn}^s = \dfrac{\partial}{\partial z^m}F_{rn}^s - \dfrac{\partial}{\partial z^n}F_{rm}^s + F_{rn}^p F_{pm}^s - F_{rm}^p F_{pn}^s.$

From Equation (77.3) it follows by the tests for tensor character that $R_{.rmn}^s$ has the tensor character indicated by its suffixes. It is called the mixed curvature tensor.

The covariant curvature tensor is

(77.5) $\qquad\qquad\qquad R_{rsmn} = g_{rt}R_{.smn}^t.$

This tensor plays an important role in mathematical physics. For any coordinate system in three dimensional space, this tensor vanishes, since it vanishes for rectangular cartesian coordinates. On the other hand, if for any one coordinate system on a surface this tensor vanishes, then there exists for this surface a curvilinear coordinate system such that

$$g_{rs} = 1 \quad \text{if} \quad r = s$$
$$\phantom{g_{rs}} = 0 \quad \text{if} \quad r = s.$$

78. *Cartesian tensors.* A tensor is said to be cartesian when the transformations involved are from one set of rectangular cartesian coordinates to another. In § 47 the special case of such transformations was considered when the transformation is a rotation about the origin. In the general case, the transformation is a rotation plus a translation. If we superimpose a translation on the rotation considered in § 47, the equations of transformation are

(78.1) $\qquad\qquad x'_s = a_{sr}x_r + a_s, \quad x_s = a_{rs}x'_r + a'_s,$

where a_{rs} are the constants considered in § 47 satisfying the orthogonality conditions

(78.2) $$a_{rt}\, a_{st} = \delta_{rs}, \quad a_{tr}\, a_{ts} = \delta_{rs}.$$

Also, a_s and a'_s are constants such that $a'_s = -\, a_{rs}\, a_r$. Just as in § 47, we have the relations

(78.3) $$\frac{\partial x'_s}{\partial x^r} = a_{sr} = \frac{\partial x_r}{\partial x'_s}.$$

The Jacobian I of the transformation is

$$I = \left| \frac{\partial x_r}{\partial x'_s} \right| = |a_{sr}|.$$

Hence by the rule for the multiplication of determinants, we have

(78.4) $$I^2 = |a_{sr}| \cdot |a_{mn}| = |a_{tr}\, a_{tn}| = |\delta_{rn}| = 1,$$

so $I = \pm 1$.

Theorem 1. For cartesian tensors there is no distinction between contravariant and covariant character.

Proof. Because of Equation (78.3) it follows that the laws of transformation of contravariant components and covariant components are the same. Further

$$g_{mn} = \delta_{mn}, \quad g = 1, \quad g^{mn} = \delta_{mn},$$

so that the raising or lowering of a suffix does not change the values of the components.

Because of this theorem, when dealing with cartesian tensors we do not need both superscripts and subscripts, so subscripts will be used exclusively.

In § 6 we introduced the orthogonal projections of a vector on rectangular cartesian coordinate axes, calling these projections the components of a vector. Throughout the rest of this book we shall refer to these as the physical components of a vector for rectangular cartesian coordinates.

Theorem 2. The physical components of a vector for rectangular cartesian coordinates constitute a cartesian tensor of the first order.

Proof. The nine constants a_{rs} in Equations (78.1) are the cosines of the angles between the axes of two rectangular cartesian coordinate systems. Hence, if **b** is a vector with physical components b_r and b'_r for these two systems of coordinates, then just as in § 47 we have

$$b_s' = a_{sr}\, b_r$$
$$= \frac{\partial x_s'}{\partial x_r}\, b_r.$$

This is the law of transformation of a cartesian tensor of the first order, so the proof is complete.

When the coordinates are rectangular cartesian, the Christoffel symbols vanish, and so the absolute derivative becomes the ordinary derivative and the covariant derivative becomes the partial derivative. For example, $\delta b_r/\delta u$ becomes db_r/du, and $b_{r|s}$ reduces to $\partial b_r/\partial x_s$. Thus we conclude that the directional derivatives of the physical components of a vector for rectangular cartesian coordinates constitute a cartesian tensor of the first order, and the nine partial derivatives of the physical components of a vector constitute a cartesian tensor of the second order.

79. *Oriented cartesian tensors.* Equation (78.4) shows that the Jacobian I of a transformation from one set of rectangular cartesian coordinates to another is equal to either plus one or minus one. The former case arises when the transformation is between coordinates whose axes have the same orientation (both right-handed or both left-handed), and the latter case arises when the orientations are opposite. A set of quantities is said to constitute an oriented cartesian tensor if it is a cartesian tensor when $I = 1$ and is not a cartesian tensor when $I = -1$.

In two-dimensional problems, suffixes have the range 1, 2. For such problems we introduce a *permutation symbol* c_{rs} defined as follows:

(79.1) $$c_{11} = c_{22} = 0, \quad c_{12} = 1, \quad c_{21} = -1.$$

In the three dimensional case, the *permutation symbol* c_{rst} has the definition

180

$$c_{rst} = 0 \text{ if two suffixes are equal}$$

(79.2)
$$= 1 \text{ if } (rst) \text{ is an even permutation of } (123)$$
$$= -1 \text{ if } (rst) \text{ is an odd permutation of } (123),$$

a single permutation of (rst) being an interchange of any two of r, s and t, and an even or odd permutation meaning an even or odd number of single permutations. Thus, for example,

$$c_{123} = c_{312} = 1, \quad c_{321} = -1, \quad c_{113} = 0.$$

In Theorem 4 of the next section we shall see that both of these permutation symbols are oriented cartesian tensors.

We can now express in tensor notation many of the formulas and equations of the earlier chapters of this book. Thus, the scalar and vector products of two vectors **a** and **b** are respectively

$$a_r b_r, \quad c_{rst} a_s b_t.$$

We note that this vector product is an oriented cartesian tensor. The scalar triple product $\mathbf{a} \cdot (\mathbf{b} \times \mathbf{c})$ is

$$c_{rst} a_r b_s c_t.$$

The expressions ∇f, $\nabla \cdot \mathbf{b}$ and $\nabla \times \mathbf{b}$ become

$$\frac{\partial f}{\partial x_r}, \quad \frac{\partial b_r}{\partial x_r}, \quad c_{rst} \frac{\partial b_t}{\partial x_s},$$

respectively. The differentiation formulas (48.1)–(48.11) may also be expressed in this notation; when this is done (Problem 36 at the end of this chapter), some of the formulas become trivial, and the truth of others follows at once from the identity

(79.3)
$$c_{rmn} c_{rst} = \delta_{ms} \delta_{nt} - \delta_{mt} \delta_{ns},$$

the proof of which is left to the reader (Problem 34 at the end of this chapter).

80. *Relative tensors.* The Jacobian I of a transformation from one set of curvilinear coordinates z^r to another set $z^{\prime r}$ is given by the relation

$$I = \left| \frac{\partial z^r}{\partial z^{\prime s}} \right|.$$

181

We now introduce the following definition: a set of quantities A^r is a relative contravariant vector of weight W, if it transforms according to the equation

$$A'^r = \frac{\partial z'^r}{\partial z^s} A^s I^W,$$

W being an integer. Relative contravariant tensors of higher order are defined analogously, as are relative covariant tensors, relative mixed tensors, and relative invariants. For example, $A^r_{.st}$ is a relative mixed tensor of weight W if it has the law of transformation

$$A'^r_{.st} = \frac{\partial z'^r}{\partial z^m} \frac{\partial z^n}{\partial z'^s} \frac{\partial z^p}{\partial z'^t} A^m_{.np} I^W.$$

A relative tensor of weight one is called a *tensor density*.

When it becomes necessary to distinguish between the kind of tensors considered heretofore and relative tensors we refer to the former type as absolute tensors. The following properties of relative tensors are easily established: (i) If a relative tensor vanishes in one coordinate system, it vanishes in all coordinate systems. (ii) The transformation of relative tensors is transitive. (iii) The sum of two relative tensors of the same order and weight is a relative tensor of this same weight. (iv) Both the inner and outer products of two relative tensors yield relative tensors whose weights are equal to the sum of the weights of the two tensors. (v) Contraction does not change the weight of a relative tensor.

Theorem 1. The determinant $g = |g_{rs}|$ is a relative tensor of weight two.

Proof. Because of the rule for the multiplication of determinants, we have

$$(80.1) \qquad g' = |g'_{rs}| = \left| \frac{\partial z^t}{\partial z'^r} \frac{\partial z^u}{\partial z'^s} g_{tu} \right|$$

$$= \left| \frac{\partial z^t}{\partial z'^r} \right| \cdot \left| \frac{\partial z^u}{\partial z'^s} \right| \cdot |g_{vw}|$$

$$= I^2 g,$$

which completes the proof.

Let us now introduce a covariant permutation symbol c_{rst} and a contravariant permutation symbol c^{rst}, both defined numerically just as in Equation (79.2).

Theorem 2. The covariant permutation symbol is a relative covariant tensor of weight −1.

Proof. We must show that

$$(80.2) \qquad c'_{rst} = \frac{\partial z^m}{\partial z'^r} \frac{\partial z^n}{\partial z'^s} \frac{\partial z^p}{\partial z'^t} c_{mnp} \, I^{-1}.$$

Let us denote the right side of this equation by $I^{-1} \Phi_{rst}$. Then

$$(80.3) \qquad \Phi_{123} = \frac{\partial z^m}{\partial z'^1} \frac{\partial z^n}{\partial z'^2} \frac{\partial z^p}{\partial z'^3} c_{mnp}.$$

But the expression on the right side here is just the expansion of the determinant I, so $\Phi_{123} = I$. In a similar manner, we see that each component of Φ_{rst} is equal to a determinant. If the suffixes on any one component are subjected to a single permutation, two rows or columns of the corresponding determinant are interchanged, and so the sign of the component is changed. We thus have the results: (i) $\Phi_{rst} = 0$ if two suffixes are equal, (ii) $\Phi_{rst} = I$ if (rst) is an even permutation of (123), (iii) $\Phi_{rst} = -I$ if (rst) is an odd permutation of (123). Thus we may write

$$\Phi_{rst} = I \, c'_{rst},$$

and so the proof is complete.

Theorem 3. The contravariant permutation symbol is a relative contravariant tensor of weight one.

Proof. This proof is quite similar to that of Theorem 2 above, and is hence omitted.

Theorem 4. The permutation symbols are oriented cartesian tensors.

Proof. When the coordinates are rectangular cartesian, we see from Equation (80.2) that c_{rst} is an absolute tensor only when $I = 1$. Hence it is an oriented cartesian tensor. The proof is similar for c^{rst}.

Because of Theorem 1 above, we may change the weight of a tensor by multiplying the tensor by a power of g. Let us assume that g is positive. We can then construct the *absolute permutation symbols* as follows:

$$(80.4) \qquad \eta_{rst} = \sqrt{g}\, c_{rst}, \qquad \eta^{rst} = \frac{c^{rst}}{\sqrt{g}}.$$

Because of Theorems 1, 3 and 4 above, we see that η_{rst} is an absolute covariant tensor, while η^{rst} is an absolute contravariant tensor.

Let $A^{\cdots}_{\cdots}$ denote a general relative tensor of weight W. Then $g^{\frac{1}{2}W} A^{\cdots}_{\cdots}$ is an absolute tensor. The covariant derivative of $A^{\cdots}_{\cdots}$ is defined to be

$$(80.5) \qquad A^{\cdots}_{\cdots\,|r} = g^{\frac{1}{2}W} \left(g^{-\frac{1}{2}W} A^{\cdots}_{\cdots} \right)_{|r}.$$

We note that $A^{\cdots}_{\cdots\,|r}$ has the same weight as $A^{\cdots}_{\cdots}$. The absolute derivatives of relative tensors are defined analogously. It can be proved that both the covariant and absolute derivatives of relative tensors obey the same product rule as do ordinary derivatives.

81. *Physical components of tensors.* In Theorem 2 of § 78 it was stated that the physical components b_r of a vector **b** for rectangular cartesian coordinates constitute a cartesian tensor of the first order. We shall now define the contravariant and covariant component of the vector **b** for curvilinear coordinates z^r. Denoting these components by B^r and B_r, we make the definitions

$$(81.1) \qquad B^r = \frac{\partial z^r}{\partial x_s}\, b_s, \qquad B_r = \frac{\partial x_s}{\partial z^r}\, b_s.$$

It is easily proved that $B_r = g_{rs} B^s$. The quantities B^r and B_r describe the vector **b** in a certain manner, and have the tensor character indicated by their suffixes.

In § 72 of the present chapter we defined abstractly the magnitude of a contravariant vector. According to this definition, the magnitude of B^r is

$$B = \sqrt{g_{rs}\, B^r B^s}.$$

Since the right side of this equation is an invariant, and since δ_{rs} is the metric tensor of rectangular cartesian coordinates, we have

$$B = \sqrt{\delta_{mn} b_m b_n} = \sqrt{b_m b_m} = b.$$

184

Thus the abstract definition of magnitude of a vector given in § 72 agrees with the definition of magnitude given in § 1. In a similar fashion, the abstract definition given in § 72 for the angle between two vectors agrees with our physical notions of angle.

Let us consider a unit vector having components λ^r for a curvilinear coordinate system z^r. The physical component of B^r in the direction of λ^r is defined to be the invariant

$$B_\lambda = g_{rs} B^r \lambda^s.$$

If θ is the angle between B^r and λ^r, then by § 72 we have

$$\cos \theta = g_{rs} \frac{B^r}{b} \lambda^s.$$

Thus $B_\lambda = b \cos \theta$, as might be expected.

The physical components of a vector B^r in the directions of the parametric lines of the coordinates z^r are called the physical components of B^r for the curvilinear coordinates z^r. Let us denote them by $B_{(r)}$. When the curvilinear coordinates are orthogonal, then as mentioned in § 49, we have

$$(81.2) \qquad (ds)^2 = (h_1 dz^1)^2 + (h_2 dz^2)^2 + (h_3 dz^3)^2.$$

If $\lambda_{(1)}^r$ is a unit vector in the direction of the parametric line of z^1, then

$$(81.3) \qquad \lambda_{(1)}^1 = \frac{dz^1}{ds} = \frac{1}{h_1}, \qquad \lambda_{(1)}^2 = \lambda_{(1)}^3 = 0.$$

By lowering suffixes, we also have

$$(81.4) \qquad \lambda_{(1)1} = h_1, \quad \lambda_{(1)2} = \lambda_{(1)3} = 0.$$

Thus

$$B_{(1)} = g_{rs} B^r \lambda_{(1)}^s = B^r \lambda_{(1)r} = B^1 h_1.$$

In a similar dashion we get $B_{(2)}$ and $B_{(3)}$, so that the physical components of the vector **b** relative to the curvilinear coordinate system z^r are

$$B^1 h_1, \quad B^2 h_2, \quad B^3 h_3.$$

By lowering suffixes, we may also express these physical components in the form

185

(81.5)
$$\frac{B_1}{h_1}, \quad \frac{B_2}{h_2}, \quad \frac{B_3}{h_3}.$$

There is a similar procedure for tensors of higher order. For example, let t_{rs} be a set of nine quantities which are the components of a cartesian tensor. The stress components of elasticity form such a set. We define the tensorial components of this tensor for curvilinear coordinates z' in terms of t_{rs} by the appropriate laws of tensor transformation. Let us denote these components by the symbols T^{rs}, $T^r_{.s}$, $T^{.s}_r$ and T_{rs}. The physical component of this tensor along the directions of two unit vectors λ' and μ' is defined to be $T^{rs}\lambda_r\mu_s$. The physical components of this tensor for the curvilinear coordinates z' are defined to be the physical components obtained by taking λ' and μ' in the directions of the parametric lines of the coordinates. Let us denote these nine physical components by $T_{(rs)}$. Then

$$T_{(rs)} = T^{mn}\lambda_{(r)m}\lambda_{(s)n},$$

$\lambda'_{(s)}$ being the three unit vectors in the directions of the parametric lines of the coordinates. When the coordinates z' are orthogonal, then $\lambda'_{(1)}$ is as given in Equation (81.3), and there are two similar relations for $\lambda'_{(2)}$ and $\lambda'_{(3)}$. We then get for $T_{(rs)}$ the expressions

$$h_1^2 T^{11}, \quad h_1 h_2 T^{12}, \quad h_1 h_3 T^{13},$$

(81.6)
$$h_2 h_1 T^{21}, \quad h_2^2 T^{22}, \quad h_2 h_3 T^{23},$$

$$h_3 h_1 T^{31}, \quad h_3 h_2 T^{32}, \quad h_3^2 T^{33}.$$

There are other expressions for $T_{(rs)}$ in terms of the covariant components T_{rs}, as well as in terms of mixed components.

Physical components of tensors of higher order can be defined analogously.

82. *Applications.* We shall consider now the problem of expressing the fundamental equations of mathematical physics in terms of quantities pertaining to curvilinear coordinates.

Dynamics of a particle. Let x_r be the rectangular cartesian coordinates of a particle at time t. Its velocity and acceleration are then

186

$$(82.1) \qquad v_r = \frac{dx_r}{dt}, \qquad a_r = \frac{dv_r}{dt}.$$

If f_r is the force acting on the particle and m is its mass, then by Newton's second law we have

$$(82.2) \qquad m\, a_r = f_r.$$

Let z^r be curvilinear coordinates of the particle, V^r, A^r and F^r being contravariant component of velocity, acceleration and force for this coordinate system. We have by definition

$$(82.3) \qquad V^r = \frac{\partial z^r}{\partial x_s}\, v_s = \frac{\partial z^r}{\partial x_s} \frac{dx_s}{dt} = \frac{dz^r}{dt}.$$

We could define A^r similarly in terms of a_r, but it is simpler to write

$$(82.4) \qquad A^r = \frac{\delta V^r}{\delta t} = \frac{dV^r}{dt} + F^r_{mn}\, V^m \frac{dz^n}{dt}.$$

We could define F^r in terms of f_r, but it is easier to use the relation

$$(82.5) \qquad dW = f_r dx_r = F_r dz^r,$$

where dW is the work done in an infinitesimal displacement with components dx_r and dz^r. By substitution in this equation for dx_r in terms of dz^s, we get F_r by equating coefficients of dz^r.

We now write the following expressions tentatively for the equations of motion in terms of curvilinear coordinates:

$$(82.6) \qquad m\, A^r = F^r.$$

To check these we note that they are tensor equations, and are true when the coordinates are rectangular cartesian since in this case they reduce to (82.2). Hence they are true for all coordinate systems.

The mathematical theory of elasticity. Using rectangular cartesian coordinates x_r, we have the displacement u_r, the strain components e_{rs} and the stress components T_{rs}. For the determination of these, we have the equations

$$(82.7) \qquad e_{rs} = \tfrac{1}{2}\left(\frac{\partial u_r}{\partial x_s} + \frac{\partial u_s}{\partial x_r}\right),$$

$$(82.8) \qquad \frac{\partial^2 e_{rm}}{\partial x_s \partial x_m} + \frac{\partial^2 e_{sm}}{\partial x_r \partial x_n} = \frac{\partial^2 e_{rm}}{\partial x_s \partial x_n} + \frac{\partial^2 e_{sn}}{\partial x_r \partial x_m},$$

187

$$(82.9) \qquad T_{rs} = k_{rsmn}\, e_{mn},$$

$$(82.10) \qquad \frac{\partial T_{rs}}{\partial x_s} + X_r = \rho\, \frac{\partial^2 u_r}{\partial t},$$

together with certain boundary conditions. In the above, k_{rsmn} are elastic constants, X_r is the external force per unit volume, ρ is the density and t is the time. If the body is at rest, the right side of (82.10) vanishes. If the body is isotropic, that is, it has no preferred directions elastically, Equation (82.9) reduces to

$$(82.11) \qquad T_{rs} = \lambda\theta\delta_{rs} + 2\mu e_{rs},$$

where λ and μ are elastic constants, and

$$(82.12) \qquad \theta = e_{rr} = \frac{\partial u_r}{\partial x_r}.$$

The quantities in the above equations are all cartesian tensors.

Let us now introduce curvilinear coordinates z^r. For this coordinate system the quantities corresponding to u_r, e_{rs}, t_{rs}, k_{rsmn} and X_r are defined by use of the laws of tensor transformation, as before. There is no difficulty if we use the same principal letter to designate these quantities for both coordinate systems. We now wish to convert Equations (82.7)–(82.12) to curvilinear coordinate. We write tentatively:

$$(82.13) \qquad e_{rs} = \tfrac{1}{2}(u_{r|s} + u_{s|r}),$$

$$(82.14) \qquad e_{rn|sm} + e_{sm|rn} = e_{rm|sn} + e_{sn|rm},$$

$$(82.15) \qquad T_{rs} = k_{rsmn} e^{mn},$$

$$(82.16) \qquad T^{rs}_{\cdot\cdot|s} + X^r = \rho\, \frac{\partial^2 u^r}{\partial t^2},$$

$$(82.17) \qquad T_{rs} = \lambda\theta g_{rs} + 2\mu e_{rs},$$

$$(82.18) \qquad \theta = e^r_{\cdot r} = u^r_{\cdot|r}.$$

These equations are tensor equations, and reduce to Equations (82.7)–(82.12) when the coordinates are rectangular cartesian coordinates. Hence Equations (82.13)–(82.18) are true for all coordinate systems, and are the desired equations. (Note that the term $\partial^2 u^r / \partial t^2$

188

in Equation (82.16) is a tensor; see Problem 45 at the end of this chapter.)

Hydrodynamics. In terms of rectangular cartesian coordinates, the fundamental equations for a perfect fluid are

$$(82.19) \qquad \frac{\partial \rho}{\partial t} + \frac{\partial}{\partial x_r}(\rho v_r) = 0,$$

$$(82.20) \qquad \frac{\partial v_r}{\partial t} + \frac{\partial v_r}{\partial x_s} v_s = X_r - \frac{1}{\rho} \frac{\partial p}{\partial x_r},$$

where ρ is the density, t is the time, v_r is the velocity, X_r is the external force per unit volume, and p is the pressure. We convert these to curvilinear coordinates in a manner analogous to that used for elasticity, obtaining the equations

$$(82.21) \qquad \frac{\partial \rho}{\partial t} + (\rho v^r)_{|r} = 0,$$

$$(82.22) \qquad \frac{\partial v^r}{\partial t} + v^r_{\cdot|s} v^s = X^r - \frac{1}{\rho} g^{rs} \frac{\partial p}{\partial z^s}.$$

In a similar manner, we can obtain in terms of curvilinear coordinates the fundamental equations of other branches of mathematical physics, such as electricity and magnetism, geometrical optics and heat conduction.

Problems

1. Prove that
$$(A_{rs} + A_{sr})z^r z^s = 2A_{rs} z^r z^s.$$

2. If $A = A_{rs}z^r z^s$, where A_{rs} are constants, prove that
$$\frac{\partial A}{\partial z^r} = (A_{rs} + A_{sr})z^s, \qquad \frac{\partial^2 A}{\partial z^r \, \partial z^s} = A_{rs} + A_{sr}.$$

3. Evaluate $\delta^r_r, \; \delta^r_s \delta^s_r, \; \delta^r_s \delta^s_t \delta^t_r$.

4. Prove that
$$\delta^r_s A_{rt} = A_{st}, \qquad \delta^r_s \delta^u_t A^t_r = A^u_s.$$

5. By differentiating Equation (62.7) with respect to z_u, prove that

189

$$\frac{\partial^2 z''^r}{\partial z^s \partial z^t} = -\frac{\partial z'^r}{\partial z^u}\frac{\partial z'^v}{\partial z^s}\frac{\partial z'^w}{\partial z^t}\frac{\partial^2 z^u}{\partial z'^v \partial z'^w}.$$

6. Let b_r denote the covariant components of a vector for rectangular cartesian coordinates. Find the covariant components of this vector for cylindrical coordinates r, θ, z in terms of b_r and r, θ, z.

7. If z^r are curvilinear coordinates and Φ is an invariant, do the expressions $\dfrac{\partial^2 \Phi}{\partial z^r \partial z^s}$ constitute a tensor?

8. Prove that the sum of two tensors A^r_{st} and B^r_{st} is a tensor.

9. Prove that the outer product of two tensors A^r_s and B^r_{st} is a tensor.

10. If A^r_{st} is a tensor, prove that A^r_{rt} is a tensor.

11. In three-dimensional space, how many different expressions are represented by $A^m_n B^n_{pq} C^{qr}_s$? When each such expression is written out explicitly, how many terms does it contain?

12. Prove that the tensor A^{rs}_t is transitive.

13. Let A^r_s be a set of nine quantities such that $A^r_s X^s_r$ is an invariant, where X^s_r is an arbitrary mixed tensor of the second order. Prove that A^r_s is a mixed tensor of the second order.

14. Let A_{rst} be a set of quantities such that $A_{rst} X^t$ is a covariant tensor of the second order, where X^t is an arbitrary contravariant vector. Establish the tensor character of A_{rst}.

15. If $g_{rs} = 0$ for $\neq r\ s$, prove that

$$g^{11} = \frac{1}{g_{11}}, \quad g^{22} = \frac{1}{g_{22}}, \quad g^{33} = \frac{1}{g_{33}},$$
$$g^{23} = g^{31} = g^{12} = 0.$$

16. Find the components of g^{rs} for cylindrical coordinates r, θ, z.

17. Find the components of g^{rs} for spherical polar coordinates r, θ, φ.

18. Let z^1 and z^2 be plane oblique cartesian coordinates whose axes have an angle β between them. For these coordinates find g_{rs} and g^{rs}.

19. Prove that $g_{rs} g^{rs} = 3$.

20. Prove that

$$\frac{\partial g}{\partial g_{mn}} = g\, g^{mn}, \quad \frac{\partial}{\partial z^r} \ln g = g^{mn} \frac{\partial g_{mn}}{\partial z^r}.$$

190

21. Using the results of Problem 20, prove that

$$F^s_{rs} = \frac{1}{\sqrt{g}} \frac{\partial}{\partial z^r} \sqrt{g}.$$

22. Prove that

$$[rm, n] + [rn, m] = \frac{\partial g_{mn}}{\partial z^r}, \quad [mn, r] = g_{rt} F^t_{mn}.$$

23. Compute the Christoffel symbols for cylindrical coordinates r, θ, z.

24. Compute the Christoffel symbols for spherical polar coordinates.

25. By using rectangular cartesian coordinates and Equations (73.14), show that the geodesics in three-dimensional space are straight lines.

26. Deduce the differential equations of the geodesics in three dimensional space, in terms of cylindrical coordinates.

27. Deduce the law of transformation of the Christoffel symbols of the first kind in the form

$$[pq, s]' = \frac{\partial z^m}{\partial z'^p} \frac{\partial z^n}{\partial z'^q} \frac{\partial z^r}{\partial z'^s} [mn, r] + g_{mn} \frac{\partial^2 z^m}{\partial z'^p \partial z'^q} \frac{\partial z^n}{\partial z'^s}.$$

28. Prove that

$$\frac{\delta g_{mn}}{\delta u} = 0, \quad \frac{\delta}{\delta u} \delta^m_n = 0, \quad \frac{\delta g^{mn}}{\delta u} = 0.$$

29. Prove that

$$\frac{\delta}{\delta u} (A^r_{.s} B_t) = \frac{\delta A^r_{.s}}{\delta u} B_t + A^r_{.s} \frac{\delta B_t}{\delta u}.$$

30. Using the results of Problem 21, prove that

$$A^r_{.|r} = \frac{1}{\sqrt{g}} \frac{\partial}{\partial z^r} (\sqrt{g} A^r).$$

31. If f is an invariant, use the results of Problem 30 to prove that the invariant $g^{rs} f_{|rs} = \nabla^2 f$, where ∇^2 is the Laplacian operator discussed in the second last paragraph of § 48; hence show that

$$\nabla^2 f = \frac{1}{\sqrt{g}} \frac{\partial}{\partial z^r} \left(\sqrt{g} \; g^{rs} \frac{\partial f}{\partial z^s} \right).$$

191

32. If f is an invariant, use the results of Problem 31 to evaluate $\nabla^2 f$ in terms of cylindrical coordinates r, θ, z, comparing the result with that in Problem 33 of Chapter IV.

33. Prove that the permutation symbols c_{rs} for two dimensional problems satisfies the identity

$$c_{rs}c_{rt} = \delta_{st}.$$

34. Prove Equation (79.3).

35. Express in cartesian tensor form the vector identity

$$\mathbf{a} \times (\mathbf{b} \times \mathbf{c}) = \mathbf{b}(\mathbf{a} \cdot \mathbf{c}) - \mathbf{c}(\mathbf{a} \cdot \mathbf{b}),$$

and prove it by use of Equation (79.3).

36. Express the eleven equations (48.1)–(48.11) in cartesian tensor form, and then verify them.

37. If A^{rs} is an absolute tensor, prove that the determinant $|A^{rs}|$ is a relative invariant of weight -2. Establish the tensor characters of $|A^r_{\cdot s}|$ and $|A_{rs}|$.

38. Prove that $c_{rst}c^{rst} = 6$, where c_{rst} and c^{rst} are the permutation symbols.

39. Prove that $\dfrac{\delta g}{\delta u} = 0$, where g is the determinant of the metric tensor.

40. If A^r is a relative tensor of weight one, prove that

$$A^r_{\cdot|r} = \frac{\partial A^r}{\partial z^r}.$$

41. If B_r are the covariant components of a vector for orthogonal curvilinear coordinates z^r whose metric form is given in Equation (81.2), show that the physical components of this vector for the curvilinear coordinates z^r are as given in (81.5).

42. If T^{rs} are the components of a tensor for the coordinates z^r in Problem 41, find the physical components of T^{rs} for these coordinates in terms of mixed components.

43. Let r, θ and φ be the spherical polar coordinates of a particle. Prove that for these coordinates the contravariant, covariant and physical components of velocity are respectively

$$\left(\frac{dr}{dt}, \frac{d\theta}{dt}, \frac{d\varphi}{dt}\right), \quad \left(\frac{dr}{dt}, r^2 \frac{d\theta}{dt}, r^2 \sin^2 \theta \frac{d\varphi}{dt}\right),$$

$$\left(\frac{dr}{dt}, r\frac{d\theta}{dt}, r \sin \theta \frac{d\varphi}{dt}\right).$$

44. Let r, θ and z be the cylindrical coordinates of a particle. Find the physical components of acceleration for these coordinates, in terms of r, θ, z and their time derivatives.

45. Let $A\colon\colon$ be a general tensor which is a function of a parameter t as well as of the coordinates. Prove that, for any transformation independent of t, the derivatives of $A\colon\colon$ with respect to t are tensors with the same tensor character as $A\colon\colon$.

46. In the theory of electricity and magnetism, Maxwell's equations for free space are

$$\nabla \times \mathbf{H} = k\frac{\partial \mathbf{E}}{\partial t}, \quad \nabla \times \mathbf{E} = -\mu\frac{\partial \mathbf{H}}{\partial t},$$

$$\nabla \cdot \mathbf{E} = 0, \qquad \nabla \cdot \mathbf{H} = 0,$$

where $\mathbf{H}$ is the magnetic intensity, k is the dielectric constant, $\mathbf{E}$ is the electric intensity, μ is the permeability and t is the time. Express these equations in tensor form for general curvilinear coordinates z^r.

GUIDE TO THE LITERATURE OF MATHEMATICS AND PHYSICS

Including Related Works on Engineering Science
by Nathan Brier Parke III

WHAT literature is available and WHERE can it be found? Fully revised —and for the first time available in a handy, inexpensive edition— this unique, up-to-date GUIDE TO THE LITERATURE OF MATHEMATICS AND PHYSICS puts a comprehensive library catalogue at your finger tips.

Over 5,000 entries (more than double the number in the first edition) are included under approximately 120 subject headings, further subdivided by an average of 6 subheadings. Every branch of physics, mathematics, and related engineering science is fully represented. For example, 28 books appear under the subhead, Projective Geometry; 78 under Geometrical Optics; 22 under Cosmic Rays; not including cross-references and general works.

All books were selected by a practicing mathematician and physicist on the basis of current significance, fullness of treatment, and the ability to give clues to further material on a subject. Citations are as full as possible—giving author, title, edition, publisher, place, data, number of volumes or number of pages. Many recently available Russian works are included. Discussions of the literature under each heading define the subject matter and provide numerous cross-references and suggestions for further investigation. The GUIDE also contains an extensive listing of bibliographical aids: abstracts, indexes, periodicals, reviews, bibliographies, directories, encyclopedias, documentary reproductions, guides, and library resources. A complete Author and Subject Index allows instantaneous location of the bibliographical data on any book.

This GUIDE will not only save you countless hours and help you locate much difficult-to-find material; it will often help you shape your problem and prevent a duplication of work by showing you exactly what has been done on a subject. With the literature grown to such huge proportions, the GUIDE TO THE LITERATURE OF MATHEMATICS AND PHYSICS has become an indispensable research assistant for every physicist, mathematician, engineer, scientist, student, and researcher. 2nd revised edition. Over 5,000 entries. 71-page introduction. Indexes.

pp. 5⅜ x 8.   Paperbound $

ADVANCED CALCULUS
by Edwin Bidwell Wilson

It is a tribute to Edwin Wilson's judgment and industry that, in spite of newer books in the field, most educators still regard "Advanced Calculus" as one of the most comprehensive and useful texts in its subject. It contains an immense amount of material, all of which is fundamental and well-presented. It can be used by students with the equivalent of only one year's study of calculus, and many chapters, such as the chapters on vector functions, ordinary differential equations, special functions, the calculus of variations, elliptic functions, and partial differential equations are excellent as introductions to these various branches of higher mathematics.

Throughout, a due level of mathematical rigor is maintained; but the book is also expressly designed as a text or reference for physicists, engineers, and others who need a sound working knowledge of advanced calculus. More than 1300 separately numbered exercises (hundreds of them are multiple-part exercises) are included in small groups placed in juxtaposition to the sections in the text to which they are related. This vast number of exercises is intended not only to facilitate the reader's ability to handle the mathematical tools of advanced calculus, but to give him abundant and varied practice in the use of these tools on the types of problems to which advanced calculus is applicable.

Contents. Introductory Review: Review of Fundamental Rules; Review of Fundamental Theory. Part I: Differential Calculus: Taylor's Formula and Allied Topics; Partial Differentiation—Explicit Functions; Partial Differentiation—Implicit Functions; Complex Numbers and Vectors. Part II: Differential Equations: General Introduction to Differential Equations; The Commoner Ordinary Differential Equations; Additional Types of Ordinary Equations; Differential Equations in More than Two Variables. Part III: Integral Calculus: On Simple Integrals; On Multiple Integrals; On Infinite Integrals; Special Functions Defined by Integrals; The Calculus of Variations. Part IV: Theory of Functions: Infinite Series; Special Infinite Developments; Functions of a Complex Variable; Elliptic Functions and Integrals; Functions of Real Variables.

Index. More than 1300 exercises. ix + 566pp. 5⅜ x 8.

Paperbound $

INTRODUCTION TO THE THEORY OF FOURIER'S SERIES AND INTEGRALS

by H. S. Carslaw

As an introductory explanation of the theory of Fourier's series, this clear detailed text has long been recognized as outstanding. This third revised edition contains tests for uniform convergence of series; a thorough treatment of term by term integration and the Second Theorem of Mean Value; enlarged sets of examples on Infinite Series and Integrals; and a section dealing with the Riemann-Lebesgue Theorem and its consequences. An appendix compares the Lebesgue Definite Integral with the classical Riemann Integral.

CONTENTS: Historical Introduction. Rational and irrational numbers. Infinite sequences and series. Functions of single variable. Limits and continuity. Definite integral. Theory of infinite series, whose terms are functions of a single variable. Definite integrals containing an arbitrary parameter. Fourier's series. Nature of convergence of Fourier's series and some properties of Fourier's constants. Approximation curves and Gibbs' phenomenon in Fourier's series. Fourier's integrals. Appendices: Practical harmonic analysis and periodogram analysis; Lebesque's theory of the definite integral.

"For the serious student of mathematical physics, anxious to have a firm grasp of Fourier theory as far as the Riemann integral will serve, Carslaw is still unsurpassed," MATHEMATICAL GAZETTE.

Bibliography. Index. 39 figures. 96 examples for students. xiii + 368pp. 5⅜ x 8.

S48 Paperbound **$2.00**

INTRODUCTION TO SYMBOLIC LOGIC
by Susanne Langer

This is probably the clearest book ever written on symbolic logic for the philosopher, general scientist and layman. It will be particularly appreciated by those who have been rebuffed by other introductory works because of insufficient mathematical training. No special knowledge of mathematics is required. Even if you have forgotten most of your high school algebra, you can learn to use mathematical logic by following the directions in this book. You start with the simplest symbols and conventions and end up with a remarkable grasp of the Boole-Schroeder and Russell-Whitehead systems.

"One of the clearest and simplest introductions to a subject which is very much alive. The style is easy, symbolism is introduced gradually, and the intelligent non-mathematician should have no difficulty in following the argument," MATHEMATICS GAZETTE.

Partial contents. Study of forms. Essentials of logical structure. Generalization. Classes. Principal relations among classes. Universe of classes. The deductive system of classes. The algebra of logic. Abstraction of interpretation. Calculus of propositions. The assumptions of PRINCIPIA MATHEMATICA by Whitehead and Russell. Logistics. Symbolic logic and the logic of the syllogism. Proofs of theorems.

Second edition, with many additions and revisions. New appendix on truth-value tables. 368pp. 5⅜ x 8.

S164 Paperbound **$1.75**

MATHEMATICAL TABLES
by Herbert B. Dwight

This set of tables is unique in English mathematical literature for its coverage, in one handy inexpensive volume, of almost every function of importance in applied mathematics, engineering, and the physical sceinces. Statisticians, electrical, civil, mechanical, nuclear engineers, aero- and hydronamicists, physicists, chemists, astrophysicists, meteorologists, biochemists, biomathematicians, geologists—everyone concerned with the evaluation of mathematical formulae used in various branches of science will find this book a gold-mine of information otherwise difficult or impossible to obtain in one volume.

In addition to extremely fine tables of the 3 trigonometric functions sine, cosine and tangent, and their inverse functions to thousandths of radians, natural and common logarithms, squares, cubes, square and cube roots, reciprocals, and the exponential functions e^x and e^{-x}, Mr Dwight hs included tables of the hyperbolic functions and the inverse hyperbolic functions, (a^2+b^2) exp. $1/2a$, complete elliptic integrals of the firist and second kind, the sine and cosine integrals, the exponential integrals $Ei(x)$ and $Ei(-x)$, binomial coefficients, factorials to 250, Gregory-Newton interpolation coefficients, Lagrangean interpolation coefficients (3, 5, and 7 tabulated values), surface zonal Harmonics and first derivatives, Bernoulli and Euler numbers and their logarithms to the base 10, the Gamma functions, the normal probability integral, the error function, over 60 pages of Bessel functions, roots of Bessel function equations, and the Riemann Zeta function. Each table is followed by a short note giving the formulae generally used in connection with the table, sources of more extensive tables, interpolation data, etc. Over half of the tables are provided with columns of differences to facilitate interpolation.

Revised and corrected new edition. Introduction. Index. viii + 231pp. 5 ⅜ x 8.

S445 Paperbound **$1.75**

VECTOR AND TENSOR ANALYSIS
by A. P. Wills

This is one of the clearest, most comprehensive expositions of vector and tensor analysis available in English. Assuming no prior training in vector or tensor methods, and only a good working knowledge of calculus, the author (late Professor of Mathematics at Columbia University) develops the elements of vector algebra and calculus, the theory of scalar and vector fields and potential functions, transformations of volume and surface integrals, linear vector functions and dyadics, co-ordinate systems, transformation theory, non-euclidean manifolds, and tensor theory. From the elementary notion of a vector as a magnitude plus a direction to such topics as dyads, absolute differentiation, the Lamé operator, the Riemann-Christoffel and Ricci-Einstein tensors, and the calculation of the Gaussian curvature of a surface, every topic is developed fully.

Pure and applied mathematicians, physicists, engineers, students and teachers of the physical sciences, will find this text an admirably clear introduction to a subject which has seen increasing application in such fields as electrical engineering, relativity theory, astrophysics, quantum mechanics, mechanics of continuous media, dynamics, study of magnetic phenomena, etc. 114 carefully selected problems at chapter endings illustrate and extend each concept and enable the student to develop facility in handling vector and tensor notation.

19 page historical introduction. 44 diagrams. 114 problems. Bibliography. Index. xxxii + 285pp. 5⅜ x 8.

S454 Paperbound **$0.00**

MECHANICS OF THE GYROSCOPE
The Dynamics of Rotation
by Richard F. Deimel

Applications of gyroscopic phenomena are stressed in this elementary general treatment of the dynamics of rotation. Discussion of the subject begins with fundamentals; and while an understanding of college physics is assumed, no knowledge of vectors is required.

Velocity on a moving curve — rotating axes — acceleration of a point — Euler's equations — the inertia ellipsoid — and other fundamental topics are covered in the first three chapters. Important theorems are introduced, along with numerous practical exercises. The remainder of the book takes up gyroscopic phenomena and apparatus such as artificial horizons — free gyros — tops — motion of discs — the damped gyro — and many others. A 46-page chapter is devoted to the gyro-compass, while a final chapter discusses stabilizers as applied to ships and monorail vehicles.

"Remarkably concise and generous treatment of gyroscopic theory," INDUSTRIAL LABORATORIES. "This exceptional treatment of a complex subject well merits a place for this text in the laboratory of the practicing engineer," PROFESSIONAL ENGINEERING NEWS.

Index. 75 figures. 135 exercises. ix + 192pp. 5⅜ x 8.

S66 Paperbound $1.60

HYDRODYNAMICS
by Sir Horace Lamb

This internationally famous work on dynamics of liquids and gases enjoys a unique position in technical literature. Most authors refer their readers to it rather than to other works for fundamental theorems, equations, and detailed methods of solution. It has never been superseded as an encyclopedic coverage of all aspects of classical hydodynamics.

This is an unabridged reproduction of the 6th enlarged revised edition. No change, however, has been made in the general plan and arrangement of the book, which decades of specialists and beginners have found most satisfactory. The clarity and lucidity of the original volume are still unimpaired.

Individual chapters cover: The Equations of Motion. Integration of the Equations in Special Cases. Irrotational Motion. Motion of a Liquid in Two Dimensions. Irrotational Motion of a Liquid: Problems in Three Dimensions. On the Motion of Solids through a Liquid: Dynamical Theory. Vortex Motion. Tidal Waves. Surface Waves. Waves of Expansion. Viscosity. Rotating Masses of Liquids.

"The leading treatise on classical hydrodynamics," MATHEMATICAL GAZETTE. "Difficult to find a writer on any mathematical topic with (equal) clearness and lucidity," PHILOSOPHICAL MAGAZINE.

Sixth enlarged edition. Index. Over 900 footnotes, mostly bibliographical. 119 figures. xv + 738pp. 6⅛ x 9¼.

S256 Paperbound **$2.95**

THEORY OF VIBRATIONS
by N. W. McLachlan

Based upon an enormously successful series of graduate lectures given at Brown University, this volume presents a concise analytical coverage of vibration theory. Individual chapters cover linear systems with one degree of freedom; forced vibrations of simple linear systems; non-linear systems with one degree of freedom; systems with more than one degree of freedom; vibration of flexible strings; longitudinal and torsional vibration of uniform bars and tubes; transverse vibration of bars and tubes; vibration of circular and annular membranes; transverse vibration of circular plate; sound waves of finite amplitude.

This book differs from other texts on the subject in its free use of the operational method for impulses, the use of Bessel functions, inclusion of modern versions of certain non-linear problems, use of frequency spectra, considerations of electro-mechanical system. The book is stimulating and clear throughout, with material presented in logical sequence and in order of analytical difficulty. An elementary knowledge of Bessel functions, Fourier's theorem, and operational calculus is desirable for the reader.

"Of special value to the practicing engineer for its application of operational calculus to vibration problems and for exact solutions of circular plates," JOURNAL, FRANKLIN INSTITUTE. "It is remarkable that the author should have lucidly presented such a vast amount of information in such a short space," APPLIED MECHANICS REVIEW.

Glossary of symbols. Bibliography. Index. 99 diagrams. vi + 154pp. 5⅜ x 8.

S190 Paperbound $1.35

HIGHER MATHEMATICS FOR STUDENTS
OF CHEMISTRY AND PHYSICS
by J. W. Mellor

This standard text, which has aided generations of physicists and chemists, has not been superseded as a practical introduction to higher mathematics. Practical in approach rather than abstract, it builds its many examples and exercises out of familiar material from actual laboratory situations, and presupposes only a working knowledge of elementary algebra and the meaning of a few trigonometric formulas.

Beginning with differential calculus, the author proceeds through analytical geometry, infinite series, probability, determinants, and similar topics. Treatment is full and detailed, and presentation is exceptionally clear.

CONTENTS: Differential calculus. Coordinate or analytical geometry. Functions with singular properties. Integral calculus. Infinite series and their uses. How to solve numerical equations. How to solve differential equations. Fourier's theorem. Probability and the theory of errors. Calculus of variations. Determinants. Appendix I: Collection of formulae and tables of reference. Appendix II: Reference tables.

"An excellent reference work. If the reader is not familiar with this book . . . it will repay him to examine it," CHEMICAL AND ENGINEERING NEWS. "Has served generations of physicists, chemists and astronomers . . . a classic," ASTROPHYSICAL JOURNAL. "An eminently readable and thoroughly practical treatise," NATURE (London).

Unabridged republication of 4th edition. Prefatory note by Donald G. Miller. Index. 800 problems. 189 figures. xxi + 641pp. 5⅜ x 8.
S193   Paperbound   **$2.00**

"Thorough and yet not overdetailed. Unreservedly recommended,"
NATURE (London).

FOUNDATIONS OF PHYSICS
by Robert Bruce Lindsay and Henry Margenau

A bridge between semipopular works for the general reader and
technical treatises written for specialists, this excellent work discusses the foundation ideas and background of modern physics. It
is not a text on theoretical physics, but a discussion of the methods
of physical description and construction of theory. It is especially
valuable for the physicist with a background in elementary calculus
who is interested in the ideas which give meaning to the data and
tools of modern physics.

Contents include a thorough discussion of theory, data, symbolism,
mathematical equations; space and time in physics, foundations of
mechanics; probability and its application; the statistical point of
view; the physics and continua; the electron theory and special relativity; the general theory of relativity; quantum mechanics; the
problem of causality.

Unabridged, newly corrected edition. New listing of recommended
readings. 35 illustrations. xi + 537pp. 5⅜ x 8. Paperbound **$2.45**

AN INTRODUCTION TO RELAXATION METHODS
by F. S. Shaw

This is an introduction to the use of relaxation methods for the solution of differential equations. Written by a coworker with Sir Richard Southwell, who developed relaxation methods, this useful volume describes almost all the manipulative resources that have been found of value. Treatment is mathematical rather than physical.

This book deals with the application of a general computational process which has been extended to include almost all branches of applied mechanics and physics. Approximate numerical methods are demonstrated, although high accuracy is obtainable by these methods without undue expenditure of time. Many examples are solved in detail to demonstrate relaxation methods.

Chapters cover: I. Linear algebraic simultaneous equations. II. Finite difference approximations. III. Linear ordinary differential equations. IV, V, VI, Second order linear partial differential equations. VII. Fourth order linear partial differential equations. VIII. Eigen value problems. IX. Free surface problems, integral equations, accuracy, non-dimensional treatment. 48 pages of tables for computing irregular star first and second derivatives, irregular star coefficients for second order equations, for fourth order equations. 10-page bibliography of works dealing with relaxation methods.

"Detailed and clear . . . an excellent introduction," PHYSIKALISCHE BLAETTER. "Useful . . . exposition is clear, simple . . . no previous acquaintance with numerical methods is assumed," SCIENCE PROGRESS. "Fills a gap," JOURNAL OF THE ROYAL AERONAUTICAL SOCIETY.

Index. Bibliography. 253 diagrams, 72 tables. 400pp. 5⅜ x 8.
S244 Paperbound **$2.45**

THE THEORY OF SOUND
by Lord Rayleigh

This major work of the Nobel Laureate and great 19th century physicist is a standard compendium of classical physics which has served generations of acousticians, physicists, mathematical physicists as the standard coverage of all aspects of sound, both experimental and theoretical.

It both sums up previous research and offers original contributions by Lord Rayleigh. It is not only a reference book; it is also a work of great practical utility for all persons concerned with scientific aspects of sound.

> "An outstanding treatise," Review of Scientific Instruments. "Astonishing how this treatise . . . still retains a place of preeminence in modern acoustical literature," Electronics Industry.

Partial contents. Volume I. Harmonic vibrations. Systems with 1 degree of freedom. Vibrating systems in general. Transverse vibrations of strings. Longitudinal, torsional vibration of bars. Vibration of membranes, plates. Curved shells, plates. Electrical vibrations. Volume II. Aerial vibrations. Vibrations in tubes. Reflection, refraction of plane waves. General equations. Theory of resonators. Laplace's functions and acoustics. Spherical sheets of air. Vibration of solid bodies. Facts and theories of audition.

Historical introduction by R. B. Lindsay, Brown University. Bibliography. 3 appendixes. 97 figures. Total of 1042pp.

2 volume set, paperbound, the set **$3.90**

SPINNING TOPS AND GYROSCOPIC MOTION
by John Perry

This well-known classic of science demonstrates, on an elementary level, the importance of studying the behavior of spinning tops and gyroscopes. It shows how a knowledge of this phenomenon can be of great value in scientific fields such as physics, geology and astronomy. Although it was written about 50 years ago, it has not been superseded as an accurate delightful exposition.

The author approaches his subject informally. Employing numerous helpful illustrations and avoiding difficult technical language, he first shows how quasi-rigidity is induced even in flexible and fluid bodies by rapid motions. Examples cited include a disc of thin paper, a ring of chain, a soft hat, smoke rings, and numerous others. The nature of this quasi-rigidity is then explained as a resistance to change of direction of the axis of spinning. Reference is made to projectiles fired from guns, a man on a bicycle, the earth pointing to the pole star, and other examples.

Particularly lucid explanations show why a gyrostat falls and why a top rises; the nature and effect on climatic conditions of the earth's precessional movement; and the effect of internal fluidity on rotating bodies. There is an absorbing discussion of light and magnetism and spinning tops, and an Appendix describing the practical uses to which gyroscopes have been put, such as in ships, compasses, and monorail transportation.

Appendixes. 62 figures. 128pp. 5⅜ x 8.

T416 Paperbound $1.00

INTRODUCTION TO SYMBOLIC LOGIC
by Susanne Langer

This is probably the clearest book ever written on symbolic logic for the philosopher, general scientist and layman. It will be particularly appreciated by those who have been rebuffed by other introductory works because of insufficient mathematical training. No special knowledge of mathematics is required. Even if you have forgotten most of your high school algebra, you can learn to use mathematical logic by following the directions in this book. You start with the simplest symbols and conventions and end up with a remarkable grasp of the Boole-Schroeder and Russell-Whitehead systems.

"One of the clearest and simplest introductions to a subject which is very much alive. The style is easy, symbolism is introduced gradually, and the intelligent non-mathematician should have no difficulty in following the argument," MATHEMATICS GAZETTE.

Partial contents. Study of forms. Essentials of logical structure. Generalization. Classes. Principal relations among classes. Universe of classes. The deductive system of classes. The algebra of logic. Abstraction of interpretation. Calculus of propositions. The assumptions of PRINCIPIA MATHEMATICA by Whitehead and Russell. Logistics. Symbolic logic and the logic of the syllogism. Proofs of theorems.

Second edition, with many additions and revisions. New appendix on truth-value tables. 368pp. 5⅜ x 8.

S164 Paperbound **$1.75**

TABLES OF FUNCTIONS WITH FORMULAE AND CURVES

by Eugene Jahnke and Fritz Emde

This new edition of Jahnke and Emde's TABLES OF FUNCTIONS contains corrections of 396 tabular errors detected in the preceding edition, and a supplementary bibliography of 43 titles. Also added is an exhaustive 76-page appendix of tables and formulae of elementary functions. This appendix does not appear in other American editions of Jahnke and Emde. Hundreds of reliefs of functions give a helpful picture of functional relations.

PARTIAL CONTENTS. 1. Sine, cosine, and logarithmic integral. 2. Factorial function. 3. Error integral and related functions. 4. Theta-functions. 5. Elliptic integrals. 6. Elliptic functions. 7. Legendre functions. 8. Bessel functions. 9. The Riemann-Zeta function. 10. Confluent hypergeometric functions. 11. Mathieu functions. 12. Some often used constants. 13. Table of powers. 14. Auxiliary tables for computation with complex numbers. 15. Cubic equations. 16. Elementary transcendental equations. 17. Exponential function. 18. Planck's radiation function. 19. Source functions of heat conduction. 20. The hyperbolic functions. 21. Circular and hyperbolic functions of a complex variable. Bibliography and supplementary bibliography. Indexed.

Fourth revised edition. 212 figures. 400pp. (Text in both English and German.) 5⅜ x 8.

"There is hardly any single volume which could be more useful to the general applied mathematician and the mathematical physicist than this remarkable work of Jahnke and Emde," BULLETIN, NATIONAL RESEARCH COUNCIL.

"Most physicists probably know the tables of Jahnke and Emde, in which many of us look for those out-of-the-way functions for which we know no other source," SCIENTIFIC COMPUTING SERVICE LTD.

S133 Paperbound **$2.00**

FOUNDATIONS OF POTENTIAL THEORY
by Oliver Dimon Kellogg

This book offers a systematic treatment of potential functions. It serves as an introduction for students with a knowledge of partial derivatives, multiple and line integrals; and provides a fundamental treatment that enables the reader to proceed at once to applications.

Numerous exercises illustrate or extend the theory. Proofs, given by rigorous methods, lead to numerous results not easily available elsewhere — proof for the general regular region of the divergence theorem on reduction of volume to surface integrals; treatment of fundamental existence theorems by means of integral equations, etc.

CONTENTS: Force of Gravity. Fields of Force. Potential. Divergence Theorem. Properties of Newtonian Potentials at Points of Free Space, at Points Occupied by Masses. Potentials as Solutions of Laplace's Equation; Electrostatics. Harmonic Functions. Electric Images; Green's Function. Sequences of Harmonic Functions. Fundamental Existence Theorems. Logarithmic Potential.

"Excellent value . . . best introduction in English," MATHEMATICAL GAZETTE. "Important for anyone in hydrodynamics, aerodynamics, physics, electrical engineering and pure mathematics," INDUSTRIAL BULLETIN.

Unaltered, unabridged reissue of 1st edition. Bibliography. Index. 30 figures. ix + 384pp. 5⅜ x 8.

S144 Paperbound **$1.98**

ORDINARY DIFFERENTIAL EQUATIONS
by E. L. Ince

The theory of ordinary differential equations in real and complex domains is here clearly explained and analyzed. The author covers not only classical theory, but also main developments of more recent times.

The pure mathematician will find valuable exhaustive sections on existence and nature of solutions, continuous transformation groups, the algebraic theory of linear differential systems, and the solution of differential equations by contour integration. The engineer and physicist will be interested in an especially fine treatment of the equations of Legendre, Bessel, and Mathieu; the transformations of Laplace and Mellin; the conditions for the oscillatory character of solutions of a differential equation; the relation between a linear differential system and an integral equation; the asymptotic development of characteristic numbers and functions; and many other topics.

PARTIAL CONTENTS: **Real Domain.** Elementary methods of integration. Existence and nature of solutions. Continuous transformation-groups. Linear differential equations — theory of, with constant coefficients, solutions of, algebraic theory of. Sturmian theory, its later developments. Boundary problems. **Complex Domain.** Existence theorems. Equations of first order. Non-linear equations of higher order. Solutions, systems, classifications of linear equations. Oscillation theorems.

"Will be welcomed by mathematicians, engineers, and others," MECH. ENGINEERING. " Highly recommended," ELECTRONICS INDUSTRIES. "Deserves the highest praise," BULLETIN, AM. MATH. SOC.

Historical appendix. Bibliography. Index. 18 figures. viii + 558pp. 5⅜ x 8.

S349 Paperbound $2.45

PARTIAL DIFFERENTIAL EQUATIONS OF MATHEMATICAL PHYSICS

by A. G. Webster

Still one of the most important treatises on partial differential equations in any language, this comprehensive work by one of America's greatest mathematical physicists covers the basic method, theory and application of partial differential equations. There are clear and full chapters on

Fourier series
integral equations
elliptic equations
spherical, cylindrical, ellipsoidal harmonics
Cauchy's method
boundary problems
method of Riemann-Volterra
and many other topics

This is a book complete in itself, developing fully the needed theory and application of every important field.

vibration
elasticity
potential theory
theory of sound
wave propagation
heat conduction
and others

Professor Webster's work is a keystone book in the library of every mature physicist, mathematical physicist, mathematician, and research engineer. It can also serve as an introduction and supplementary text for the student.

Edited by Samuel J. Plimpton. Second corrected edition. 97 illustrations. vii + 440pp. 5⅜ x 8.

S263 Paperbound **$1.98**

TRIGONOMETRY REFRESHER FOR TECHNICAL MEN

by A. Albert Klaf

This modern question and answer text covers most important aspects of plane and spherical trigonometry. 913 specially selected questions and detailed answers will help you to brush up your trigonometry or clear up difficulties on special areas.

The first portion of this book discusses plane trigonometry, covering angles, quadrants, trigonometrical functions, graphical representation, interpolation, equations, logarithms, solution of triangles, and the use of the slide rule, and similar topics. 188 pages then discuss the application of plane trigonometry to special problems in navigation, surveying, elasticity, architecture, and various fields of engineering. Small angles, periodic functions, vectors, polar coordinates, De Moivre's theorem are fully examined. The third section of the book then discusses spherical trigonometry and the solution of spherical triangles, with their application in terrestrial and astronomical problems.

Methods of saving time in numerical calculations, a simplification of the principal functions of an angle by use of a "shadow and perpendicular" concept, and much practical information on calculation aids make this an especially valuable book.

913 questions answered for you. 1738 problems to test your progress; answers to odd numbers. 494 figures. 24 pages of useful formulaes, functions. Index. x + 629pp. 5⅜ x 8. Paperbound **$1.95**

Catalogue of Dover
SCIENCE BOOKS

DIFFERENTIAL EQUATIONS
(ORDINARY AND PARTIAL DIFFERENTIAL)

INTRODUCTION TO THE DIFFERENTIAL EQUATIONS OF PHYSICS, L. Hopf. Especially valuable to engineer with no math beyond elementary calculus. Emphasizes intuitive rather than formal aspects of concepts. Partial contents: Law of causality, energy theorem, damped oscillations, coupling by friction, cylindrical and spherical coordinates, heat source, etc. 48 figures. 160pp. 5⅜ x 8.   S120 Paperbound **$1.25**

INTRODUCTION TO BESSEL FUNCTIONS, F. Bowman. Rigorous, provides all necessary material during development, includes practical applications. Bessel functions of zero order, of any real order, definite integrals, asymptotic expansion, circular membranes, Bessel's solution to Kepler's problem, much more. "Clear . . . useful not only to students of physics and engineering, but to mathematical students in general," Nature. 226 problems: Short tables of Bessel functions. 27 figures. x + 135pp. 5⅜ x 8.   S462 Paperbound **$1.35**

DIFFERENTIAL EQUATIONS, F. R. Moulton. Detailed, rigorous exposition of all non-elementary processes of solving ordinary differential equations. Chapters on practical problems; more advanced than problems usually given as illustrations. Includes analytic differential equations; variations of a parameter; integrals of differential equations; analytic implicit functions; problems of elliptic motion; sine-amplitude functions; deviation of formal bodies; Cauchy-Lipshitz process; linear differential equations with periodic coefficients; much more. Historical notes. 10 figures. 222 problems. xv + 395pp. 5⅜ x 8.   S451 Paperbound **$2.00**

PARTIAL DIFFERENTIAL EQUATIONS OF MATHEMATICAL PHYSICS, A. G. Webster. Valuable sections on elasticity, compression theory, potential theory, theory of sound, heat conduction, wave propagation, vibration theory. Contents include: deduction of differential equations, vibrations, normal functions, Fourier's series. Cauchy's method, boundary problems, method of Riemann-Volterra, spherical, cylindrical, ellipsoidal harmonics, applications, etc. 97 figures. vii + 440pp. 5⅜ x 8.   S263 Paperbound **$2.00**

ORDINARY DIFFERENTIAL EQUATIONS, E. L. Ince. A most compendious analysis in real and complex domains. Existence and nature of solutions, continuous transformation groups, solutions in an infinite form, definite integrals, algebraic theory. Sturmian theory, boundary problems, existence theorems, 1st order, higher order, etc. "Deserves highest praise, a notable addition to mathematical literature," Bulletin, Amer. Math. Soc. Historical appendix. 18 figures. viii + 558pp. 5⅜ x 8.   S349 Paperbound **$2.55**

ASYMPTOTIC EXPANSIONS, A. Erdélyi. Only modern work available in English; unabridged reproduction of monograph prepared for Office of Naval Research. Discusses various procedures for asymptotic evaluation of integrals containing a large parameter; solutions of ordinary linear differential equations. vi + 108pp. 5⅜ x 8.   S318 Paperbound **$1.35**

LECTURES ON CAUCHY'S PROBLEM, J. Hadamard. Based on lectures given at Columbia, Rome, discusses work of Riemann, Kirchhoff, Volterra, and author's own research on hyperbolic case in linear partial differential equations. Extends spherical cylindrical waves to apply to all (normal) hyperbolic equations. Partial contents: Cauchy's problem, fundamental formula, equations with odd number, with even number of independent variables; method of descent. 32 figures. iii + 316pp. 5⅜ x 8.   S105 Paperbound **$1.75**

NUMBER THEORY

INTRODUCTION TO THE THEORY OF NUMBERS, L. E. Dickson. Thorough, comprehensive, witn adequate coverage of classical literature. Not beyond beginners. Chapters on divisibility, congruences, quadratic residues and reciprocity, Diophantine equations, etc. Full treatment of binary quadratic forms without usual restriction to integral coefficients. Covers infinitude of primes, Fermat's theorem, Legendre's symbol, automorphs, Recent theorems of Thue, Siegal, much more. Much material not readily available elsewhere. 239 problems. 1 figure. viii + 183pp. 5⅜ x 8.   S342 Paperbound **$1.65**

ELEMENTS OF NUMBER THEORY, I. M. Vinogradov. Detailed 1st course for persons without advanced mathematics; 95% of this book can be understood by readers who have gone no farther than high school algebra. Partial contents: divisibility theory, important number theoretical functions, congruences, primitive roots and indices, etc. Solutions to problems, exercises. Tables of primes, indices, etc. Covers almost every essential formula in elementary number theory! "Welcome addition . . . reads smoothly," Bull. of the Amer. Math. Soc. 233 problems. 104 exercises. viii + 227pp. 5⅜ x 8.   S259 Paperbound **$1.60**

PROBABILITY THEORY AND INFORMATION THEORY

SELECTED PAPERS ON NOISE AND STOCHASTIC PROCESSES, edited by Prof. Nelson Wax, U. of Illinois. 6 basic papers for those whose work involves noise characteristics. Chandrasekhar, Uhlenback and Ornstein, Uhlenbeck and Ming, Rice, Doob. Included is Kac's Chauvenet-Prize winning "Random Walk." Extensive bibliography lists 200 articles, through 1953. 21 figures. 337pp. 6⅛ x 9¼.   S262 Paperbound **$2.35**

A PHILOSOPHICAL ESSAY ON PROBABILITIES, Marquis de Laplace. This famous essay explains without recourse to mathematics the principle of probability, and the application of probaiilty to games of chance, natural philosophy, astronomy, many other fields. Translated from 6th French edition by F. W. Truscott, F. L. Emory. Intro. by E. T. Bell. 204pp. 5⅜ x 8.   S166 Paperbound **$1.25**

MATHEMATICAL FOUNDATIONS OF INFORMATION THEORY, A. I. Khinchin. For mathematicians, statisticians, physicists, cyberneticists, communications engineers, a complete, exact introduction to relatively new field. Entropy as a measure of a finite scheme, applications to coding theory, study of sources, channels and codes, detailed proofs of both Shannon theorems for any ergodic source and any stationary channel with finite memory, much more. "Presents for the first time rigorous proofs of certain fundamental theorems . . . quite complete . . . amazing expository ability," American Math. Monthly. vii + 120pp. 5⅜ x 8.   S434 Paperbound **$1.35**

VECTOR AND TENSOR ANALYSIS AND MATRIX THEORY

VECTOR AND TENSOR ANALYSIS, G. E. Hay. One of clearest introductions to increasingly important subject. Start with simple definitions, finish with sure mastery of oriented Cartesian vectors, Christoffel symbols, solenoidal tensors. Complete breakdown of plane, solid, analytical, differential geometry. Separate chapters on application. All fundamental formulae listed, demonstrated. 195 problems. 66 figures. viii + 193pp. 5⅜ x 8.   S109 Paperbound **$1.75**

APPLICATIONS OF TENSOR ANALYSIS, A. J. McConnell. Excellent text for applying tensor methods to such familiar subjects as dynamics, electricity, elasticity, hydrodynamics. Explains fundamental ideas and notation of tensor theory, geometrical treatment of tensor algebra, theory of differentiation of tensors, and a wealth of practical material. "The variety of fields treated and the presence of extremely numerous examples make this volume worth much more than its low price," Alluminio. Formerly titled "Applications of the Absolute Differential Calculus." 43 illustrations. 685 problems. xii + 381pp.   S373 Paperbound **$1.85**

VECTOR AND TENSOR ANALYSIS, A. P. Wills. Covers entire field, from dyads to non-Euclidean manifolds (especially detailed), absolute differentiation, the Riemann-Christoffel and Ricci-Einstein tensors, calculation of Gaussian curvature of a surface. Illustrations from electrical engineering, relativity theory, astro-physics, quantum mechanics. Presupposes only working knowledge of calculus. Intended for physicists, engineers, mathematicians. 44 diagrams. 114 problems. xxxii + 285pp. 5⅜ x 8.   S454 Paperbound **$1.75**

DOVER SCIENCE BOOKS

PHYSICS, ENGINEERING

MECHANICS, DYNAMICS, THERMODYNAMICS, ELASTICITY

MATHEMATICAL ANALYSIS OF ELECTRICAL AND OPTICAL WAVE-MOTION, H. Bateman. By one of century's most distinguished mathematical physicists, a practical introduction to developments of Maxwell's electromagnetic theory which directly concern the solution of partial differential equation of wave motion. Methods of solving wave-equation, polar-cylindrical coordinates, diffraction, transformation of coordinates, homogeneous solutions, electromagnetic fields with moving singularities, etc. 168pp. 5⅜ x 8. S14 Paperbound **$1.60**

THERMODYNAMICS, Enrico Fermi. Unabridged reproduction of 1937 edition. Remarkable for clarity, organization; requires no knowledge of advanced math beyond calculus, only familiarity with fundamentals of thermometry, calorimetry. Partial Contents: Thermodynamic systems, 1st and 2nd laws, potentials; Entropy, phase rule; Reversible electric cells; Gaseous reactions: Van't Hoff reaction box, principle of LeChatelier; Thermodynamics of dilute solutions: osmotic, vapor pressures; boiling, freezing point; Entropy constant. 25 problems. 24 illustrations. x + 160pp. 5⅜ x 8. S361 Paperbound **$1.75**

FOUNDATIONS OF POTENTIAL THEORY, O. D. Kellogg. Based on courses given at Harvard, suitable for both advanced and beginning mathematicians, Proofs rigorous, much material here not generally available elsewhere. Partial contents: gravity, fields of force, divergence theorem, properties of Newtonian potentials at points of free space, potentials as solutions of LaPlace's equation, harmonic functions, electrostatics, electric images, logarithmic potential, etc. ix + 384pp. 5⅜ x 8. S144 Paperbound **$1.98**

DIALOGUES CONCERNING TWO NEW SCIENCES, Galileo Galilei. Classic of experimental science, mechanics, engineering, as enjoyable as it is important. Characterized by author as "superior to everything else of mine." Offers a lively exposition of dynamics, elasticity, sound, ballistics, strength of materials, scientific method. Translated by H. Grew, A. de Salvio. 126 diagrams. xxi + 288pp. 5⅜ x 8. S99 Paperbound **$1.65**

THEORETICAL MECHANICS; AN INTRODUCTION TO MATHEMATICAL PHYSICS, J. S. Ames, F. D. Murnaghan. A mathematically rigorous development for advanced students, with constant practical applications. Used in hundreds of advanced courses. Unusually thorough coverage of gyroscopic baryscopic material, detailed analyses of Corilis acceleration, applications of Lagrange's equations, motion of double pendulum, Hamilton-Jacobi partial differential equations, group velocity, dispersion, etc. Special relativity included. 159 problems. 44 figures. ix + 462pp. 5⅜ x 8. S461 Paperbound **$2.00**

STATICS AND THE DYNAMICS OF A PARTICLE, W. D. MacMillan. This is Part One of "Theoretical Mechanics." For over 3 decades a self-contained, extremely comprehensive advanced undergraduate text in mathematical physics, physics, astronomy, deeper foundations of engineering. Early sections require only a knowledge of geometry; later, a working knowledge of calculus. Hundreds of basic problems including projectiles to moon, harmonic motion, ballistics, transmission of power, stress and strain, elasticity, astronomical problems. 340 practice problems, many fully worked out examples. 200 figures. xvii + 430pp. 5⅜ x 8. S467 Paperbound **$2.00**

THE THEORY OF THE POTENTIAL, W. D. MacMillan. This is Part Two of "Theoretical Mechanics." Comprehensive, well-balanced presentation, serving both as introduction and reference with regard to specific problems, for physicists and mathematicians. Assumes no prior knowledge of integral relations, all math is developed as needed. Includes: Attraction of Finite Bodies; Newtonian Potential Function; Vector Fields, Green and Gauss Theorems; Two-layer Surfaces; Spherical Harmonics; etc. "The great number of particular cases . . . should make the book valuable to geo-physicists and others actively engaged in practical applications of the potential theory," Review of Scientific Instruments. xii + 469pp. 5⅜ x 8. S486 Paperbound **$2.25**

DYNAMICS OF A SYSTEM OF RIGID BODIES (Advanced Section), E. J. Routh. Revised 6th edition of a classic reference aid. Partial contents: moving axes, relative motion, oscillations about equilibrium, motion. Motion of a body under no forces, any forces. Nature of motion given by linear equations and conditions of stability. Free, forced vibrations, constants of integration, calculus of finite differences, variations, procession and mutation, motion of the moon, motion of string, chain, membranes. 64 figures. 498pp. 5⅜ x 8. S229 Paperbound **$2.35**

THE DYNAMICS OF PARTICLES AND OF RIGID, ELASTIC, AND FLUID BODIES: BEING LECTURES ON MATHEMATICAL PHYSICS, A. G. Webster. Reissuing of classic fills need for comprehensive work on dynamics. Covers wide range in unusually great depth, applying ordinary, partial differential equations. Partial contents: laws of motion, methods applicable to systems of all sorts; oscillation, resonance, cyclic systems; dynamics of rigid bodies; potential theory; stress and strain; gyrostatics; wave, vortex motion; kinematics of a point; Lagrange's equations; Hamilton's principle; vectors; deformable bodies; much more not easily found together in one volume. Unabridged reprinting of 2nd edition. 20 pages on differential equations, higher analysis. 203 illustrations. xi + 588pp. 5⅜ x 8. S522 Paperbound **$2.35**

PRINCIPLES OF MECHANICS, Heinrich Hertz. A classic of great interest in logic of science. Last work by great 19th century physicist, created new system of mechanics based upon space, time, mass; returns to axiomatic analysis, understanding of formal, structural aspects of science, taking into account logic, observation, a priori elements. Of great historical importance to Poincaré, Carnap, Einstein, Milne. 20 page introduction by R. S. Cohen, Wesleyan U., analyzes implications of Hertz's thought and logic of science. 13 page introduction by Helmholtz. xlii + 274pp. 5⅜ x 8.   S316 Clothbound **$3.50**
                                                                                S317 Paperbound **$1.75**

MATHEMATICAL FOUNDATIONS OF STATISTICAL MECHANICS, A. I. Khinchin. A thoroughly up-to-date introduction, offering a precise and mathematically rigorous formulation of the problems of statistical mechanics. Provides analytical tools to replace many commonly used cumbersome concepts and devices. Partial contents: Geometry, kinematics of phase space; ergodic problem; theory of probability; central limit theorem; ideal monatomic gas; foundation of thermodynamics; dispersion, distribution of sum functions; etc. "Excellent introduction . . . clear, concise, rigorous," Quarterly of Applied Mathematics. viii + 179pp. 5⅜ x 8.   S146 Clothbound **$2.95**
                                                                                S147 Paperbound **$1.35**

MECHANICS OF THE GYROSCOPE, THE DYNAMICS OF ROTATION, R. F. Deimel, Prof. of Mechanical Engineering, Stevens Inst. of Tech. Elementary, general treatment of dynamics of rotation, with special application of gyroscopic phenomena. No knowledge of vectors needed. Velocity of a moving curve, acceleration to a point, general equations of motion, gyroscopic horizon, free gyro, motion of discs, the damped gyro, 103 similar topics. Exercises. 75 figures. 208pp. 5⅜ x 8.   S66 Paperbound **$1.65**

MECHANICS VIA THE CALCULUS, P. W. Norris, W. S. Legge. Wide coverage, from linear motion to vector analysis; equations determining motion, linear methods, compounding of simple harmonic motions, Newton's laws of motion, Hooke's law, the simple pendulum, motion of a particle in 1 plane, centers of gravity, virtual work, friction, kinetic energy of rotating bodies, equilibrium of strings, hydrostatics, sheering stresses, elasticity, etc. Many worked-out examples. 550 problems. 3rd revised edition. xii + 367pp.   S207 Clothbound **$3.95**

A TREATISE ON THE MATHEMATICAL THEORY OF ELASTICITY, A. E. H. Love. An indispensable reference work for engineers, mathematicians, physicists, the most complete, authoritative treatment of classical elasticity in one volume. Proceeds from elementary notions of extension to types of strain, cubical dilatation, general theory of strains. Covers relation between mathematical theory of elasticity and technical mechanics; equilibrium of isotropic elastic solids and aelotropic solid bodies; nature of force transmission; Volterra's theory of dislocations; theory of elastic spheres in relation to tidal, rotational, gravitational effects on earth; general theory of bending; deformation of curved plates; buckling effects; much more. "The standard treatise on elasticity," American Math. Monthly. 4th revised edition. 76 figures. xviii + 643pp. 6⅛ x 9¼.   S174 Paperbound **$2.95**

NUCLEAR PHYSICS, QUANTUM THEORY, RELATIVITY

MESON PHYSICS, R. E. Marshak. Presents basic theory, and results of experiments with emphasis on theoretical significance. Phenomena involving mesons as virtual transitions avoided, eliminating some of least satisfactory predictions of meson theory. Includes production study of π mesons at nonrelativistic nucleon energies contracts between π and u, mesons, phenomena associated with nuclear interaction of π mesons, etc. Presents early evidence for new classes of particles, indicates theoretical difficulties created by discovery of heavy mesons and hyperons. viii + 378pp. 5⅜ x 8.   S500 Paperbound **$1.95**

THE FUNDAMENTAL PRINCIPLES OF QUANTUM MECHANICS, WITH ELEMENTARY APPLICATIONS, E. C. Kemble. Inductive presentation, for graduate student, specialists in other branches of physics. Apparatus necessary beyond differential equations and advanced calculus developed as needed. Though general exposition of principles, hundreds of individual problems fully treated. "Excellent book . . . of great value to every student . . . rigorous and detailed mathematical discussion . .. has succeeded in keeping his presentation clear and understandable," Dr. Linus Pauling, J. of American Chemical Society. Appendices: calculus of variations, math. notes, etc. 611pp. 5⅝ x 8⅜.   T472 Paperbound **$2.95**

WAVE PROPAGATION IN PERIODIC STRUCTURES, L. Brillouin. General method, application to different problems: pure physics—scattering of X-rays in crystals, thermal vibration in crystal lattices, electronic motion in metals; problems in electrical engineering. Partial contents: elastic waves along 1-dimensional lattices of point masses. Propagation of waves along 1-dimensional lattices. Energy flow. 2, 3 dimensional lattices. Mathieu's equation. Matrices and propagation of waves along an electric line. Continuous electric lines. 131 illustrations. xii + 253pp. 5⅜ x 8.   S34 Paperbound **$1.85**

4

THEORY OF ELECTRONS AND ITS APPLICATION TO THE PHENOMENA OF LIGHT AND RADIANT HEAT, H. Lorentz. Lectures delivered at Columbia Univ., by Nobel laureate. Unabridged, form historical coverage of theory of free electrons, motion, absorption of heat, Zeeman effect, optical phenomena in moving bodies, etc. 109 pages notes explain more advanced sections. 9 figures. 352pp. 5⅜ x 8. S173 Paperbound **$1.85**

SELECTED PAPERS ON QUANTUM ELECTRODYNAMICS, edited by J. Schwinger. Facsimiles of papers which established quantum electrodynamics; beginning to present position as part of larger theory. First book publication in any language of collected papers of Bethe, Bloch, Dirac, Dyson, Fermi, Feynman, Heisenberg, Kusch, Lamb, Oppenheimer, Pauli, Schwinger, Tomonaga, Weisskopf, Wigner, etc. 34 papers: 29 in English, 1 in French, 3 in German, 1 in Italian. Historical commentary by editor. xvii + 423pp. 6⅛ x 9¼. S444 Paperbound **$2.45**

FOUNDATIONS OF NUCLEAR PHYSICS, edited by R. T. Beyer. 13 of the most important papers on nuclear physics reproduced in facsimile in the original languages; the papers most often cited in footnotes, bibliographies. Anderson, Curie, Joliot, Chadwick, Fermi, Lawrence, Cockroft, Hahn, Yukawa. Unparalleled bibliography: 122 double columned pages, over 4,000 articles, books, classified. 57 figures. 288pp. 6⅛ x 9¼. S19 Paperbound **$1.75**

THE THEORY OF GROUPS AND QUANTUM MECHANICS, H. Weyl. Schroedinger's wave equation, de Broglie's waves of a particle, Jordon-Hoelder theorem, Lie's continuous groups of transformations, Pauli exclusion principle, quantization of Mawell-Dirac field equations, etc. Unitary geometry, quantum theory, groups, application of groups to quantum mechanics, symmetry permutation group, algebra of symmetric transformations, etc. 2nd revised edition. xxii + 422pp. 5⅜ x 8. S268 Clothbound **$4.50**
S269 Paperbound **$1.95**

PHYSICAL PRINCIPLES OF THE QUANTUM THEORY, Werner Heisenberg. Nobel laureate discusses quantum theory; his own work, Compton, Schroedinger, Wilson, Einstein, many others. For physicists, chemists, not specialists in quantum theory. Only elementary formulae considered in text; mathematical appendix for specialists. Profound without sacrificing clarity. Translated by C. Eckart, F. Hoyt. 18 figures. 192pp. 5⅜ x 8. S113 Paperbound **$1.25**

INVESTIGATIONS ON THE THEORY OF THE BROWNIAN MOVEMENT, Albert Einstein. Reprints from rare European journals, translated into English. 5 basic papers, including Elementary Theory of the Brownian Movement, written at request of Lorentz to provide a simple explanation. Translated by A. D. Cowper. Annotated, edited by R. Fürth. 33pp. of notes elucidate, give history of previous investigations. 62 footnotes. 124pp. 5⅜ x 8. S304 Paperbound **$1.25**

THE PRINCIPLE OF RELATIVITY, E. Einstein, H. Lorentz, M. Minkowski, H. Weyl. The 11 basic papers that founded the general and special theories of relativity, translated into English. 2 papers by Lorentz on the Michelson experiment, electromagnetic phenomena. Minkowski's "Space and Time," and Weyl's "Gravitation and Electricity." 7 epoch-making papers by Einstein: "Electromagnetics of Moving Bodies," "Influence of Gravitation in Propagation of Light," "Cosmological Considerations," "General Theory," 3 others. 7 diagrams. Special notes by A. Sommerfeld. 224pp. 5⅜ x 8. S93 Paperbound **$1.75**

STATISTICS

ELEMENTARY STATISTICS, WITH APPLICATIONS IN MEDICINE AND THE BIOLOGICAL SCIENCES, F. E. Croxton. Based primarily on biological sciences, but can be used by anyone desiring introduction to statistics. Assumes no prior acquaintance, requires only modest knowledge of math. All basic formulas carefully explained, illustrated; all necessary reference tables included. From basic terms and concepts, proceeds to frequency distribution, linear, non-linear, multiple correlation, etc. Contains concrete examples from medicine, biology. 101 charts. 57 tables. 14 appendices. lv + 376pp. 5⅜ x 8. S506 Paperbound **$1.95**

ANALYSIS AND DESIGN OF EXPERIMENTS, H. B. Mann. Offers method for grasping analysis of variance, variance design quickly. Partial contents: Chi-square distribution, analysis of variance distribution, matrices, quadratic forms, likelihood ration tests, test of linear hypotheses, power of analysis, Galois fields, non-orthogonal data, interblock estimates, etc. 15pp. of useful tables. x + 195pp. 5 x 7⅜. S180 Paperbound **$1.45**

FREQUENCY CURVES AND CORRELATION, W. P. Elderton. 4th revised edition of standard work on classical statistics. Practical, one of few books constantly referred to for clear presentation of basic material. Partial contents: Frequency Distributions; Pearsons Frequency Curves; Theoretical Distributions; Standard Errors; Correlation Ratio—Contingency; Corrections for Moments, Beta, Gamma Functions; etc. Key to terms, symbols. 25 examples. 40 tables. 16 figures. xi + 272pp. 5½ x 8½. Clothbound **$1.49**

HYDRODYNAMICS, ETC.

HYDRODYNAMICS, Horace Lamb. Standard reference work on dynamics of liquids and gases. Fundamental theorems, equations, methods, solutions, background for classical hydrodynamics. Chapters: Equations of Motion, Integration of Equations in Special Gases, Vortex Motion, Tidal Waves, Rotating Masses of Liquids, etc. Excellently planned, arranged, Clear, lucid presentation. 6th enlarged, revised edition. Over 900 footnotes, mostly bibliographical. 119 figures. xv + 738pp. 6⅛ x 9¼. S256 Paperbound **$2.95**

HYDRODYNAMICS, A STUDY OF LOGIC, FACT, AND SIMILITUDE, Garrett Birkhoff. A stimulating application of pure mathematics to an applied problem. Emphasis is on correlation of theory and deduction with experiment. Examines recently discovered paradoxes, theory of modelling and dimensional analysis, paradox and error in flows and free boundary theory. Classical theory of virtual mass derived from homogenous spaces; group theory applied to fluid mechanics. 20 figures, 3 plates. xiii + 186pp. 5⅜ x 8. S22 Paperbound **$1.85**

HYDRODYNAMICS, H. Dryden, F. Murhaghan, H. Bateman. Published by National Research Council, 1932. Complete coverage of classical hydrodynamics, encyclopedic in quality. Partial contents: physics of fluids, motion, turbulent flow, compressible fluids, motion in 1, 2, 3 dimensions; laminar motion, resistance of motion through viscous fluid, eddy viscosity, discharge of gases, flow past obstacles, etc. Over 2900-item bibliography. 23 figures. 634pp. 5⅜ x 8. S303 Paperbound **$2.75**

ACOUSTICS AND OPTICS

PRINCIPLES OF PHYSICAL OPTICS, Ernst Mach. Classical examination of propagation of light, color, polarization, etc. Historical, philosophical treatment unequalled for breadth and readability. Contents: Rectilinear propagation, reflection, refraction, dioptrics, composition of light, periodicity, theory of interference, polarization, mathematical representation of properties, etc. 279 illustrations. 10 portraits. 324pp. 5⅜ x 8. S170 Paperbound **$1.75**

THE THEORY OF SOUND, Lord Rayleigh. Written by Nobel laureate, classical methods here will cover most vibrating systems likely to be encountered in practice. Complete coverage of experimental, mathematical aspects. Partial contents: Harmonic motions, lateral vibrations of bars, curved plates or shells, applications of Laplace's functions to acoustical problems, fluid friction, etc. First low-priced edition of this great reference-study work. Historical introduction by R. B. Lindsay. 1040pp. 97 figures. 5⅜ x 8. S292, S293, Two volume set, paperbound **$4.00**

THEORY OF VIBRATIONS, N. W. McLachlan. Based on exceptionally successful graduate course, Brown University. Discusses linear systems having 1 degree of freedom, forced vibrations of simple linear systems, vibration of flexible strings, transverse vibrations of bars and tubes, of circular plate, sound waves of finite amplitude, etc. 99 diagrams. 160pp. 5⅜ x 8. S190 Paperbound **$1.35**

APPLIED OPTICS AND OPTICAL DESIGN, A. E. Conrady. Thorough systematic presentation of physical and mathematical aspects, limited mostly to "real optics." Stresses practical problem of maximum aberration permissible without affecting performance. Ordinary ray tracing methods; complete theory ray tracing methods, primary aberrations; enough higher aberration to design telescopes, low powered microscopes, photographic equipment. Covers fundamental equations, extra-axial image points, transverse chromatic aberration, angular magnification, similar topics. Tables of functions of N. Over 150 diagrams. x + 518pp. 5⅜ x 8⅝. S366 Paperbound **$2.98**

RAYLEIGH'S PRINCIPLE AND ITS APPLICATIONS TO ENGINEERING, G. Temple, W. Bickley. Rayleigh's principle developed to provide upper, lower estimates of true value of fundamental period of vibrating system, or condition of stability of elastic system. Examples, rigorous proofs. Partial contents: Energy method of discussing vibrations, stability. Perturbation theory, whirling of uniform shafts. Proof, accuracy, successive approximations, applications of Rayleigh's theory. Numerical, graphical methods. Ritz's method. 22 figures. ix + 156pp. 5⅜ x 8. S307 Paperbound **$1.50**

OPTICKS, Sir Isaac Newton. In its discussion of light, reflection, color, refraction, theories of wave and corpuscular theories of light, this work is packed with scores of insights and discoveries. In its precise and practical discussions of construction of optical apparatus, contemporary understanding of phenomena, it is truly fascinating to modern scientists. Foreword by Albert Einstein. Preface by I. B. Cohen, Harvard. 7 pages of portraits, facsimile pages, letters, etc. cxvi + 414pp. 5⅜ x 8. S205 Paperbound **$2.00**

DOVER SCIENCE BOOKS

ON THE SENSATIONS OF TONE, Hermann Helmholtz. Using acoustical physics, physiology, experiment, history of music, covers entire gamut of musical tone: relation of music science to acoustics, physical vs. physiological acoustics, vibration, resonance, tonality, progression of parts, etc. 33 appendixes on various aspects of sound, physics, acoustics, music, etc. Translated by A. J. Ellis. New introduction by H. Margenau, Yale. 68 figures. 43 musical passages analyzed. Over 100 tables. xix + 576pp. 6⅛ x 9¼.
S114 Clothbound **$4.95**

ELECTROMAGNETICS, ENGINEERING, TECHNOLOGY

INTRODUCTION TO RELAXATION METHODS, F. S. Shaw. Describes almost all manipulative resources of value in solution of differential equations. Treatment is mathematical rather than physical. Extends general computational process to include almost all branches of applied math and physics. Approximate numerical methods are demonstrated, although high accuracy is obtainable without undue expenditure of time. 48pp. of tables for computing irregular star first and second derivatives, irregular star coefficients for second order equations, for fourth order equations. "Useful. . . . exposition is clear, simple . . . no previous acquaintance with numerical methods is assumed," Science Progress. 253 diagrams. 72 tables. 400pp. 5⅜ x 8.
S244 Paperbound **$2.45**

THE ELECTROMAGNETIC FIELD, M. Mason, W. Weaver. Used constantly by graduate engineers. Vector methods exclusively; detailed treatment of electrostatics, expansion methods, with tables converting any quantity into absolute electromagnetic, absolute electrostatic, practical units. Discrete charges, ponderable bodies. Maxwell field equations, etc. 416pp. 5⅜ x 8.
S185 Paperbound **$2.00**

ELASTICITY, PLASTICITY AND STRUCTURE OF MATTER, R. Houwink. Standard treatise on rheological aspects of different technically important solids: crystals, resins, textiles, rubber, clay, etc. Investigates general laws for deformations; determines divergences. Covers general physical and mathematical aspects of plasticity, elasticity, viscosity. Detailed examination of deformations, internal structure of matter in relation to elastic, plastic behaviour, formation of solid matter from a fluid, etc. Treats glass, asphalt, balata, proteins, baker's dough, others. 2nd revised, enlarged edition. Extensive revised bibliography in over 500 footnotes. 214 figures. xvii + 368pp. 6 x 9¼.
S385 Paperbound **$2.45**

DESIGN AND USE OF INSTRUMENTS AND ACCURATE MECHANISM, T. N. Whitehead. For the instrument designer, engineer; how to combine necessary mathematical abstractions with independent observations of actual facts. Partial contents: instruments and their parts, theory of errors, systematic errors, probability, short period errors, erratic errors, design precision, kinematic, semikinematic design, stiffness, planning of an instrument, human factor, etc. 85 photos, diagrams. xii + 288pp. 5⅜ x 8.
S270 Paperbound **$1.95**

APPLIED HYDRO- AND AEROMECHANICS, L. Prandtl, O. G. Tietjens. Presents, for most part, methods valuable to engineers. Flow in pipes, boundary layers, airfoil theory, entry conditions, turbulent flow, boundary layer determining drag from pressure and velocity, etc. "Will be welcomed by all students of aerodynamics," Nature. Unabridged, unaltered. An Engineering Society Monograph, 1934. Index. 226 figures. 28 photographic plates illustrating flow patterns. xvi + 311pp. 5⅜ x 8.
S375 Paperbound **$1.85**

FUNDAMENTALS OF HYDRO- AND AEROMECHANICS, L. Prandtl, O. G. Tietjens. Standard work, based on Prandtl's lectures at Goettingen. Wherever possible hydrodynamics theory is referred to practical considerations in hydraulics, unifying theory and experience. Presentation extremely clear. Though primarily physical, proofs are rigorous and use vector analysis to a great extent. An Engineering Society Monograph, 1934. "Still recommended as an excellent introduction to this area," Physikalische Blätter. 186 figures. xvi + 270pp. 5⅜ x 8.
S374 Paperbound **$1.85**

GASEOUS CONDUCTORS: THEORY AND ENGINEERING APPLICATIONS, J. D. Cobine. Indispensable text, reference, to gaseous conduction phenomena, with engineering viewpoint prevailing throughout. Studies kinetic theory of gases, ionization, emission phenomena; gas breakdown, spark characteristics, glow, discharges; engineering applications in circuit interrupters, rectifiers, etc. Detailed treatment of high pressure arcs (Suits); low pressure arcs (Langmuir, Tonks). Much more. "Well organized, clear, straightforward," Tonks, Review of Scientific Instruments. 83 practice problems. Over 600 figures. 58 tables. xx + 606pp. 5⅜ x 8.
S442 Paperbound **$2.75**

PHOTOELASTICITY: PRINCIPLES AND METHODS, H. T. Jessop, F. C. Harris. For engineer, specific problems of stress analysis. Latest time-saving methods of checking calculations in 2-dimensional design problems, new techniques for stresses in 3 dimensions, lucid description of optical systems used in practical photoelectricity. Useful suggestions, hints based on on-the-job experience included. Partial contents: strain, stress-strain relations, circular disc under thrust along diameter, rectangular block with square hold under vertical thrust, simply supported rectangular beam under central concentrated load, etc. Theory held to minimum, no advanced mathematical training needed. 164 illustrations. viii + 184pp. 6⅛ x 9¼.
S137 Clothbound **$3.75**

MICROWAVE TRANSMISSION DESIGN DATA, T. Moreno. Originally classified, now rewritten, enlarged (14 new chapters) under auspices of Sperry Corp. Of immediate value or reference use to radio engineers, systems designers, applied physicists, etc. Ordinary transmission line theory; attenuation; parameters of coaxial lines; flexible cables; tuneable wave guide impedance transformers; effects of temperature, humidity; much more. "Packed with information . . . theoretical discussions are directly related to practical questions," U. of Royal Naval Scientific Service. Tables of dielectrics, flexible cable, etc. ix + 248pp. 5⅜ x 8.
S549 Paperbound **$1.50**

THE THEORY OF THE PROPERTIES OF METALS AND ALLOYS, H. F. Mott, H. Jones. Quantum methods develop mathematical models showing interrelationship of fundamental chemical phenomena wtih crystal structure, electrical, optical properties, etc. Examines electron motion in applied field, cohesion, heat capacity, refraction, noble metals, transition and di-valent metals, etc. "Exposition is as clear . . . mathematical treatment as simple and reliable as we have become used to expect of . . . Prof. Mott," Nature. 138 figures. xiii + 320pp. 5⅜ x 8.
S456 Paperbound **$1.85**

THE MEASUREMENT OF POWER SPECTRA FROM THE POINT OF VIEW OF COMMUNICATIONS ENGINEERING, R. B. Blackman, J. W. Tukey. Pathfinding work reprinted from "Bell System Technical Journal." Various ways of getting practically useful answers in power spectra measurement, using results from both transmission and statistical estimation theory. Treats: Autocovariance, Functions and Power Spectra, Distortion, Heterodyne Filtering, Smoothing, Decimation Procedures, Transversal Filtering, much more. Appendix reviews fundamental Fourier techniques. Index of notation. Glossary of terms. 24 figures. 12 tables. 192pp. 5⅝ x 8⅝.
S507 Paperbound **$1.85**

TREATISE ON ELECTRICITY AND MAGNETISM, James Clerk Maxwell. For more than 80 years a seemingly inexhaustible source of leads for physicists, mathematicians, engineers. Total of 1082pp. on such topics as Measurement of Quantities, Electrostatics, Elementary Mathematical Theory of Electricity, Electrical Work and Energy in a System of Conductors, General Theorems, Theory of Electrical Images, Electrolysis, Conduction, Polarization, Dielectrics, Resistance, much more. "The greatest mathematical physicist since Newton," Sir James Jeans. 3rd edition. 107 figures, 21 plates. 1082pp. 5⅜ x 8.
S186 Clothbound **$4.95**

CHEMISTRY AND PHYSICAL CHEMISTRY

THE PHASE RULE AND ITS APPLICATIONS, Alexander Findlay. Covers chemical phenomena of 1 to 4 multiple component systems, the "standard work on the subject" (Nature). Completely revised, brought up to date by A. N. Campbell, N. O. Smith. New material on binary, tertiary liquid equilibria, solid solutions in ternary systems, quinary systems of salts, water, etc. Completely revised to triangular coordinates in ternary systems, clarified graphic representation, solid models, etc. 9th revised edition. 236 figures. 505 footnotes, mostly bibliographic. xii + 449pp. 5⅜ x 8.
S92 Paperbound **$2.45**

DYNAMICAL THEORY OF GASES, James Jeans. Divided into mathematical, physical chapters for convenience of those not expert in mathematics. Discusses mathematical theory of gas in steady state, thermodynamics, Bolzmann, Maxwell, kinetic theory, quantum theory, exponentials, etc. "One of the classics of scientific writing . . . as lucid and comprehensive an exposition of the kinetic theory as has ever been written," J. of Institute of Engineers. 4th enlarged edition, with new material on quantum theory, quantum dynamics, etc. 28 figures. 444pp. 6⅛ x 9¼.
S136 Paperbound **$2.45**

POLAR MOLECULES, Pieter Debye. Nobel laureate offers complete guide to fundamental electrostatic field relations, polarizability, molecular structure. Partial contents: electric intensity, displacement, force, polarization by orientation, molar polarization, molar refraction, halogen-hydrides, polar liquids, ionic saturation, dielectric constant, etc. Special chapter considers quantum theory. "Clear and concise . . . coordination of experimental results with theory will be readily appreciated," Electronics Industries. 172pp. 5⅜ x 8.
S63 Clothbound **$3.50**
S64 Paperbound **$1.50**

ATOMIC SPECTRA AND ATOMIC STRUCTURE, G. Herzberg. Excellent general survey for chemists, physicists specializing in other fields. Partial contents: simplest line spectra, elements of atomic theory; multiple structure of line spectra, electron spin; building-up principle, periodic system of elements; finer details of atomic spectra; hyperfine structure of spectral lines; some experimental results and applications. 80 figures. 20 tables. xiii + 257pp. 5⅜ x 8.
S115 Paperbound **$1.95**

TREATISE ON THERMODYNAMICS, Max Planck. Classic based on his original papers. Brilliant concepts of Nobel laureate make no assumptions regarding nature of heat, rejects earlier approaches of Helmholtz, Maxwell, to offer uniform point of view for entire field. Seminal work by founder of quantum theory, deducing new physical, chemical laws. A standard text, an excellent introduction to field for students with knowledge of elementary chemistry, physics, calculus. 3rd English edition. xvi + 297pp. 5⅜ x 8.
S219 Paperbound **$1.75**

DOVER SCIENCE BOOKS

KINETIC THEORY OF LIQUIDS, J. Frenkel. Regards kinetic theory of liquids as generalization, extension of theory of solid bodies, covers all types of arrangements of solids; thermal displacements of atoms; interstitial atoms, ions; orientational, rotational motion of molecules; transition between states of matter. Mathematical theory developed close to physical subject matter. "Discussed in a simple yet deeply penetrating fashion . . . will serve as seeds for a great many basic and applied developments in chemistry," J. of the Amer. Chemical Soc. 216 bibliographical footnotes. 55 figures. xi + 485pp. 5⅜ x 8.

S94 Clothbound **$3.95**
S95 Paperbound **$2.45**

ASTRONOMY

OUT OF THE SKY, H. H. Nininger. Non-technical, comprehensive introduction to "meteoritics" —science concerned with arrival of matter from outer space. By one of world's experts on meteorites, this book defines meteors and meteorites; studies fireball clusters and processions, meteorite composition, size, distribution, showers, explosions, origins, much more. viii + 336pp. 5⅜ x 8.

T519 Paperbound **$1.85**

AN INTRODUCTION TO THE STUDY OF STELLAR STRUCTURE, S. Chandrasekhar. Outstanding treatise on stellar dynamics by one of greatest astro-physicists. Examines relationship between loss of energy, mass, and radius of stars in steady state. Discusses thermodynamic laws from Caratheodory's axiomatic standpoint; adiabatic, polytropic laws; work of Ritter, Emden, Kelvin, etc.; Stroemgren envelopes as starter for theory of gaseous stars; Gibbs statistical mechanics (quantum); degenerate stellar configuration, theory of white dwarfs; etc. "Highest level of scientific merit," Bulletin. Amer. Math. Soc. 33 figures. 509pp. 5⅜ x 8.

S413 Paperbound **$2.75**

LES MÉTHODES NOVELLES DE LA MÉCANIQUE CÉLESTE, H. Poincaré. Complete French text of one of Poincaré's most important works. Revolutionized celestial mechanics: first use of integral invariants, first major application of linear differential equations, study of periodic orbits, lunar motion and Jupiter's satellites, three body problem, and many other important topics. "Started a new era . . . so extremely modern that even today few have mastered his weapons," E. T. Bell. 3 volumes. Total 1282pp. 6⅛ x 9¼.

Vol. 1 S401 Paperbound **$2.75**
Vol. 2 S402 Paperbound **$2.75**
Vol. 3 S403 Paperbound **$2.75**
The set **$7.50**

THE REALM OF THE NEBULAE, E. Hubble. One of the great astronomers of our time presents his concept of "island universes," and describes its effect on astronomy. Covers velocity-distance relation; classification, nature, distances, general field of nebulae; cosmological theories; nebulae in the neighborhood of the Milky way; etc. 39 photos, including velocity-distance relations shown by spectrum comparison. "One of the most progressive lines of astronomical research," The Times, London. New Introduction by A. Sandage. 55 illustrations. xxiv + 201pp. 5⅜ x 8.

S455 Paperbound **$1.50**

HOW TO MAKE A TELESCOPE, Jean Texereau. Design, build an f/6 or f/8 Newtonian type reflecting telescope, with altazimuth Couder mounting, suitable for planetary, lunar, and stellar observation. Covers every operation step-by-step, every piece of equipment. Discusses basic principles of geometric and physical optics (unnecessary to construction), comparative merits of reflectors, refractors. A thorough discussion of eyepieces, finders, grinding, installation, testing, etc. 241 figures, 38 photos, show almost every operation and tool. Potential errors are anticipated. Foreword by A. Couder. Sources of supply. xiii + 191pp. 6¼ x 10.

T464 Clothbound **$3.50**

BIOLOGICAL SCIENCES

THE BIOLOGY OF THE AMPHIBIA, G. K. Noble, Late Curator of Herpetology at Am. Mus. of Nat. Hist. Probably most used text on amphibia, most comprehensive, clear, detailed. 19 chapters, 85 page supplement: development; heredity; life history; speciation; adaptation; sex, integument, respiratory, circulatory, digestive, muscular, nervous systems; instinct, intelligence, habits, economic value classification, environment relationships, etc. "Nothing comparable to it," C. H. Pope, curator of Amphibia, Chicago Mus. of Nat. Hist. 1047 item bibliography. 174 illustrations. 600pp. 5⅜ x 8.

S206 Paperbound **$2.98**

THE ORIGIN OF LIFE, A. I. Oparin. A classic of biology. This is the first modern statement of theory of gradual evolution of life from nitrocarbon compounds. A brand-new evaluation of Oparin's theory in light of later research, by Dr. S. Margulis, University of Nebraska. xxv + 270pp. 5⅜ x 8.

S213 Paperbound **$1.75**

THE BIOLOGY OF THE LABORATORY MOUSE, edited by G. D. Snell. Prepared in 1941 by staff of Roscoe B. Jackson Memorial Laboratory, still the standard treatise on the mouse, assembling enormous amount of material for which otherwise you spend hours of research. Embryology, reproduction, histology, spontaneous neoplasms, gene and chromosomes mutations, genetics of spontaneous tumor formations, of tumor transplantation, endocrine secretion and tumor formation, milk influence and tumor formation, inbred, hybrid animals, parasites, infectious diseases, care and recording. "A wealth of information of vital concern. . . . recommended to all who could use a book on such a subject," Nature. Classified bibliography of 1122 items. 172 figures, including 128 photos. ix + 497pp. 6⅛ x 9¼.
S248 Clothbound **$6.00**

THE TRAVELS OF WILLIAM BARTRAM, edited by Mark Van Doren. Famous source-book of American anthropology, natural history, geography, is record kept by Bartram in 1770's on travels through wilderness of Florida, Georgia, Carolinas. Containing accurate, beautiful descriptions of Indians, settlers, fauna, flora, it is one of finest pieces of Americana ever written. 13 original illustrations. 448pp. 5⅜ x 8.
T13 Paperbound **$2.00**

BEHAVIOUR AND SOCIAL LIFE OF THE HONEYBEE, Ronald Ribbands. Outstanding scientific study; a compendium of practically everything known of social life of honeybee. Stresses behaviour of individual bees in field, hive. Extends von Frisch's experiments on communication among bees. Covers perception of temperature, gravity, distance, vibration; sound production; glands; structural differences; wax production; temperature regulation; recognition, communication; drifting, mating behaviour, other highly interesting topics. "This valuable work is sure of a cordial reception by laymen, beekeepers and scientists," Prof. Karl von Frisch, Brit. J. of Animal Behaviour. Bibliography of 690 references. 127 diagrams, graphs, sections of bee anatomy, fine photographs. 352pp.
S410 Clothbound **$4.50**

ELEMENTS OF MATHEMATICAL BIOLOGY, A. J. Lotka. Pioneer classic, 1st major attempt to apply modern mathematical techniques on large scale to phenomena of biology, biochemistry, psychology, ecology, similar life sciences. Partial contents: Statistical meaning of irreversibility; Evolution as redistribution; Equations of kinetics of evolving systems; Chemical, inter-species equilibrium; parameters of state; Energy transformers of nature, etc. Can be read with profit by even those having no advanced math; unsurpassed as study-reference. Formerly titled "Elements of Physical Biology." 72 figures. xxx + 460pp. 5⅜ x 8.
S346 Paperbound **$2.45**

TREES OF THE EASTERN AND CENTRAL UNITED STATES AND CANADA, W. M. Harlow. Serious middle-level text covering more than 140 native trees, important escapes, with information on general appearance, growth habit, leaf forms, flowers, fruit, bark, commercial use, distribution, habitat, woodlore, etc. Keys within text enable you to locate various species easily, to know which have edible fruit, much more useful, interesting information. "Well illustrated to make identification very easy," Standard Cat. for Public Libraries. Over 600 photographs, figures. xiii + 288pp. 5⅝ x 6½.
T395 Paperbound **$1.35**

FRUIT KEY AND TWIG KEY TO TREES AND SHRUBS (Fruit key to Northeastern Trees, Twig key to Deciduous Woody Plants of Eastern North America), W. M. Harlow. Only guides with photographs of every twig, fruit described. Especially valuable to novice. Fruit key (both deciduous trees, evergreens) has introduction on seeding, organs involved, types, habits. Twig key introduction treats growth, morphology. In keys proper, identification is almost automatic. Exceptional work, widely used in university courses, especially useful for identification in winter, or from fruit or seed only. Over 350 photos, up to 3 times natural size. Index of common, scientific names, in each key. xvii + 125pp. 5⅝ x 8⅜.
T511 Paperbound **$1.25**

INSECT LIFE AND INSECT NATURAL HISTORY, S. W. Frost. Unusual for emphasizing habits, social life, ecological relations of insects rather than more academic aspects of classification, morphology. Prof. Frost's enthusiasm and knowledge are everywhere evident as he discusses insect associations, specialized habits like leaf-rolling, leaf mining, case-making, the gall insects, boring insects, etc. Examines matters not usually covered in general works: insects as human food; insect music, musicians; insect response to radio waves; use of insects in art, literature. "Distinctly different, possesses an individuality all its own," Journal of Forestry. Over 700 illustrations. Extensive bibliography. x + 524pp. 5⅜ x 8.
T519 Paperbound **$2.49**

A WAY OF LIFE, AND OTHER SELECTED WRITINGS, Sir William Osler. Physician, humanist, Osler discusses brilliantly Thomas Browne, Gui Patin, Robert Burton, Michael Servetus, William Beaumont, Laennec. Includes such favorite writing as title essay, "The Old Humanities and the New Science," "Books and Men," "The Student Life," 6 more of his best discussions of philosophy, literature, religion. "The sweep of his mind and interests embraced every phase of human activity," G. L. Keynes. 5 photographs. Introduction by G. L. Keynes, M.D., F.R.C.S. xx + 278pp. 5⅜ x 8.
T488 Paperbound **$1.50**

THE GENETICAL THEORY OF NATURAL SELECTION, R. A. Fisher. 2nd revised edition of vital reviewing of Darwin's Selection Theory in terms of particulate inheritance, by one of greatest authorities on experimental, theoretical genetics. Theory stated in mathematical form. Special features of particulate inheritance are examined: evolution of dominance, maintenance of specific variability, mimicry, sexual selection, etc. 5 chapters on man's special circumstances as a social animal. 16 photographs. x + 310pp. 5⅜ x 8.
S466 Paperbound **$1.85**

THE AUTOBIOGRAPHY OF CHARLES DARWIN, AND SELECTED LETTERS, edited by Francis Darwin. Darwin's own record of early life; historic voyage aboard "Beagle;" furore surrounding evolution, his replies; reminiscences of his son. Letters to Henslow, Lyell, Hooker, Huxley, Wallace, Kingsley, etc., and thoughts on religion, vivisection. We see how he revolutionized geology with concepts of ocean subsidence; how his great books on variation of plants and animals, primitive man, expression of emotion among primates, plant fertilization, carnivorous plants, protective coloration, etc., came into being. 365pp. 5⅜ x 8.
T479 Paperbound **$1.65**

ANIMALS IN MOTION, Eadweard Muybridge. Largest, most comprehensive selection of Muybridge's famous action photos of animals, from his "Animal Locomotion." 3919 high-speed shots of 34 different animals, birds, in 123 types of action; horses, mules, oxen, pigs, goats, camels, elephants, dogs, cats guanacos, sloths, lions, tigers, jaguars, raccoons, baboons, deer, elk, gnus, kangaroos, many others, walking, running, flying, leaping. Horse alone in over 40 ways. Photos taken against ruled backgrounds; most actions taken from 3 angles at once: 90°, 60°, rear. Most plates original size. Of considerable interest to scientists as biology classic, records of actual facts of natural history, physiology. "Really marvelous series of plates," Nature. "Monumental work," Waldemar Kaempffert. Edited by L. S. Brown, 74 page introduction on mechanics of motion. 340pp. of plates. 3919 photographs. 416pp. Deluxe binding, paper. (Weight: 4½ lbs.) 7⅛ x 10⅝.
T203 Clothbound **$10.00**

THE HUMAN FIGURE IN MOTION, Eadweard Muybridge. New edition of great classic in history of science and photography, largest selection ever made from original Muybridge photos of human action: 4789 photographs, illustrating 163 types of motion: walking, running, lifting, etc. in time-exposure sequence photos at speeds up to 1/6000th of a second. Men, women, children, mostly undraped, showing bone, muscle positions against ruled backgrounds, mostly taken at 3 angles at once. Not only was this a great work of photography, acclaimed by contemporary critics as work of genius, but it was also a great 19th century landmark in biological research. Historical introduction by Prof. Robert Taft, U. of Kansas. Plates original size, full of detail. Over 500 action strips. 407pp. 7¾ x 10⅝. Deluxe edition.
7204 Clothbound **$10.00**

AN INTRODUCTION TO THE STUDY OF EXPERIMENTAL MEDICINE, Claude Bernard. 90-year old classic of medical science, only major work of Bernard available in English, records his efforts to transform physiology into exact science. Principles of scientific research illustrated by specified case histories from his work; roles of chance, error, preliminary false conclusion, in leading eventually to scientific truth; use of hypothesis. Much of modern application of mathematics to biology rests on foundation set down here. "The presentation is polished . . . reading is easy," Revue des questions scientifiques. New foreword by Prof. I. B. Cohen, Harvard U. xxv + 266pp. 5⅜ x 8.
T400 Paperbound **$1.50**

STUDIES ON THE STRUCTURE AND DEVELOPMENT OF VERTEBRATES, E. S. Goodrich. Definitive study by greatest modern comparative anatomist. Exhaustive morphological, phylogenetic expositions of skeleton, fins, limbs, skeletal visceral arches, labial cartilages, visceral clefts, gills, vascular, respiratory, excretory, periphal nervous systems, etc., from fish to higher mammals. "For many a day this will certainly be the standard textbook on Vertebrate Morphology in the English language," Journal of Anatomy. 754 illustrations. 69 page biographical study by C. C. Hardy. Bibliography of 1186 references. Two volumes, total 906pp. 5⅜ x 8.
Two vol. set S449, 450 Paperbound **$5.00**

EARTH SCIENCES

THE EVOLUTION OF IGNEOUS BOOKS, N. L. Bowen. Invaluable serious introduction applies techniques of physics, chemistry to explain igneous rock diversity in terms of chemical composition, fractional crystallization. Discusses liquid immiscibility in silicate magmas, crystal sorting, liquid lines of descent, fractional resorption of complex minerals, petrogen, etc. Of prime importance to geologists, mining engineers; physicists, chemists working with high temperature, pressures. "Most important," Times, London. 263 bibliographic notes. 82 figures. xviii + 334pp. 5⅜ x 8.
S311 Paperbound **$1.85**

GEOGRAPHICAL ESSAYS, M. Davis. Modern geography, geomorphology rest on fundamental work of this scientist. 26 famous essays present most important theories, field researches. Partial contents: Geographical Cycle; Plains of Marine, Subaerial Denudation; The Peneplain; Rivers, Valleys of Pennsylvania; Outline of Cape Cod; Sculpture of Mountains by Glaciers; etc. "Long the leader and guide," Economic Geography. "Part of the very texture of geography . . . models of clear thought," Geographic Review. 130 figures. vi + 777pp. 5⅜ x 8.
S383 Paperbound **$2.95**

URANIUM PROSPECTING, H. L. Barnes. For immediate practical use, professional geologist considers uranium ores, geological occurrences, field conditions, all aspects of highly profitable occupation. "Helpful information . . . easy-to-use, easy-to-find style," Geotimes. x + 117pp. 5⅜ x 8.
T309 Paperbound **$1.00**

DE RE METALLICA, Georgius Agricola. 400 year old classic translated, annotated by former President Herbert Hoover. 1st scientific study of mineralogy, mining, for over 200 years after its appearance in 1556 the standard treatise. 12 books, exhaustively annotated, discuss history of mining, selection of sites, types of deposits, making pits, shafts, ventilating, pumps, crushing machinery; assaying, smelting, refining metals; also salt alum, nitre, glass making. Definitive edition, with all 289 16th century woodcuts of original. Biographical, historical introductions. Bibliography, survey of ancient authors. Indexes. A fascinating book for anyone interested in art, history of science, geology, etc. Deluxe Edition. 289 illustrations. 672pp. 6¾ x 10. Library cloth. S6 Clothbound **$10.00**

INTERNAL CONSTITUTION OF THE EARTH, edited by Beno Gutenberg. Prepared for National Research Council, this is a complete, thorough coverage of earth origins, continent formation, nature and behaviour of earth's core, petrology of crust, cooling forces in core, seismic and earthquake material, gravity, elastic constants, strain characteristics, similar topics. "One is filled with admiration . . . a high standard . . . there is no reader who will not learn something from this book," London, Edinburgh, Dublin, Philosophic Magazine. Largest Bibliography in print: 1127 classified items. Table of constants. 43 diagrams. 439pp. 6⅛ x 9¼. S414 Paperbound **$2.45**

THE BIRTH AND DEVELOPMENT OF THE GEOLOGICAL SCIENCES, F. D. Adams. Most thorough history of earth sciences ever written. Geological thought from earliest times to end of 19th century, covering over 300 early thinkers and systems; fossils and their explanation, vulcanists vs. neptunists, figured stones and paleontology, generation of stones, dozens of similar topics. 91 illustrations, including Medieval, Renaissance woodcuts, etc. 632 footnotes, mostly bibliographical. 511pp. 5⅜ x 8. T5 Paperbound **$2.00**

HYDROLOGY, edited by O. E. Meinzer, prepared for the National Research Council. Detailed, complete reference library on precipitation, evaporation, snow, snow surveying, glaciers, lakes, infiltration, soil moisture, ground water, runoff, drought, physical changes produced by water hydrology of limestone terranes, etc. Practical in application, especially valuable for engineers. 24 experts have created "the most up-to-date, most complete treatment of the subject," Am. Assoc. of Petroleum Geologists. 165 illustrations. xi + 712pp. 6⅛ x 9¼. S191 Paperbound **$2.95**

LANGUAGE AND TRAVEL AIDS FOR SCIENTISTS

SAY IT language phrase books

"SAY IT" in the foreign language of your choice! We have sold over ½ million copies of these popular, useful language books. They will not make you an expert linguist overnight, but they do cover most practical matters of everyday life abroad.

Over 1000 useful phrases, expressions, additional variants, substitutions.

Modern! Useful! Hundreds of phrases not available in other texts: "Nylon," "air-conditioned," etc.

The ONLY inexpensive phrase book **completely indexed.** Everything is available at a flip of your finger, ready to use.

Prepared by native linguists, travel experts.

Based on years of travel experience abroad.

May be used by itself, or to supplement any other text or course. Provides a living element. Used by many colleges, institutions: Hunter College; Barnard College; Army Ordinance School, Aberdeen; etc.

Available, 1 book per language:

Danish (T818) 75¢
Dutch (T817) 75¢
English (for German-speaking people) (T801) 60¢
English (for Italian-speaking people) (T816) 60¢
English (for Spanish-speaking people) (T802) 60¢
Esperanto (T820) 75¢
French (T803) 60¢
German (T804) 60¢
Modern Greek (T813) 75¢
Hebrew (T805) 60¢

Italian (T806) 60¢
Japanese (T807) 75¢
Norwegian (T814) 75¢
Russian (T810) 75¢
Spanish (T811) 60¢
Turkish (T821) 75¢
Yiddish (T815) 75¢
Swedish (T812) 75¢
Polish (T808) 75¢
Portuguese (T809) 75¢

DOVER SCIENCE BOOKS

MONEY CONVERTER AND TIPPING GUIDE FOR EUROPEAN TRAVEL, C. Vomacka. Purse-size handbook crammed with information on currency regulations, tipping for every European country, including Israel, Turkey, Czechoslovakia, Rumania, Egypt, Russia, Poland. Telephone, postal rates; duty-free imports, passports, visas, health certificates; foreign clothing sizes; weather tables. What, when to tip. 5th year of publication. 128pp. 3½ x 5¼.   T260 Paperbound **60¢**

NEW RUSSIAN-ENGLISH AND ENGLISH-RUSSIAN DICTIONARY, M. A. O'Brien. Unusually comprehensive guide to reading, speaking, writing Russian, for both advanced, beginning students. Over 70,000 entries in new orthography, full information on accentuation, grammatical classifications. Shades of meaning, idiomatic uses, colloquialisms, tables of irregular verbs for both languages. Individual entries indicate stems, transitiveness, perfective, imperfective aspects, conjugation, sound changes, accent, etc. Includes pronunciation instruction. Used at Harvard, Yale, Cornell, etc. 738pp. 5⅜ x 8.   T208 Paperbound **$ 2.00**

PHRASE AND SENTENCE DICTIONARY OF SPOKEN RUSSIAN, English-Russian, Russian-English. Based on phrases, complete sentences, not isolated words—recognized as one of best methods of learning idiomatic speech. Over 11,500 entries, indexed by single words, over 32,000 English, Russian sentences, phrases, in immediately useable form. Shows accent changes in conjugation, declension; irregular forms listed both alphabetically, under main form of word. 15,000 word introduction covers Russian sounds, writing, grammar, syntax. 15 page appendix of geographical names, money, important signs, given names, foods, special Soviet terms, etc. Originally published as U.S. Gov't Manual TM 30-944. iv + 573pp. 5⅜ x 8.   T496 Paperbound **$2.75**

PHRASE AND SENTENCE DICTIONARY OF SPOKEN SPANISH, Spanish-English, English-Spanish. Compiled from spoken Spanish, based on phrases, complete sentences rather than isolated words—not an ordinary dictionary. Over 16,000 entries indexed under single words, both Castilian, Latin-American. Language in immediately useable form. 25 page introduction provides rapid survey of sounds, grammar, syntax, full consideration of irregular verbs. Especially apt in modern treatment of phrases, structure. 17 page glossary gives translations of geographical names, money values, numbers, national holidays, important street signs, useful expressions of high frequency, plus unique 7 page glossary of Spanish, Spanish-American foods. Originally published as U.S. Gov't Manual TM 30-900. iv + 513pp. 5⅝ x 8⅜.   T495 Paperbound **$1.75**

SAY IT CORRECTLY language record sets

The best inexpensive pronunciation aids on the market. Spoken by native linguists associated with major American universities, each record contains:

> 14 minutes of speech—12 minutes of normal, relatively slow speech, 2 minutes of normal conversational speed.

> 120 basic phrases, sentences, covering nearly every aspect of everyday life, travel—introducing yourself, travel in autos, buses, taxis, etc., walking, sightseeing, hotels, restaurants, money, shopping, etc.

> 32 page booklet containing everything on record plus English translations easy-to-follow phonetic guide.

> Clear, high-fidelity recordings.

> Unique bracketing systems, selection of basic sentences enabling you to expand use of SAY IT CORRECTLY records with a dictionary, to fit thousands of additional situations.

Use this record to supplement any course or text. All sounds in each language illustrated perfectly—imitate speaker in pause which follows each foreign phrase in slow section, and be amazed at increased ease, accuracy of pronounciation. Available, one language per record for

French	**Spanish**	**German**
Italian	**Dutch**	**Modern Greek**
Japanese	**Russian**	**Portuguese**
Polish	**Swedish**	**Hebrew**
English (for German-speaking people)		**English (for Spanish-speaking people)**

7″ (33 1/3 rpm) record, album, booklet. **$1.00 each.**

SPEAK MY LANGUAGE: SPANISH FOR YOUNG BEGINNERS, M. Ahlman, Z. Gilbert. Records provide one of the best, most entertaining methods of introducing a foreign language to children. Within framework of train trip from Portugal to Spain, an English-speaking child is introduced to Spanish by native companion. (Adapted from successful radio program of N.Y. State Educational Department.) A dozen different categories of expressions, including greeting, numbers, time, weather, food, clothes, family members, etc. Drill is combined with poetry and contextual use. Authentic background music. Accompanying book enables a reader to follow records, includes vocabulary of over 350 recorded expressions. Two 10″ 33 1/3 records, total of 40 minutes. Book. 40 illustrations. 69pp. 5¼ x 10½.   T890 The set **$4.95**

LISTEN & LEARN language record sets

LISTEN & LEARN is the only extensive language record course designed especially to meet your travel and everyday needs. Separate sets for each language, each containing three 33 1/3 rpm long-playing records—1 1/2 hours of recorded speech by eminent native speakers who are professors at Columbia, New York U., Queens College.

Check the following features found only in LISTEN & LEARN:

> Dual language recording. 812 selected phrases, sentences, over 3200 words, spoken first in English, then foreign equivalent. Pause after each foreign phrase allows time to repeat expression.

> 128-page manual (196 page for Russian)—everything on records, plus simple transcription. Indexed for convenience. Only set on the market completely indexed.

> Practical. No time wasted on material you can find in any grammar. No dead words. Covers central core material with phrase approach. Ideal for person with limited time. Living, modern expressions, not found in other courses. Hygienic products, modern equipment, shopping, "air-conditioned," etc. Everything is immediately useable.

> High-fidelity recording, equal in clarity to any costing up to $6 per record.

"Excellent . . . impress me as being among the very best on the market," Prof. Mario Pei, Dept. of Romance Languages, Columbia U. "Inexpensive and well done . . . ideal present," Chicago Sunday Tribune. "More genuinely helpful than anything of its kind," Sidney Clark, well-known author of "All the Best" travel books.

UNCONDITIONAL GUARANTEE. Try LISTEN & LEARN, then return it within 10 days for full refund, if you are not satisfied. It is guaranteed after you actually use it.

6 modern languages—FRENCH, SPANISH, GERMAN, ITALIAN, RUSSIAN, or JAPANESE *—one language to each set of 3 records (33 1/3 rpm). 128 page manual. Album.

Spanish	the set $4.95	**German**	the set $4.95	**Japanese***	the set $5.95
French	the set $4.95	**Italian**	the set $4.95	**Russian**	the set $5.95

* Available Oct. 1959.

TRÜBNER COLLOQUIAL SERIES

These unusual books are members of the famous Trübner series of colloquial manuals. They have been written to provide adults with a sound colloquial knowledge of a foreign language, and are suited for either class use or self-study. Each book is a complete course in itself, with progressive, easy to follow lessons. Phonetics, grammar, and syntax are covered, while hundreds of phrases and idioms, reading texts, exercises, and vocabulary are included. These books are unusual in being neither skimpy nor overdetailed in grammatical matters, and in presenting up-to-date, colloquial, and practical phrase material. Bilingual presentation is stressed, to make thorough self-study easier for the reader.

COLLOQUIAL HINDUSTANI, A. H. Harley, formerly Nizam's Reader in Urdu, U. of London. 30 pages on phonetics and scripts (devanagari & Arabic-Persian) are followed by 29 lessons, including material on English and Arabic-Persian influences. Key to all exercises. Vocabulary. 5 x 7½. 147pp. Clothbound **$1.75**

COLLOQUIAL ARABIC, DeLacy O'Leary. Foremost Islamic scholar covers language of Egypt, Syria, Palestine, & Northern Arabia. Extremely clear coverage of complex Arabic verbs & noun plurals; also cultural aspects of language. Vocabulary. xviii + 192pp. 5 x 7½. Clothbound **$1.75**

COLLOQUIAL GERMAN, P. F. Doring. Intensive thorough coverage of grammar in easily-followed form. Excellent for brush-up, with hundreds of colloquial phrases. 34 pages of bilingual texts. 224pp. 5 x 7½. Clothbound **$1.75**

COLLOQUIAL SPANISH, W. R. Patterson. Castilian grammar and colloquial language, loaded with bilingual phrases and colloquialisms. Excellent for review or self-study. 164pp. 5 x 7½. Clothbound **$1.75**

COLLOQUIAL FRENCH, W. R. Patterson. 16th revised edition of this extremely popular manual. Grammar explained with model clarity, and hundreds of useful expressions and phrases; exercises, reading texts, etc. Appendixes of new and useful words and phrases. 223pp. 5 x 7½. Clothbound **$1.75**

DOVER SCIENCE BOOKS

COLLOQUIAL PERSIAN, L. P. Elwell-Sutton. Best introduction to modern Persian, with 90 page grammatical section followed by conversations, 35 page vocabulary. 139pp. Clothbound **$1.75**

COLLOQUIAL CZECH, J. Schwarz, former headmaster of Lingua Institute, Prague. Full easily followed coverage of grammar, hundreds of immediately useable phrases, texts. Perhaps the best Czech grammar in print. "An absolutely successful textbook," JOURNAL OF CZECHO-SLOVAK FORCES IN GREAT BRITAIN. 252pp. 5 x 7½. Clothbound **$2.50**

COLLOQUIAL RUMANIAN, G. Nandris, Professor of University of London. Extremely thorough coverage of phonetics, grammar, syntax; also included 70 page reader, and 70 page vocabulary. Probably the best grammar for this increasingly important language. 340pp. 5 x 7½.
Clothbound **$2.50**

COLLOQUIAL ITALIAN, A. L. Hayward. Excellent self-study course in grammar, vocabulary, idioms, and reading. Easy progressive lessons will give a good working knowledge of Italian in the shortest possible time. 5 x 7½. Clothbound **$1.75**

MISCELLANEOUS

TREASURY OF THE WORLD'S COINS, Fred Reinfeld. Finest general introduction to numismatics; non-technical, thorough, always fascinating. Coins of Greece, Rome, modern countries of every continent, primitive societies, such oddities as 200-lb stone money of Yap, nail coinage of New England; all mirror man's economy, customs, religion, politics, philosophy, art. Entertaining, absorbing study; novel view of history. Over 750 illustrations. Table of value of coins illustrated. List of U.S. coin clubs. 224pp. 6½ x 9¼.
T433 Paperbound **$1.75**

ILLUSIONS AND DELUSIONS OF THE SUPERNATURAL AND THE OCCULT, D. H. Rawcliffe. Rationally examines hundreds of persistent delusions including witchcraft, trances, mental healing, peyotl, poltergeists, stigmata, lycanthropy, live burial, auras, Indian rope trick, spiritualism, dowsing, telepathy, ghosts, ESP, etc. Explains, exposes mental, physical deceptions involved, making this not only an exposé of supernatural phenomena, but a valuable exposition of characteristic types of abnormal psychology. Originally "The Psychology of the Occult." Introduction by Julian Huxley. 14 illustrations. 551pp. 5⅜ x 8.
T503 Paperbound **$2.00**

HOAXES, C. D. MacDougall. Shows how art, science, history, journalism can be perverted for private purposes. Hours of delightful entertainment, a work of scholarly value, often shocking. Examines nonsense news, Cardiff giant, Shakespeare forgeries, Loch Ness monster, biblical frauds, political schemes, literary hoaxers like Chatterton, Ossian, disumbrationist school of painting, lady in black at Valentino's tomb, over 250 others. Will probably reveal truth about few things you've believed, will help you spot more easily the editorial "gander" or planted publicity release. "A stupendous collection . . . and shrewd analysis," New Yorker. New revised edition. 54 photographs. 320pp. 5⅜ x 8. T465 Paperbound **$1.75**

YOGA: A SCIENTIFIC EVALUATION, Kovoor T. Behanan. Book that for first time gave Western readers a sane, scientific explanation, analysis of yoga. Author draws on laboratory experiments, personal records of year as disciple of yoga, to investigate yoga psychology, physiology, "supernatural" phenomena, ability to plumb deepest human powers. In this study under auspices of Yale University Institute of Human Relations, strictest principles of physiological, psychological inquiry are followed. Foreword by W. A. Miles, Yale University. 17 photographs. xx + 270pp. 5⅜ x 8. T505 Paperbound **$1.65**